ANALYSIS AND DESIGN OF EXPERIMENTS

Other Dover Series Books in Mathematics & Physics

THEORY OF SETS by E. Kamke. *Translated by Frederick Bagemihl, University of Rochester.*

STATISTICAL MECHANICS by A. Khinchin. *Translated by G. Gamow, George Washington University.*

PROBLEM BOOK IN THE THEORY OF FUNCTIONS, Volume I: Problems in the Elementary Theory of Functions by Konrad Knopp. *Translated by Lipman Bers, Syracuse University.*

INTRODUCTION TO THE DIFFERENTIAL EQUATIONS OF PHYSICS by L. Hopf. *Translated by Walter Nef, University of Fribourg.*

A CONCISE HISTORY OF MATHEMATICS by Dirk J. Struik, Massachusetts Institute of Technology. 2 volumes.

ANALYSIS AND DESIGN OF EXPERIMENTS

Analysis of Variance and Analysis of Variance Designs

H. B. MANN
PROFESSOR OF MATHEMATICS,
THE OHIO STATE UNIVERSITY

NEW YORK
DOVER PUBLICATIONS, INC.

THE DOVER SERIES IN MATHEMATICS AND PHYSICS

W. PRAGER, *Consulting Editor*

Printed & Bound in the U.S.A.

To Harold Hotelling

Contents

Introduction

THE IDEA TO DESIGN experiments systematically and with a view to their statistical analysis was first promoted by R. A. Fisher in his well known book "The Design of Experiments". Fisher also proposed the majority of the designs discussed in the present volume. Several designs of great importance, notably the quasifactorial designs and the incomplete balanced block designs, were discovered by F. Yates. R. A. Fisher's book, however, as well as other publications by R. A. Fisher and F. Yates and their school are not written for mathematicians. Thus the main emphasis is placed on the explanation of the procedure with little or no attention being paid to a mathematical formulation of the assumptions and to the principles of statistical inference which lead from the assumption to the statistical method. Moreover, also in many other important papers on analysis of variance and design of experiments proofs and derivations of formulae are barely sketched if not totally omitted. The present book tries to fill this gap and the main emphasis is therefore given to a rigorous mathematical treatment of the subject.

In writing this volume the author had in mind a reader with a mathematical background of a student, who majors in mathematics and is in his senior year. References are given whenever the text exceeds this background.

The book is designed to serve three different purposes. First, it was intended to enable a mature mathematician with no background in statistics to study the analysis of variance and analysis of variance designs within a reasonably short time. Secondly, it is intended to serve as a text book for a graduate or advanced undergraduate course in the subject. Finally, it is hoped that this book will be studied by practical experimenters and statisticians who wish to study the mathematical methods used in the analysis of variance and in the construction of analysis of variance designs and are willing and able to expend the time and effort necessary for this purpose.

My thanks are due to the Iowa State College Press for their kind permission to include in this book the tables of the F-distribution of G. W. Snedecor's "Statistical Methods" and to the Department of Statistics, University of London, University College for their kind permission to republish P. C. Tang's tables of the power function of the analysis of variance test from the second volume of the "Statistical Research Memoirs".

I am indebted to Mr. Ransom Whitney who has assisted me in reading the manuscript and the proofs. I also wish to acknowledge my indebtedness to Professor W. G. Cochran for a very helpful letter.

CHAPTER I

Chi-square Distribution and Analysis of Variance Distribution

IN THIS CHAPTER certain fundamental concepts of the probability calculus are used. The reader who is not acquainted with these concepts should first acquire the necessary background by reading, for instance, Uspensky's, "Introduction to Mathematical Probability," Chapter XII. Sec. 8, example 3, Chapter XIII. Secs. 1-4 and 6, Chapter XV, Secs. 1-6.

Let $x_1, \cdots, x_N$ be normally and independently distributed variables with variances 1 and means 0. We wish to calculate the distribution of the expression

$$\chi^2 = x_1^2 + x_2^2 + \cdots + x_N^2 . \tag{1.1}$$

The joint distribution of $x_1, \cdots, x_N$ is given by the probability density function,

$$P(x_1, \cdots, x_N) = \frac{1}{(2\pi)^{N/2}} \exp\left[-(x_1^2 + \cdots + x_N^2)/2\right].$$

Hence the probability that

$$\chi^2 = x_1^2 + \cdots + x_N^2 \leq R^2$$

is given by

$$\int_S \frac{1}{(2\pi)^{N/2}} e^{-\chi^2/2}\, dx_1 \cdots dx_N$$

where S is the sphere with radius R^2 and center 0. The probability that

$$R^2 \leq \chi^2 \leq (R + \Delta R)^2$$

is, therefore, given by

$$C \int e^{-\chi^2/2}\, dx_1 \cdots dx_N$$

$$R^2 \leq \chi^2 \leq (R + \Delta R)^2$$

where C is a certain constant independent of R. If we denote the probability that $\chi^2 \leq R^2$ by $P(\chi^2 \leq R^2)$ we, therefore, have

$$\Delta[P(\chi^2 \leq R^2)] = C\, e^{-\chi^{*2}/2}\, \Delta v$$

where $R^2 \leq \chi^{*2} \leq (R + \Delta R)^2$ and Δv is the volume of the spherical shell $R^2 \leq \chi^2 \leq (R + \Delta R)^2$. This volume is given by $\Delta v = C' R^{N-1} \Delta R$. If now ΔR approaches 0, we obtain

$$\frac{dP\,(\chi^2 \leq R^2)}{dR} = C''\, e^{-R^2/2}\, R^{N-1}.$$

Hence since $\chi^2 \geq 0$

$$P(\chi^2 \leq R^2) = \int_0^R C''\, e^{-\chi^2/2}\, \chi^{N-1}\, d\chi$$

$$= \int_0^{R^2} \bar{C}(\chi^2)^{(N-2)/2}\, e^{-\chi^2/2}\, d\chi^2.$$

The probability density of χ^2 is therefore,

$$P(\chi^2) = \bar{C}(\chi^2)^{(N-2)/2}\, e^{-\chi^2/2} \qquad \text{for } \chi^2 \geq 0$$

$$= 0 \qquad \text{for } \chi^2 < 0.$$

The constant $\bar{C}$ still remains to be determined. We must have

$$\bar{C} \int_0^\infty (\chi^2)^{(N-2)/2}\, e^{-\chi^2/2}\, d\chi^2 = 1.$$

Hence

$$\frac{1}{\bar{C}} = \int_0^\infty (\chi^2)^{(N-2)/2}\, e^{-\chi^2/2}\, d\chi^2 = \int_0^\infty 2^{N/2}\left(\frac{\chi^2}{2}\right)^{(N-2)/2} e^{-\chi^2/2}\, d\left(\frac{\chi^2}{2}\right)$$

$$= 2^{N/2} \int_0^\infty x^{(N-2)/2}\, e^{-x}\, dx = 2^{N/2}\Gamma\left(\frac{N}{2}\right),$$

where

$$\Gamma(z) = \int_0^\infty x^{z-1}\, e^{-x}\, dx$$

is the well known Γ function.

Hence we finally have

$$(1.2) \qquad P(\chi^2) = \frac{1}{2^{N/2}\Gamma(N/2)} (\chi^2)^{(N-2)/2} e^{-\chi^2/2}.$$

The number N in this distribution is called the number of degrees of freedom.

This distribution is tabulated in almost every modern book on statistics for all degrees of freedom under 31. For larger values of N the quantity $(2\chi^2)^{\frac{1}{2}} - (2N - 1)^{\frac{1}{2}}$ is approximately normally distributed with mean 0 and variance 1. For large values of N also $(\chi^2 - N)/(2N)^{\frac{1}{2}}$ is approximately so distributed.

If χ_1^2 has n_1 degrees of freedom and χ_2^2 has n_2 degrees of freedom, then χ_1^2, (χ_2^2) is distributed as is the sum of n_1, (n_2) independently and normally distributed variates. Hence we have

THEOREM 1.1: *Let $\chi_1^2, \chi_2^2, \cdots, \chi_s^2$ be independently distributed variables such that χ_i^2 has the χ^2 distribution with n_i degrees of freedom then*

$$\chi^2 = \chi_1^2 + \chi_2^2 + \cdots + \chi_s^2$$

has the χ^2 distribution with $n_1 + n_2 + \cdots + n_s = n$ degrees of freedom.

All of the theory of analysis and design of experiments which is presented in this book is based on the distribution of the ratio of two independent chi-square expressions. We therefore, proceed to derive this distribution.

Suppose that χ_1^2 is distributed according to 1.2 with n_1 degrees of freedom, and χ_2^2 with n_2 degrees of freedom and suppose that χ_1^2 and χ_2^2 are independently distributed. The joint distribution of χ_1^2 and χ_2^2 is then given by its density function

$$P(\chi_1^2, \chi_2^2) = \frac{1}{2^{(n_1+n_2)/2}\Gamma(n_1/2)\Gamma(n_2/2)} \cdot (\chi_1^2)^{(n_1-2)/2}(\chi_2^2)^{(n_2-2)/2} \exp\left[-(\chi_1^2 + \chi_2^2)/2\right].$$

We put

$$(1.3) \qquad \frac{\chi_1^2}{\chi_2^2} = y, \qquad \chi_1^2 + \chi_2^2 = z.$$

To every pair of values $y \geq 0$, $z \geq 0$, there exists one and only one pair of values $\chi_1^2 \geq 0$, $\chi_2^2 \geq 0$. We, therefore, obtain the probability density of y and z by transforming $P(\chi_1^2, \chi_2^2)$ by means of 1.3. From 1.3 we have

$$\begin{vmatrix} \dfrac{\partial \chi_1^2}{\partial y} & \dfrac{\partial \chi_1^2}{\partial z} \\[2ex] \dfrac{\partial \chi_2^2}{\partial y} & \dfrac{\partial \chi_2^2}{\partial z} \end{vmatrix} = \begin{vmatrix} \dfrac{z}{(1+y)^2} & \dfrac{y}{1+y} \\[2ex] \dfrac{-z}{(1+y)^2} & \dfrac{1}{1+y} \end{vmatrix} = \frac{z}{(1+y)^2}.$$

Hence the probability density of y and z is given by

$$\frac{1}{2\Gamma(n_1/2)\Gamma(n_2/2)} \frac{y^{(n_1-2)/2}}{(1+y)^{(n_1+n_2)/2}} \left(\frac{z}{2}\right)^{(n_1+n_2-2)/2} e^{-z/2}$$

for $z \geq 0$, $y \geq 0$,

and is 0 for either $z < 0$ or $y < 0$.

Integrating out with respect to z from 0 to ∞, we obtain the density function of y

$$(1.4) \qquad H(y) = \frac{\Gamma\left(\dfrac{n_1+n_2}{2}\right) y^{\frac{n_1-2}{2}}}{\Gamma\left(\dfrac{n_1}{2}\right)\Gamma\left(\dfrac{n_2}{2}\right)(1+y)^{\frac{n_1+n_2}{2}}}.$$

Hence the probability that $y > \bar{y} > 0$ is given by

$$(1.5) \qquad \int_{\bar{y}}^{\infty} H(y)\, dy.$$

The variable y was defined as the quotient of two independent chi-square expressions χ_1^2 and χ_2^2 with n_1 and n_2 degrees of freedom respectively. We shall consider the variable F given by

$$F = \frac{n_2}{n_1}\frac{\chi_1^2}{\chi_2^2}, \qquad \frac{n_1}{n_2} F = y.$$

The probability of obtaining an F larger or equal to $\bar{F}$ is according to 1.5 and 1.4 given by

$$\int_{\bar{F}}^{\infty} H\left(\frac{n_1}{n_2} F\right) \frac{n_1}{n_2}\, dF$$

$$= \int_{\bar{F}}^{\infty} \frac{\Gamma([n_1 + n_2]/2)}{\Gamma(n_1/2)\Gamma(n_2/2)} \frac{(n_1/n_2)^{n_1/2} F^{(n_1-2)/2}}{(1 + n_1F/n_2)^{(n_1+n_2)/2}}\, dF \tag{1.6}$$

$$= G(\bar{F}).$$

The values $\bar{F}$ and $\bar{\bar{F}}$ for which

$$G(\bar{F}) = .05, \qquad G(\bar{\bar{F}}) = .01.$$

have been tabulated by G. W. Snedecor in his books "Statistical Methods" and "Analysis of Variance and Covariance," which also contain a large collection of interesting applications of the χ^2 and F statistic.

CHAPTER II

Matrices, Quadratic Forms, and the Multivariate Normal Distribution

A MATRIX is a rectangular array of coefficients

$$\begin{pmatrix} \sigma_{11}, & \cdots, & \sigma_{1n} \\ \\ \sigma_{m1}, & \cdots, & \sigma_{mn} \end{pmatrix}.$$

We shall denote such a matrix by (σ_{ij}) whenever the meaning of the numbers m and n will be clear from the context.

Consider a system of linear forms

$$L_i = a_{i1}x_1 + \cdots + a_{in}x_n, \qquad i = 1, \cdots, m. \tag{2.1}$$

The matrix (a_{ij}) is called the matrix of the linear forms L_i in $x_1, \cdots, x_n$. Suppose now that the x_i are themselves linear forms in the variables $y_1, \cdots, y_s$

$$x_j = b_{j1}y_1 + \cdots + b_{js}y_s. \tag{2.2}$$

Then

$$L_i = \sum_{j=1}^{n} a_{ij}x_j = \sum_{j=1}^{n} \sum_{k=1}^{s} a_{ij}b_{jk}y_k = \sum_{k=1}^{s} y_k \sum_{j=1}^{n} a_{ij}b_{jk},$$

$$i = 1, \cdots, m.$$

The L_i are therefore linear forms in the variables $y_1, \cdots, y_s$ with the matrix (c_{ik}) where

$$c_{ik} = \sum_{j=1}^{n} a_{ij}b_{jk}, \qquad i = 1, \cdots, m, k = 1, \cdots, s.$$

It is therefore natural to define the product of two matrices by

$$(a_{ij})(b_{jk}) = \left(\sum_{j=1}^{n} a_{ij}b_{jk} \right). \tag{2.3}$$

Note that the product is only defined if (a_{ij}) has as many columns as (b_{jk}) has rows.

If we put

$$(L) = \begin{pmatrix} L_1 \\ \cdot \\ \cdot \\ \cdot \\ L_m \end{pmatrix} \qquad (x) = \begin{pmatrix} x_1 \\ \cdot \\ \cdot \\ \cdot \\ x_m \end{pmatrix}$$

we may rewrite (2.1) in matrix form as

$$(2.4) \qquad (L) = (a_{ij})(x).$$

To a limited extent matrix notation and some of the most elementary theorems on matrices will be used in this book. If the reader is not familiar with the most elementary aspects of the theory of matrices, he should acquire the necessary background by reading, for instance, in A. A. Albert's book "Introduction to Higher Algebraic Theories" Chapter 2 and Chapter 3, Section 1 to 11. Albert's book will be referred to as (AAA). We shall review here some elementary theorems which will be used in this chapter.

The multiplication of matrices is associative (AAA III. 2.) That is to say, if A, B, C are matrices such that (AB) and (BC) are defined then

$$(2.5) \qquad (AB)C = A(BC).$$

The multiplication of matrices is not commutative. That means that AB is not always the same as BA. In fact AB may be defined whilst BA is not.

The determinant of a square matrix $(a_{ij}) = A$ will be denoted by $| a_{ij} |$ or $| A |$. The equation

$$(2.6) \qquad | AB | = | A | \, | B |$$

holds (AAA, III, 5).

The matrix

$$(2.7)\qquad \begin{pmatrix} 10 \cdots 0 \\ 01 \cdots 0 \\ \cdot \;\cdots\; \cdot \\ \cdot \;\cdots\; \cdot \\ \cdot \;\cdots\; \cdot \\ 0 \cdots 1 \end{pmatrix} = I$$

is called the unit matrix and it is easy to verify that $AI = IA = A$ for every A for which IA and AI are defined.

If and only if $|A| \neq 0$ then A is called non singular and possesses an inverse A^{-1} for which (AAA, III, 6).

$$(2.8)\qquad AA^{-1} = A^{-1}A = I.$$

We shall always use the notation $(\sigma_{ij})^{-1} = (\sigma^{ij})$.

To every matrix $(a_{ij}) = A$ we can construct the transposed matrix A' by interchanging rows and columns. One easily verifies the laws

$$(2.9)\qquad (AB)' = B'A', \quad (AB)^{-1} = B^{-1}A^{-1}, \quad (A^{-1})' = A'^{-1}.$$

The symbol A' will be reserved in this book for the transposed of A.

We consider quadratic forms

$$(2.10)\qquad Q = \sum_{i=1}^{n} \sum_{j=1}^{n} a_{ij}x_i x_j\,, \qquad a_{ij} = a_{ji}\,.$$

We may write Q in matrix form

$$(2.11)\qquad Q = x'Ax,$$

where

$$A = (a_{ij}), \qquad x = \begin{pmatrix} x_1 \\ \cdot \\ \cdot \\ x_n \end{pmatrix}.$$

A is called the matrix of Q in the variables $x_1, \cdots, x_n$.

Suppose that

$$x = Py, \qquad P = \begin{pmatrix} p_{11} & \cdots & p_{1m} \\ & & \\ p_{n1} & \cdots & p_{nm} \end{pmatrix}, \qquad y = \begin{pmatrix} y_1 \\ \cdot \\ \cdot \\ \cdot \\ y_m \end{pmatrix}.$$

Then

$$(2.12) \qquad Q = x'Ax = y'P'APy.$$

Hence the matrix of Q in terms of the variables y_1 , $\cdots$, y_m is given by $P'AP$.

A quadratic form in x_1 , $\cdots$, x_n is called positive definite if it takes only positive values when the variables x_1 , $\cdots$, x_n , take real values not all equal to 0. It is called semi-definite when it takes only non negative values (positive and 0) for real x_1 , $\cdots$, x_n . Any quadratic form may, by a non singular transformation (AAA, III, 11.)

$$\overline{L}_i = \sum_{j=1}^{n} c_{ij}x_j , \qquad i = 1, \cdots , n,$$

be transformed into

$$Q = \sum_{i=1}^{r} c_i\overline{L}_i^2 , \qquad r \leq n, \qquad c_i \neq 0.$$

The number r is called the rank of Q and is independent of the transformation provided it is non singular. The c_i must all be positive, if Q is positive semidefinite and the transformation $L_i = (c_i)^{\frac{1}{2}}\overline{L}_i$ leads to

$$Q = \sum_{i=1}^{r} L_i^2 .$$

If Q_1 has the rank n_1 and Q_2 the rank n_2 then $Q_1 + Q_2$ has at most the rank $n_1 + n_2$ for

$$Q_1 + Q_2 = \sum_{i=1}^{n_1} L_i^2 + \sum_{j=1}^{n_2} M_j^2 .$$

Some of the L_i or M_j may be represented in terms of the others. Eliminating as many of them as possible we obtain

$$Q_1 + Q_2 = \sum_{i=1}^{n'} \sum_{j=1}^{n'} t_{ij} N_i N_j \qquad n' \leq n_1 + n_2 ,$$

where the N_i are independent linear forms in the x's. Hence $Q_1 + Q_2$ has at most the rank $n_1 + n_2$. Hence we have

Lemma 2.1: *The sum of the ranks of s quadratic forms is not smaller than the rank of their sum.*

If x_1 , x_2 are two random variables with the means μ_1 and μ_2 then

$$E(x_1 - \mu_1)(x_2 - \mu_2) = \sigma_{12} ,$$

where E denotes the mathematical expectation, is called the covariance of x_1 and x_2 .

Let x_1 , $\cdots$, x_r be r jointly normally distributed variables with means 0 and covariance matrix (σ_{ij}). Their density function is given by

$$(2.13) \quad P(x_1 , \cdots , x_r) = \frac{1}{(2\pi)^{r/2} \mid \sigma_{ij} \mid^{1/2}} e^{-1/2 \sum_{i=1}^{r} \sum_{j=1}^{r} \sigma^{ij} x_i x_j} ,$$

where the quadratic form in the exponent is positive definite.

The probability $P[(x_1 , \cdots , x_r \subset T]$ that the point $(x_1 , \cdots , x_r)$ is in a subspace T of the r dimensional space is given by

$$(2.14) \quad P[(x_1 , \cdots , x_r) \subset T] = \int_T P(x_1 , \cdots , x_r)\, dx_1\, dx_2 \cdots dx_r .$$

If $E(x_i) = \mu_i \neq 0$ then we make the transformation $x_i' = x_i - \mu_i$. We shall formulate the results of this chapter for the case that $E(x_i) = 0$. It will be easy to find the proper formulation for the case $E(x_i) = \mu_i$.

We apply a non singular linear transformation (AAA, III, 6).

$$(2.15)\qquad x_i = \sum_{j=1}^{r} p_{ij}y_j\,, \qquad i = 1, \cdots, r.$$

The Jacobian determinant of this transformation is $|p_{ij}|$ and the new density function of the y's is therefore given by

$$(2.16)\qquad Q(y_1, \cdots, y_r) = \frac{\|P\|}{(2\pi)^{r/2}\,|\sigma_{ij}|^{1/2}}\, e^{-1/2\sum \sigma^{*ij} y_i y_j}\,,$$

where $(P) = (p_{ij})$, $(\sigma^{*ij}) = P'(\sigma^{ij})P$, and $\|P\|$ denotes the absolute value of $|P|$. We may then write the constant term in (2.16) as

$$\frac{\|P\|}{(2\pi)^{r/2}\,|\sigma_{ij}|^{1/2}} = \frac{1}{(2\pi)^{r/2}\,|P^{-1}(\sigma_{ij})P'^{-1}|^{1/2}} = \frac{1}{(2\pi)^{r/2}\,|\sigma^*_{ij}|}\,.$$

We see therefore that the y's are also jointly normally distributed with means 0 and covariance matrix

$$(2.17)\qquad (\sigma^*_{ij}) = P^{-1}(\sigma_{ij})P'^{-1}.$$

The matrix P is called orthogonal if

$$(2.18)\qquad P^{-1} = P' \qquad \text{or} \qquad P'P = PP' = I.$$

In terms of the coefficients p_{ik} of P this means

$$(2.19)\qquad \sum_{k=1}^{r} p_{ik}p_{lk} = \begin{cases} 1 & \text{if} \quad i = l \\ 0 & \text{if} \quad i \neq l. \end{cases}$$

If $x_1, \cdots, x_r$ are independently distributed with variance σ^2 then

$$(2.20)\qquad \sigma_{ij} = \begin{cases} 0 & \text{for} \quad i \neq j \\ \sigma^2 & \text{for} \quad i = j \end{cases}$$

and it follows from (2.17) that if P is orthogonal

$$(2.21)\qquad \begin{aligned}(\sigma^*_{ij}) &= P'\begin{pmatrix}\sigma^2 & \cdots & 0\\ \cdot & \cdots & \cdot\\ \cdot & \cdots & \cdot\\ \cdot & \cdots & \cdot\\ 0 & \cdots & \sigma^2\end{pmatrix}P\\ &= P'P\begin{pmatrix}\sigma^2 & \cdots & 0\\ \cdot & \cdots & \cdot\\ \cdot & \cdots & \cdot\\ \cdot & \cdots & \cdot\\ 0 & \cdots & \sigma^2\end{pmatrix} = \begin{pmatrix}\sigma^2 & \cdots & 0\\ \cdot & \cdots & \cdot\\ \cdot & \cdots & \cdot\\ \cdot & \cdots & \cdot\\ 0 & \cdots & \sigma^2\end{pmatrix}\end{aligned}$$

since a scalar matrix (AAA, II, 6, p. 30) commutes with every other matrix. Hence we have

Lemma 2.2: *If $x_1, \cdots, x_r$ are normally and independently distributed with means 0 and common variance σ^2 and if*

$$(2.22)\qquad x_i = \sum_{j=1}^{r} p_{ij}y_j, \qquad i = 1, 2 \cdots, r,$$

where $P = (p_{ij})$ is an orthogonal matrix then the y_i are independently and normally distributed all with the same variance σ^2.

We proceed to prove

Lemma 2.3: *Let*

$$(2.23)\qquad \sum_{i=1}^{n} x_i^2 = Q_1(x) + \cdots + Q_s(x),$$

where $Q_i(x)$ is a quadratic form in $x_1, \cdots, x_r$ of rank n_i (AAA, III, 11). *Then there exists an orthogonal transformation*

$$(2.24)\qquad x'_i = \sum_{k=1}^{n} p_{ik}x_k, \qquad i = 1, \cdots, n$$

such that

$$(2.25)\qquad Q_i = \sum_{k=n_1+\cdots+n_{i-1}+1}^{n_1+\cdots+n_i} x_k'^2, \qquad i = 1, \cdots, s$$

if and only if $n_1 + n_2 + \cdots + n_s = n$.

In the first place we have by Lemma 2.1

$$n_1 + \cdots + n_s \geq n \tag{2.26}$$

since the rank of the left side of 2.23 is n.

Suppose first that there exists an orthogonal transformation fulfilling the conditions of Lemma 2.3. Then 2.24 and 2.25 imply

$$n_1 + \cdots + n_s = n. \tag{2.27}$$

Now let $\sum n_i = n$. Since Q_i has the rank n_i there exist transformations

$$\begin{gathered} L_j = \sum_{k=1}^{n} p_{jk} x_k \\ j = n_1 + \cdots + n_{i-1} + 1, \cdots, n_1 + n_2 + \cdots + n_i \end{gathered} \tag{2.28}$$

such that

$$Q_i = \sum_{j=n_1+\cdots+n_{i-1}+1}^{j=n_1+\cdots+n_i} L_j^2 . \tag{2.29}$$

If the L_j were not independent, then the quadratic form

$$\sum Q_i = \sum_{j=1}^{n} L_j^2$$

would have a rank smaller than n. But this is impossible on account of 2.23. Hence the L_j are independent. We may regard therefore the transformation (2.28) as one non singular transformation with $j = 1, \cdots, n$. Putting

$$L = \begin{pmatrix} L_1 \\ \cdot \\ \cdot \\ \cdot \\ L_n \end{pmatrix}, \qquad X = \begin{pmatrix} x_1 \\ \cdot \\ \cdot \\ \cdot \\ x_n \end{pmatrix}, \qquad P = (p_{ij})$$

we may therefore write $L = PX$, where $P = (p_{ij})$ is non singular. Since

$$Q = \sum_{j=1}^{n} x_j^2 = \sum_{i=1}^{s} Q_i = \sum_{j=1}^{n} L_j^2 ,$$

we have

$$X'IX = L'P'^{-1}IP^{-1}L.$$

But $P'^{-1}IP^{-1}$ is the matrix of Q as a form in $L_1, \cdots, L_n$ and this matrix is the unit matrix. Hence

$$P'^{-1}P^{-1} = I.$$

P'^{-1} and therefore also P are thus orthogonal matrices and Lemma 2.3 is proved.

THEOREM 2.1: *Let $x_1, \cdots, x_n$ be normally and independently distributed variables with variance* 1. *Let*

$$Q_1 + \cdots + Q_s = \sum_{i=1}^{i=n} x_i^2, \tag{2.29}$$

where Q_i is a quadratic form of rank n_i.

The Q_i are independently distributed and Q_i has the chi square distribution with n_i degrees of freedom if and only if

$$n_1 + n_2 + \cdots + n_s = n. \tag{2.30}$$

Suppose first that the Q_i are independently distributed and that Q_i has the χ^2 distribution with n_i degrees of freedom. Then by Theorem 1.1 $Q_1 + \cdots + Q_s$ has the χ^2 distribution with $n_1 + n_2 + \cdots + n_s$ degrees of freedom but on account of (2.29) it has also the χ^2 distribution with n degrees of freedom and (2.30) follows.

On the other hand suppose that $n_1 + \cdots + n_s = n$. Then by Lemma 2.3 there exists an orthogonal transformation

$$x_j = \sum p_{jk}x'_k$$

such that

$$Q_i = \sum_{j=n_1+\cdots+n_{i-1}+1}^{n_1+\cdots+n_i} x_k'^2.$$

But by Lemma 2.2 the quantities x'_j are normally and independently distributed variables with means 0 and variance 1. Hence the Q_i are independently distributed and Q_i has by our results in chapter 1 the χ^2 distribution with n_i degrees of freedom. This proves Theorem 2.1.

Corollary to Theorem 2.1: *Let* $x_1, \cdots, x_n$ *be normally and independently distributed with means* 0 *and variance* σ^2 *and let* $Q_i (i = 1, \cdots, s)$ *be s quadratic forms in* $x_1, \cdots, x_n$ *with ranks* $n_1, \cdots, n_s$ *and*

$$Q_1 + Q_2 + \cdots + Q_s = Q = \sum_{i=1}^{n} x_i^2$$

then $n_j/n_i \; Q_i/Q_j$ *has the F distribution with* n_i *and* n_j *degrees of freedom respectively.*

The variables $x_1/\sigma, \cdots, x_n/\sigma$ are normally distributed with variance 1 and means 0. Therefore Q_i/σ^2 has by Theorem 2.1 the χ^2 distribution with n_i degrees of freedom and the corollary follows from our results in Chapter 1.

The corollary to Theorem 2.1 is of importance in the analysis of variance. Theorem 2.1 and its corollary were first formulated by W. G. Cochran.

CHAPTER III

Analysis of Variance in a One Way Classification

LET $X_1, \cdots, X_s$ be s normally and independently distributed variates with common variance σ^2, and let X_i have the mean value μ_i. For instance, consider s different races of cattle and let X_i be the birth weight of calves of the ith race. We wish to test the hypothesis that $\mu_i = \cdots = \mu_s = \mu$.

Suppose a random sample is taken of n_1 individuals of X_1, n_2 of $X_2, \cdots, n_s$ of X_s. The values obtained are $x_{11}, \cdots, x_{1n_1}$, from the first variate $x_{21}, \cdots, x_{2n_2}$ from the second and so forth. Let

$$x_i = \frac{x_{i1} + x_{i2} + \cdots + x_{in_i}}{n_i}$$

be the mean of the ith sample and let

$$x = \frac{\sum_i \sum_j x_{ij}}{n}, \qquad n = n_1 + \cdots + n_s,$$

where $\sum_i$ denotes summation over all values of i, be the total mean.

We shall first prove the following identity. Let $\alpha_1, \cdots, \alpha_t$ be t numbers,

$$\alpha = \frac{\alpha_1 + \cdots + \alpha_t}{t}$$

their mean then

$$\sum_i \alpha_i^2 = \sum_i (\alpha_i - \alpha)^2 + t\alpha^2. \tag{3.1}$$

Proof: We have

$$\sum_i \alpha_i^2 = \sum_i (\alpha_i - \alpha + \alpha)^2$$

$$= \sum_i (\alpha_i - \alpha)^2 + 2\alpha \sum_i (\alpha_i - \alpha) + t\alpha^2$$

but

$$\sum_i (\alpha_i - \alpha)\alpha = \alpha \sum_i (\alpha_i - \alpha) = \alpha(\sum_i \alpha_i - \sum_i \alpha_i) = 0$$

which proves (3.1). We apply (3.1) to $\sum_j x_{ij}^2$ and obtain

$$\sum_j (x_{ij})^2 = \sum_j (x_{ij} - x_i)^2 + n_i x_i^2 . \tag{3.2}$$

Thus

$$\sum_i \sum_j x_{ij}^2 = \sum_i \sum_j (x_{ij} - x_i)^2 + \sum_i n_i x_i^2 . \tag{3.3}$$

Next we apply (3.1) to $\sum_i n_i x_i^2$ whereby we consider $n_i x_i^2$ as the sum of n_i quantities. Then x is the mean of all the n quantities x_i and by (3.1)

$$\sum_i n_i x_i^2 = \sum_i n_i (x_i - x)^2 + nx^2. \tag{3.4}$$

Substituting (3.4) into (3.3) we finally have

$$\sum_i \sum_j x_{ij}^2 = \sum_i \sum_j (x_{ij} - x_i)^2 + \sum_i n_i (x_i - x)^2 + nx^2. \tag{3.5}$$

We shall always write $E(x)$ for the mathematical expectation of a random variable x. We put $E(x_i) = \mu_i$ and $1/n \sum_i n_i \mu_i = \mu$ then $(x_{ij} - x_i) = (x_{ij} - \mu_i) - (x_i - \mu_i)$ and by (3.1)

$$\begin{aligned} &\sum_i \sum_j (x_{ij} - x_i)^2 \\ &\qquad = \sum_i \sum_j (x_{ij} - \mu_i)^2 - \sum_i n_i (x_i - \mu_i)^2. \end{aligned} \tag{3.6}$$

By assumption $E(x_{ij} - \mu_i)^2 = \sigma^2$ independent of i and j. Since $\sigma_{x_i}^2 = \sigma^2/n_i$ we obtain from (3.6)

$$E[\sum_i \sum_j (x_{ij} - x_i)^2] = n\sigma^2 - s\sigma^2 = (n - s)\sigma^2.$$

On the other hand

$$\begin{aligned} \sum_i n_i (x_i - x)^2 &= \sum_i n_i [(x_i - \mu) - (x - \mu)]^2 \\ &= \sum_i n_i (x_i - \mu)^2 - n(x - \mu)^2. \end{aligned} \tag{3.7}$$

But

$$(x_i - \mu)^2 = (x_i - \mu_i)^2 + (\mu_i - \mu)^2 + 2(x_i - \mu)(\mu_i - \mu).$$

Hence

$$\begin{aligned} E(x_i - \mu)^2 &= E(x_i - \mu_i)^2 + (\mu_i - \mu)^2 \\ &\quad + 2(\mu_i - \mu)E(x_i - \mu_i) \qquad (3.8) \\ &= \frac{\sigma^2}{n_i} + (\mu_i - \mu)^2. \end{aligned}$$

Therefore from (3.7)

$$\begin{aligned} E[\sum_i n_i(x_i - x)^2] &= s\sigma^2 + \sum_i n_i(\mu_i - \mu)^2 - \sigma^2 \\ &= (s - 1)\sigma^2 + \sum_i n_i(\mu_i - \mu)^2. \qquad (3.9) \end{aligned}$$

Thus whilst $E[\sum_i \sum_j (x_{ij} - x_i)^2]$ is an unbiased estimate of $(n - s)\sigma^2$ regardless of any hypothesis about the μ_i we see from (3.9) that $\sum_i n_i(x_i - x)^2$ is an unbiased estimate of σ^2 only if $\mu_1 = \mu_2 = \cdots = \mu_s$. Otherwise its expectation is larger than σ^2. That is to say; if the hypothesis $\mu_1 = \mu_2 = \cdots = \mu_s = \mu$ is incorrect the ratio

$$(3.10) \qquad F = \frac{n - s}{s - 1} \frac{\sum_i n_i(x_i - x)^2}{\sum_i \sum_j (x_{ij} - x_i)^2}$$

will tend to be large. It seems therefore, reasonable to use this ratio F as a statistic for testing the hypothesis $\mu_1 = \mu_2 = \cdots = \mu_s = \mu$ and to reject this hypothesis on the level of significance α if this ratio is larger than could be expected by chance with probability α. A theoretical justification for using this F ratio will be given in chapters 4 and 6.

We shall now show that the statistic F defined by (3.10) has the F distribution of Chapter 1 with $(s - 1)$ and $(n - s)$ degrees of freedom. We first substitute in (3.5) $x_{ij} - \mu$ for x_{ij}. Then

$$\sum_i \sum_j (x_{ij} - \mu)^2 = \sum_i \sum_j (x_{ij} - x_i)^2 \tag{3.11}$$
$$+ \sum_i n_i(x_i - x)^2 + n(x - \mu)^2 .$$

We now put

$$\sum_i \sum_j (x_{ij} - x_i)^2 = Q_1 \qquad \text{of rank } m_1 ,$$

$$\sum_i n_i(x_i - x)^2 = Q_2 \qquad \text{of rank } m_2 ,$$

$$n(x - \mu)^2 = Q_3 \qquad \text{of rank } m_3 .$$

Q_1 is a sum of squares of the linear forms $L_{ij} = (x_{ij} - x_i)$. Between the L_{ij} there exist s obviously independent relations $\sum_i L_{ij} = 0$, $i = 1, \cdots, s$. Since we may put

$$L_{in_i} = - \sum_{j=1}^{n_i - 1} L_{ij} , \qquad i = (1, \cdots , s),$$

and thus write Q_1 as a quadratic form in $(n - s)$ linear forms, it follows that Q_1 has at most the rank $n - s$. Similarly Q_2 has at most the rank $s - 1$ and Q_3 has obviously the rank 1. But

$$(n - s) + (s - 1) + 1 = n. \tag{3.13}$$

It follows thus from (3.11) and Lemma 2.1 of Chapter 2 that $m_1 = n - s$, $m_2 = s - 1$, $m_3 = 1$. If $\mu_i = \mu_2 = \cdots = \mu$ then the $(x_{ij} - \mu)$ are by assumption normally and independently distributed with common variance σ^2. By the corollary to theorem 2.1

$$\frac{n - s}{s - 1} \frac{Q_2}{Q_1} \tag{3.14}$$

has the F distribution with $n - s$ and $s - 1$ degrees of freedom respectively.

If the quantities $\mu_i - \mu$ are not all equal to 0 then $\sum_i n_i(x_i - x)^2/\sigma^2$ does not have the χ^2 distribution although

$\sum_i \sum_j (x_{ij} - x_i)^2/\sigma^2 = \overline{Q}_1$ still has. This may be seen by applying (3.1) to obtain

$$\overline{Q}'_i = \sum_j (x_{ij} - \mu_i)^2 = \sum_j (x_{ij} - x_i)^2 + n_i(x_i - \mu_i)^2,$$

(3.15)
$$= \overline{Q}_i + n_i(x_i - \mu_i)^2,$$

$$i = (1, \cdots, s).$$

The rank of $\overline{Q}_i$ is at most $n_i - 1$ and it follows from Lemma 1 in Chapter 2 that $\overline{Q}_i$ has exactly the rank $n_i - 1$. From Theorem 2.1 and the independence of the x_{ij} it thus follows that

(3.15)
$$\sum_i \sum_j (x_{ij} - x_i)^2/\sigma^2$$

has the χ^2 distribution with $n - s$ degrees of freedom irrespective of any hypothesis about the μ_i.

In the comparison of classes it is very often desirable to test the significance of differences between class means. Suppose we wish to test whether there is a difference between the means of the ith and the jth class. We put

$$\frac{n_i x_i + n_j x_j}{n_i + n_j} = x'$$

and consider the expression

(3.16)
$$n_i(x_i - x)^2 + n_j(x_j - x)^2 = n_i(x_i - x')^2 + n_j(x_j - x')^2 + (n_i + n_j)(x' - x)^2.$$

It follows that

(3.17)
$$\sum_k n_k(x_k - x)^2 = \sum_{\substack{l \neq i \\ l \neq j}} n_l(x_l - x)^2 + n_i(x_i - x')^2 + n_j(x_j - x')^2 + (n_i + n_j)(x' - x)^2.$$

Substituting (3.17) in (3.11) we have, on account of (3.12),

$$\sum_i \sum_j (x_{ij} - \mu)^2 = Q_1 + \sum_{\substack{l \neq i \\ l \neq j}} n(x_l - x)^2 + n_i(x_i - x')^2$$

(3.18)

$$+ n_j(x_j - x')^2 + (n_i + n_j)(x' - x)^2 + n(x - \mu)^2.$$

The rank of

$$\sum_{\substack{l \neq i \\ l \neq j}} n_l(x_l - x)^2 + (n_i + n_j)(x' - x)^2$$

is at most $s - 2$. The rank of

$$n_i(x_i - x')^2 + n_j(x_j - x')^2 = \frac{n_i n_j}{n_i + n_j} (x_i - x_j)^2$$

is one; hence by the corollary to Theorem 2.1

$$F = \frac{n - s}{1} \frac{n_i n_j}{n_i + n_j} \frac{(x_i - x_j)^2}{Q_1} \tag{3.19}$$

has the F distribution with 1 and $n - s$ degrees of freedom respectively. We have shown before that Q_1 is not affected if $\mu_i \neq \mu_j$ but

$$E(x_i - x_j)^2 = E\{[(x_i - \mu_i) - (x_j - \mu_j) + (\mu_i - \mu_j)]^2\}$$

$$= \frac{n_i + n_j}{n_i n_j} \sigma^2 + (\mu_i - \mu_j)^2.$$

Hence $(x_i - x_j)^2$ will tend to be large if μ_i differs substantially from μ_j. It seems, therefore, reasonable to use the F statistic in (3.19) to test the hypothesis $\mu_i = \mu_j$.

CHAPTER IV

Likelihood Ratio Tests and Tests of Linear Hypothesis

LET THE VARIABLE VECTOR $x = (x_1, \cdots, x_n)$ have the distribution function $f(x, \theta_1, \cdots, \theta_k)$ depending on k parameters $\theta_1, \cdots, \theta_k$. We may know that $\theta_1, \cdots, \theta_k$ satisfy certain relations.

$$(4.1) \qquad g_i(\theta_1, \cdots, \theta_k) = 0, \qquad i = 1, \cdots, s, \qquad 0 \leq s \leq k.$$

We wish to test the hypothesis that $\theta_1, \cdots, \theta_k$ satisfy certain additional relations.

$$(4.2) \quad g_j(\theta_1, \cdots, \theta_k) = 0, \; j = s + 1, \cdots, s + r, \; 0 < r \leq k - s.$$

Let $x_1, \cdots, x_n$ be an independent sample of nx's. The distribution in the sample space is then given by its probability density

$$(4.3) \qquad p(x_1, \cdots, x_n) = \prod_i f(x_i, \theta_1, \cdots, \theta_k).$$

For a given sample $x_1, \cdots, x_n$ the density becomes a function $p(\theta_1, \cdots, \theta_k)$ of $\theta_1, \cdots, \theta_k$. Let $\hat{\theta}_1, \cdots \hat{\theta}_k$ be a set of values for which $p(\theta_1, \cdots, \theta_k)$ is maximized under the restrictions (4.1). We call $\hat{\theta}_1, \cdots, \hat{\theta}_k$ the maximum likelihood estimates of $\theta_1, \cdots, \theta_k$. Maximum likelihood estimates may also be obtained under the restrictions (4.1) and (4.2) and these estimates will be denoted by $\hat{\theta}_1', \cdots, \hat{\theta}_k'$. Clearly

$$(4.4) \qquad p(\hat{\theta}_1, \cdots, \hat{\theta}_k) \geq p(\hat{\theta}_1', \cdots, \hat{\theta}_k').$$

The ratio

$$(4.5) \qquad \frac{p(\hat{\theta}_1', \cdots, \hat{\theta}_k')}{p(\hat{\theta}_1, \cdots, \hat{\theta}_k)} = \lambda$$

is called the likelihood ratio for the hypothesis (4.2). The use of λ as a statistic to test the hypothesis (4.2) can be justified on the basis of certain criteria (see f.i. A. Wald: Tests of statistical hypothesis concerning several parameters, when the number of observations is large. Trans. Am. Math. Sec. 54, pp. 426-482). We shall at this point advance only an intuitive argument. Suppose that our hypothesis is false, then λ would tend to be smaller than if the hypothesis were true. It seems, therefore, reasonable to use λ as a statistic to test the hypothesis (4.2) and to reject it on the level of significance α if $\lambda < \lambda_0$ where λ_0 is chosen so that $P(\lambda < \lambda_0 \mid 4.2) = \alpha$ where $P(E \mid H)$ denotes the probability that the event E will happen computed under the hypothesis H.

All the tests which will be discussed in this book are tests of linear hypotheses. We consider a set of N random variables $y_1, \cdots, y_N$ and put $E(y_\alpha = \mu_\alpha)$. We shall make the following assumptions.

1) *The y_α are normally and independently distributed and their variances are equal.*
2) *The μ_α are linear functions of p parameters $\beta_1, \cdots, \beta_p$, $p \leq N$.*

$$\mu_\alpha = \sum_i g_{i\alpha}\beta_i, \qquad \alpha = 1, \cdots, N. \tag{4.6}$$

and the rank (A.A.A. II 7) *of the matrix $(g_{i\alpha})$ is equal to p.*

Eliminating the β_i from (4.6) we see that the assumption 2 is equivalent to assuming that the μ_α satisfy $N - p$ linear restrictions:

$$\begin{gathered}\sum_\alpha \lambda_{k\alpha}\mu_\alpha = 0, \qquad k = 1, \cdots, N - p, \\ \text{rank } (\lambda_{k\alpha}) = N - p.\end{gathered} \tag{4.6'}$$

The hypothesis we wish to test is *that the β_i satisfy s independent linear restrictions.*

$$\sum_j k_{ij}\beta_j = 0, \qquad i = 1, \cdots, s, \qquad s \leq p. \tag{4.7}$$

The hypothesis can, by eliminating the β_i from (4.6) and (4.7), also be written as

(4.7′)
$$\sum_{\alpha=1}^{N} \rho_{k\alpha}\mu_\alpha = 0, \qquad k = 1, \cdots, s,$$

$$\text{rank}\begin{pmatrix} \lambda_{11} & \cdots & \lambda_{1N} \\ \cdot & & \cdot \\ \cdot & & \cdot \\ \cdot & & \cdot \\ \lambda_{N-p,1} & \cdots & \lambda_{N-p,N} \\ \rho_{11} & \cdots & \rho_{1N} \\ \cdot & & \cdot \\ \cdot & & \cdot \\ \cdot & & \cdot \\ \rho_{s1} & \cdots & \rho_{sN} \end{pmatrix} = N - p + s.$$

According to assumption 1 the joint density function of $y_1, \cdots, y_N$ is given by

(4.8)
$$\frac{1}{\sigma^N (2\pi)^{N/2}} \exp\left[-\frac{1}{2} \sum_\alpha \frac{(y_\alpha - \mu_\alpha)^2}{\sigma^2} \right].$$

We now compute the likelihood ratio. The expression (4.8) is maximized if we minimize

(4.9)
$$\sum_\alpha (y_\alpha - \mu_\alpha)^2 = \sum_\alpha (y_\alpha - g_{1\alpha}\beta_1 - \cdots - g_{p\alpha}\beta_p)^2.$$

Let $b_1, \cdots, b_p$ be the maximum likelihood estimates of $\beta_1, \cdots, \beta_p$. We put

(4.10)
$$Q_a = \sum_\alpha (y_\alpha - g_{1\alpha}b_1 - \cdots - g_{p\alpha}b_p)^2.$$

Similarly the maximum likelihood estimate of σ is obtained as

(4.11)
$$\hat{\sigma}^2 = \frac{Q_a}{N}.$$

The maximum likelihood under the assumptions then becomes

$$(4.12) \qquad \Omega_{\max} = \left(\frac{N}{2\pi Q_a}\right)^{N/2} e^{-N/2}.$$

Let Q_r be the minimum of

$$\sum (y_\alpha - \mu_\alpha)^2 = \sum_\alpha (y_\alpha - g_{1\alpha}\beta_1 - \cdots - g_{p\alpha}\beta_p)^2$$

obtained under the restrictions (4.7) imposed by the hypothesis. The maximum likelihood under the restrictions (4.6) and (4.7) then becomes

$$(4.13) \qquad \omega_{\max} = \left(\frac{N}{2\pi Q_r}\right)^{N/2} e^{-N/2}.$$

Hence the likelihood ratio is given by

$$(4.14) \qquad \lambda = \left(\frac{Q_\alpha}{Q_r}\right)^{N/2}.$$

In testing a hypothesis we may instead of a given test function like λ take any monotonic function of it. Hence instead of $(Q_a/Q_r)^{N/2}$ we may take as a test function Q_r/Q_a or

$$(4.15) \qquad F = \frac{N - P}{s} \frac{Q_r - Q_a}{Q_a}.$$

We decided to reject (4.7) if $\lambda < \lambda_0$ whereby λ_0 is determined so that $P(\lambda < \lambda_0 \mid 4.7) = \alpha$. Since F is a monotonically decreasing function of λ we obtain a test equivalent to the likelihood ratio test if we reject (4.7) whenever $F \geq F_0$ where $P(F \geq F_0 \mid 4.7) = \alpha$.

We proceed to derive the distribution of the ratio (4.15) and we shall show that it has the F distribution of Chapter I with s and $N - P$ degrees of freedom respectively. We first prove:

Lemma 4.1: *Let*

$$(4.16) \qquad \sum_i a_{ij}\mu_j = 0, \qquad i = 1, \cdots, k$$

be k linearly independent linear restrictions on the values μ_1, $\cdots$, μ_N. Then there exists a system of restrictions

$$(4.16') \qquad \sum_i b_{ij}\mu_j = 0, \qquad i = 1, \cdots k$$

such that the restrictions $\sum_j a_{ij}\mu_j = 0$, $i = 1, \cdots, l \leq k$ *are equivalent to the restrictions* $\sum_j b_{ij}\mu_j = 0$, $i = 1, \cdots, l \leq k$ *and such that the rows of the matrix* (b_{ij}) *are orthogonal to each other, that is to say such that*

$$(4.17) \qquad \sum_{\alpha=1}^{\alpha=N} b_{i\alpha}b_{j\alpha} = \delta_{ij} = \begin{cases} 1 & \text{if } i = j \\ 0 & \text{if } i \neq j. \end{cases}$$

Proof: We put

$$b_{1i} = \frac{a_{1i}}{\sum a_{1j}^2}$$

$$b_{2i}^* = a_{2i} - \lambda b_{1i} \qquad \text{where} \qquad \lambda = \sum_i b_{1i}a_{2i}$$

then

$$\sum b_{1i}b_{2i}^* = \sum b_{1i}a_{2i} - \lambda = 0.$$

We then put

$$b_{2i} = \frac{b_{2i}^*}{\sum_j b_{2j}^{*2}}\,.$$

This is possible since

$$\sum_j b_{2j}^{*2} > 0.$$

Otherwise the second equation would be a multiple of the first, contradicting the assumption of independence of the system (4.16). The systems

$$\sum_j a_{ij}\mu_j = 0, \qquad \sum b_{ij}\mu_j = 0, \qquad i = 1, 2$$

are obviously equivalent. Suppose now that we have succeeded in constructing a system

$$(4.18) \qquad \sum_\alpha b_{i\alpha}\mu_\alpha = 0, \qquad i = 1, \cdots, l < k$$

fulfilling (4.17), which is equivalent to

$$\sum_\alpha a_{i\alpha}\mu_\alpha = 0, \qquad i = 1, \cdots, l < K.$$

We put

$$b^*_{l+1\alpha} = a_{l+1\alpha} - \lambda_1 b_{1\alpha} - \cdots - \lambda_l b_{l\alpha} ,$$

where

$$\lambda_i = \sum_\alpha a_{l+1\alpha} b_{i\alpha} , \qquad i = 1, \cdots , l,$$

then

$$\sum_\alpha b^*_{l+1\alpha} b_{j\alpha} = \sum_\alpha a_{l+1\alpha} b_{j\alpha} - \sum_\alpha \sum_{i=1}^{l} \lambda_i b_{i\alpha} b_{j\alpha} ,$$

$$j = 1, \cdots , l.$$

Since (4.17) is valid for $i, j \leq l$ we have

$$\sum_\alpha b^*_{l+1\alpha} b_{j\alpha} = \sum_\alpha a_{l+1} b_{j\alpha} - \lambda_j = 0.$$

Now $\sum_\alpha b^{*2}_{l+1} > 0$ since otherwise the $(l + 1)$st equation would be a linear combination of the first l equations, contradicting the assumption of independence of (4.16). We then have only to put

$$b_{l+1\alpha} = \frac{b^*_{l+1\alpha}}{\sum_\alpha b^{*2}_{l+1}}$$

to obtain the $(l + 1)$st equation of the system $\sum_\alpha b_{i\alpha}\mu_\alpha = 0$ fulfilling (4.17) and equivalent to the initial equations of (4.16). The process may be continued until all k rows of (4.16′) are obtained.

Applying Lemma 4.1 to the restrictions imposed on the μ_α by the hypothesis and the assumptions of the linear hypothesis we may assume that the rows of (4.6′) and (4.7′) are normalized and orthogonal, that is to say that

$$\sum_\alpha \lambda_{i\alpha}\lambda_{j\alpha} = \sum_\alpha \rho_{i\alpha}\rho_{j\alpha} = \delta_{ij} = \begin{cases} 0 & \text{for } i \neq j \\ 1 & \text{for } i = j. \end{cases}$$

$$\sum_\alpha \rho_{i\alpha}\lambda_{j\alpha} = 0.$$

If $p > s$ we form an additional row $\tau_{11}, \cdots, \tau_{1n}$ such that

$$\sum_i \lambda_{i\alpha}\tau_{1\alpha} = 0, \qquad i = 1, \cdots, p$$

$$\sum_i \rho_{i\alpha}\tau_{1\alpha} = 0, \qquad i = 1, \cdots, s.$$

This is possible since $N - p + s < N$ equations in N unknowns have a non trivial solution. Thus continuing we finally obtain an orthogonal matrix

$$\text{(4.19)} \qquad \begin{pmatrix} \lambda_{11}, & \cdots, \lambda_{1N} \\ \cdot & \cdot \\ \cdot & \cdot \\ \cdot & \cdot \\ \lambda_{N-p1}, & \cdots, \lambda_{N-pN} \\ \rho_{11}, & \cdots, \rho_{1N} \\ \cdot & \cdot \\ \cdot & \cdot \\ \cdot & \cdot \\ \rho_{s1}, & \cdots, \rho_{sN} \\ \tau_{11}, & \cdots, \tau_{1N} \\ \cdot & \cdot \\ \cdot & \cdot \\ \cdot & \cdot \\ \tau_{p-s1}, & \cdots, \tau_{p-sN} \end{pmatrix}.$$

We now put

$$y_i^* = \sum_\alpha \lambda_{i\alpha} y_\alpha \qquad \text{for } i = 1, \cdots, N - p;$$

$$\text{(4.20)} \qquad y_{N-p+k}^* = \sum_\alpha \rho_{k\alpha} y_\alpha \qquad \text{for } k = 1, \cdots, s;$$

$$y_{N-p+s+l}^* = \sum_\alpha \tau_{l\alpha} y_\alpha \qquad \text{for } l = 1, \cdots, p - s.$$

Let $E(y_\alpha^*) = \mu_\alpha^*$. Then

$$\mu_\alpha^* = \sum_j \lambda_{\alpha j}\mu_j, \qquad \alpha = 1, \cdots, N-p;$$

(4.21) $$\mu_{N-p+\beta}^* = \sum_j \rho_{\beta j}\mu_j, \qquad \beta = 1, \cdots, s;$$

$$\mu_{N-p+s+\gamma}^* = \sum_j \tau_{\gamma j}\mu_j, \qquad \gamma = 1, \cdots, p-s.$$

Then since (4.19) is orthogonal

$$\sum_\alpha (y_\alpha - \mu_\alpha)^2 = \sum_\alpha (y_\alpha^* - \mu_\alpha^*)^2.$$

By Lemma 2.2 the $(y_\alpha^* - \mu_\alpha^*)$ are normally and independently distributed with mean 0 and variance σ^2. The assumptions then state that $\mu_\alpha^* = 0$ for $\alpha = 1, \cdots, N-p$. Hence

(4.22) $$Q_a = \sum_{\alpha=1}^{N-p} y_\alpha^{*2}.$$

Similarly

$$Q_r = \sum_{\alpha=1}^{N-p+s} y_\alpha^{*2}$$

and

(4.23) $$Q_r - Q_a = \sum_{\alpha=N-p+1}^{N-p+s} y_\alpha^{*2}.$$

Hence under the assumptions Q_a is a sum of $N - p$ independent squares and Q_a/σ^2 has the χ^2 distribution with $N - p$ degrees of freedom. Similarly $(Q_r - Q_a)/\sigma^2$ has the χ^2 distribution with s degrees of freedom and $Q_r - Q_a$ and Q_a are independent of each other. Hence

(4.24) $$F = \frac{N-p}{s}\frac{Q_r - Q_a}{Q_a}$$

has the F distribution with s and $N - p$ degrees of freedom respectively. We, therefore, have

THEOREM 4.1: *Let $y_1, \cdots, y_N$ be normally and independently distributed variables with the same variance and means $\mu_1, \cdots, \mu_N$ respectively. Assume that the μ_α satisfy the independent relations*

$$(4.25) \qquad \sum_\alpha \lambda_{i\alpha}\mu_\alpha = 0 \qquad i = 1, \cdots, N - p.$$

To test the hypothesis that the μ_α satisfy relations

$$(4.26) \qquad \sum_\alpha \rho_{i\alpha}\mu_\alpha \qquad i = 1, \cdots, s \qquad s \leq p.$$

independent of the relations (4.25) and of each other, we form the ratio

$$(4.27) \qquad F = \frac{N-p}{s}\frac{Q_r - Q_a}{Q_a},$$

where Q_a is the minimum with respect to μ_α of $\sum_\alpha (y_\alpha - \mu_\alpha)^2$ under the restrictions (4.25) and Q_r the minimum of $\sum_\alpha (y_\alpha - \mu_\alpha)^2$ under the restrictions (4.25) and (4.26). We reject the hypothesis (4.26) if $F \geq F_0$ where $P(F \geq F_0 \mid 4.25 \ \& \ 4.26) = \alpha$ and α is a fixed constant. Then

1) *The test described is equivalent to the likelihood ratio test for the hypothesis (4.26).*
2) *The ratio (4.27) has the F distribution with s and $N - p$ degrees of freedom respectively.*

We can formulate our assumptions also in the following manner. We have

$$y_\alpha = \mu_\alpha + \epsilon_\alpha,$$

where the ϵ_α are normally and independently distributed variables. According to our assumptions (4.6) we have

$$(4.28) \qquad y_\alpha = g_{1\alpha}\beta_1 + \cdots + g_{p\alpha}\beta_p + \epsilon_\alpha, \qquad \alpha = 1, \cdots, N.$$

The equation (4.28) is called a linear regression equation of y on $g_1, \cdots, g_p$. The coefficients $\beta_1, \cdots, \beta_p$ are termed the regression coefficients of y on $g_1, \cdots, g_p$. We have shown that their maximum likelihood estimates $b_1, \cdots, b_p$ minimize the expression

(4.29) $$\sum_\alpha (y_\alpha - \beta_1 g_{1\alpha} - \cdots - \beta_p g_{p\alpha})^2.$$

Hence we must have

(4.30) $$\sum_\alpha (y_\alpha - b_1 g_{1\alpha} - \cdots - b_p g_{p\alpha}) g_{i\alpha} = 0, \qquad i = 1, \cdots, p.$$

Multiplying the ith of the equations (4.30) by b_i, adding over all equations (4.30), and putting

(4.31) $$Y_\alpha = b_1 g_{1\alpha} + \cdots + b_p g_{p\alpha}$$

we obtain

(4.32) $$\sum_\alpha (y_\alpha - Y_\alpha) Y_\alpha = 0.$$

The quantity Y_α is called the regression value of y_α on the variables $g_{1\alpha}, \cdots, g_{p\alpha}$.

The minimum Q_a under the assumptions is then given by

(4.33) $$\begin{aligned}\sum_\alpha (y_\alpha - Y_\alpha)^2 &= \sum_\alpha (y_\alpha - Y_\alpha) y_\alpha - \sum_\alpha (y_\alpha - Y_\alpha) Y_\alpha \\ &= \sum_\alpha y_\alpha^2 - \sum_\alpha Y_\alpha^2.\end{aligned}$$

Let now Y^* be the regression value of y_α on $g_{1\alpha}, \cdots, g_{p\alpha}$ under the restrictions 4.6 and 4.7. Then similarly

(4.34) $$Q_r = \sum_\alpha y_\alpha^2 - \sum_\alpha Y_\alpha^{*2}.$$

Hence

(4.35) $$Q_r - Q_a = \sum_\alpha (Y_\alpha^2 - Y_\alpha^{*2}).$$

The restrictions (4.7) are equivalent to stating that $\beta_1, \cdots, \beta_p$ may be expressed by $p - s$ parameters $\gamma_1, \cdots, \gamma_{p-s}$.

(4.36) $$\beta_i = \sum_j k_{ij} \gamma_j. \qquad i = 1, \cdots, p.$$

Let $c_1, \cdots, c_{p-s}$ be the maximum likelihood estimates of γ_i. Then

$$(4.37) \qquad Y^*_\alpha = \sum_l c_l \sum_t g_{t\alpha} k_{tl} \, .$$

Multiplying the tth of the equations (4.30) by $k_{tl}c_l$ and summing over t and l we obtain

$$(4.38) \qquad \sum_\alpha (y_\alpha - Y_\alpha) Y^*_\alpha = 0.$$

Since also $\sum_\alpha (y_\alpha - Y^*_\alpha) Y^*_\alpha = 0$ we obtain

$$\sum_\alpha (Y_\alpha - Y^*_\alpha) Y^*_\alpha = \sum_\alpha (y_\alpha - Y^*_\alpha) Y^*_\alpha - \sum_\alpha (y_\alpha - Y_\alpha) Y^*_\alpha = 0.$$

Hence

$$(4.39) \qquad \begin{aligned} \sum_\alpha (Y_\alpha - Y^*_\alpha)^2 &= \sum_\alpha (Y_\alpha - Y^*_\alpha) Y_\alpha \\ &= \sum_\alpha Y^2_\alpha - \sum_\alpha Y^{*2}_\alpha . \end{aligned}$$

Therefore

$$(4.40) \qquad Q_r - Q_a = \sum_\alpha (Y_\alpha - Y^*_\alpha)^2$$

and

$$(4.41) \qquad \begin{aligned} F &= \frac{(N-p)}{s} \frac{\sum_\alpha (Y_\alpha - Y^*_\alpha)^2}{\sum_\alpha (y_\alpha - Y_\alpha)^2} \\ &= \frac{N-p}{s} \frac{\sum_\alpha Y^2_\alpha - \sum_\alpha Y^{*2}_\alpha}{\sum_\alpha y^2_\alpha - \sum_\alpha Y^2_\alpha} \, . \end{aligned}$$

Testing a linear hypothesis means essentially testing the significance of the coefficients of a regression equation.

From (4.33) and (4.39) it follows also that

$$(4.42) \qquad \begin{aligned} \sum_\alpha (y_\alpha - Y_\alpha)^2 = \sum_\alpha y^2_\alpha - \sum_\alpha Y^{*2}_\alpha \\ - \sum (Y_\alpha - Y^*_\alpha)^2 . \end{aligned}$$

This result can easily be generalized to yield

Theorem 4.2: *Let $H_1, \cdots, H_s$ be a sequence of hypotheses on the means of the variables y_α with $E(y_\alpha) = \mu_\alpha$ of the form*

$$H_1: \qquad \mu_\alpha = \sum_{i=1}^{p} g_{i\alpha}\beta_i ,$$

$$H_t: \qquad H_1 \,\&\, H_2 \cdots \&\, H_{t-1} \,\&\, \sum_j a_{kj}\beta_j = 0,$$

$$k = s_{t-1} + 1, \cdots, s_t , \qquad s_t \leq p$$

such that the linear restrictions imposed by H_s are independent of each other. Let $Y_\alpha^{(t)}$ be the regression value of y_α obtained under the hypothesis H_t then

$$\sum_\alpha y_\alpha^2 = \sum_\alpha (y_\alpha - Y_\alpha^{(1)})^2 + \sum_\alpha (Y_\alpha^{(1)} - Y_\alpha^{(2)})^2$$

(4.43)

$$+ \cdots + \sum_\alpha (Y_\alpha^{(s-1)} - Y_\alpha^{(s)})^2 + \sum_\alpha (Y_\alpha^{(s)})^2.$$

Theorem 4.2 is very useful in reducing the labor involved in computing sums of squares of deviations from a regression value.

We now turn our attention to the solution of the equation (4.30). We write

(4.44) $$\sum_\alpha g_{i\alpha}g_{j\alpha} = a_{ij} , \qquad \sum_\alpha y_\alpha g_{i\alpha} = a_i .$$

Lemma 4.2: *Let $g = (g_{i\alpha})$, $(i = 1, \cdots, p, \alpha = 1, \cdots, N)$, be any matrix of rank $p \leq N$. Put $gg' = (a_{ij})$. Then the quadratic form $\sum_i \sum_j a_{ij}x_i x_j$ is positive definite.*

Proof: Consider

$$\sum_\alpha \left(\sum_{i=1}^{i=p} g_{i\alpha}x_i \right)^2 = \sum_\alpha \sum_i \sum_j g_{i\alpha}g_{j\alpha}x_i x_j$$

$$= \sum_i \sum_j a_{ij}x_i x_j = Q.$$

clearly Q is either positive definite or positive semi definite. If $Q = 0$ then

$$(4.45) \qquad \sum_i g_{i\alpha} x_i = 0, \qquad \alpha = 1, \cdots, N.$$

Since g has the rank p there are p linearly independent equations in (4.45). Therefore, (4.45) has only the solution $x_i = 0$, $i = 1, \cdots, p$. Hence Q is positive definite.

Corollary to lemma 4.2. *The determinant* $| a_{ij} |$ *is different from* 0.

This follows from the fact that all the principal minors of a positive definite matrix are positive.

We may rewrite (4.30) as

$$(4.46) \qquad \sum_j a_{ij} b_j = a_i , \qquad i = 1, \cdots, p,$$

or in matrix form

$$(4.47) \qquad (a_{ij})(b) = (a), \qquad b = \begin{pmatrix} b_1 \\ \cdot \\ \cdot \\ \cdot \\ b_p \end{pmatrix}, \qquad (a) = \begin{pmatrix} a_1 \\ \cdot \\ \cdot \\ \cdot \\ a_p \end{pmatrix}.$$

Since by the corollary to lemma 4.2 (a_{ij}) is non singular we have with $(a^{ij}) = (a_{ij})^{-1}$

$$(4.48) \qquad b = (a^{ij})(a)$$

or

$$(4.48') \qquad b_i = \sum_j a^{ij} a_j , \qquad i = 1, \cdots, p.$$

We see that b_i is a linear function with constant coefficients of the y_α. Hence if the y_α are jointly normally distributed, then the b_i are jointly normally distributed and their distribution is completely specified if we know their means and their covariance matrix. We have putting

$$\delta_{ij} = \begin{cases} 0 & \text{for } i \neq j \\ 1 & \text{for } i = j, \end{cases}$$

$$E(b_i) = \sum_j a^{ij} \sum_\alpha g_{j\alpha} E(y_\alpha) = \sum_j a^{ij} \sum_\alpha \sum_l g_{j\alpha} g_{l\alpha} \beta_l$$

(4.49)

$$= \sum_j \sum_l a^{ij} a_{jl} \beta_l = \sum_l \delta_{il} \beta_l = \beta_i \ .$$

Thus b_i is an unbiased estimate of β_i . Further

$$\sigma_{b_i b_j} = \sum_k \sum_l a^{ik} a^{jl} \sigma_{a_k a_l} = \sum_k \sum_l a^{ik} a^{jl} \sum_\alpha \sum_\beta g_{k\alpha} g_{l\beta} \sigma_{y_\alpha y_\beta} \ .$$

But $\sigma_{y_\alpha y_\beta} = 0$ if $\alpha \neq \beta$ and $\sigma^2_{y_\alpha} = \sigma^2$. Hence

$$\sigma_{b_i b_j} = \sigma^2 \sum_k \sum_l a^{ik} a^{jl} \sum_\alpha g_{k\alpha} g_{l\alpha} = \sigma^2 \sum_k \sum_l a^{ik} a^{jl} a_{kl}$$

(4.50)

$$= \sigma^2 \sum_k a^{ik} \delta_{jk} = a^{ij} \sigma^2.$$

We proceed to prove

THEOREM 4.3: *Let Q_a be the minimum of the quadratic form $\sum_\alpha (y_\alpha - E(y_\alpha))^2$ under the assumption*

$$(4.51) \qquad E(y_\alpha) = \sum_{i=1}^{s} \beta_i g_{i\alpha} + \sum_{d=s+1}^{p} \beta_d g_{d\alpha} \ , \qquad \alpha = 1, \cdots, N.$$

and Q_r its minimum under the restrictions $\beta_i = 0, i = 1, \cdots, s$. Let b_i , $(i = 1, \cdots, s)$, $b_d (d = s + 1, \cdots, p)$ be the least square estimates of $\beta_1, \beta_2, \cdots, \beta_p$ under the restrictions (4.51) *and put*

$$\left(\frac{\sigma_{b_i b_j}}{\sigma^2}\right)^{-1} = (c_{ij}).$$

Then

$$(4.52) \qquad Q_r - Q_a = \sum_i \sum_j c_{ij} b_i b_j \ .$$

In the following let i, j, k run from 1 to s; d, e, f from $s + 1$ to p; σ, τ from 1 to p.

Put

$$(4.53) \qquad \begin{pmatrix} a_{ij} & a_{id} \\ a_{dj} & a_{de} \end{pmatrix}^{-1} = \begin{pmatrix} a^{ij} & a^{id} \\ a^{dj} & a^{de} \end{pmatrix}, \qquad (a_{de})^{-1} = (a'^{de}).$$

Then by (4.50)

$$(a^{ij})^{-1} = (c_{ij}). \tag{4.54}$$

We have

$$\begin{aligned} Q_a &= \sum_\alpha y_\alpha^2 - \sum_\alpha Y_\alpha^2 = \sum_\alpha y_\alpha^2 - \sum_\alpha \sum_\sigma \sum_\tau g_{\sigma\alpha} g_{\tau\alpha} b_\sigma b_\tau \\ &= \sum_\alpha y_\alpha^2 - \sum_\sigma \sum_\tau a_{\sigma\tau} b_\sigma b_\tau = \sum_\alpha y_\alpha^2 - \sum_\sigma a_\sigma b_\sigma . \end{aligned} \tag{4.55}$$

Let b_d^*, $d = s + 1, \cdots p$ be the regression values for β_d obtained under the hypothesis $\beta_1 = \cdots \beta_s = 0$. Then by (4.55)

$$\begin{aligned} Q_r - Q_a &= \sum_i a_i b_i + \sum_d a_d b_d - \sum_d a_d b_d^* \\ &= \sum_i a_i b_i + \sum_d a_d (b_d - b_d^*). \end{aligned} \tag{4.56}$$

But from (4.46) we have

$$\sum_{e=s+1}^{p} a_{de}(b_e - b_e^*) = -\sum_j a_{dj} b_j .$$

Hence

$$b_e - b_e^* = -\sum_d a'^{de} \sum_j a_{dj} b_j , \tag{4.57}$$

and from (4.46), (4.56) and (4.57)

$$\begin{aligned} Q_r - Q_a &= \sum_i b_i (\sum_j a_{ij} b_j + \sum_d a_{id} b_d) \\ &\quad - \sum_d a_d \sum_e a'^{de} \sum_j a_{ej} b_j \\ &= \sum_i b_i (\sum_j a_{ij} b_j + \sum_d a_{id} b_d) \\ &\quad - \sum_d \sum_e \sum_k \sum_j a_{dk} a'^{de} a_{ej} b_j b_k \\ &\quad - \sum_d \sum_e \sum_f \sum_j a_{df} a'^{de} a_{ej} b_j b_f . \end{aligned} \tag{4.58}$$

The coefficient of $b_i b_f$ in the expression (4.58) is given by

$$a_{if} - \sum_d \sum_e a_{df} a'^{de} a_{ei} = a_{if} - \sum_e \delta_{ef} a_{ei}$$

(4.59)

$$= a_{if} - a_{fi} = 0.$$

The coefficient of $b_j b_k$ is given by

(4.60) $$a_{jk} - \sum_d \sum_e a_{dk} a'^{de} a_{ej} = \bar{c}_{jk} .$$

Our theorem is proved if we can prove that $\bar{c}_{jk} = c_{jk}$. This is proved if we can show that $\sum_i a^{ij} \bar{c}_{jk} = \delta_{ik}$. We have

(4.61) $$\sum_j a^{ij} \bar{c}_{jk} = \sum_j a^{ij} a_{jk} - \sum_j \sum_d \sum_e a^{ij} a_{dk} a'^{de} a_{ej} .$$

Now

$$\sum_j a^{ij} a_{ej} + \sum_f a^{if} a_{ef} = \delta_{ie} = 0.$$

Hence (4.61) becomes

$$\sum_j a^{ij} a_{jk} + \sum_d \sum_e \sum_f a^{if} a_{ef} a'^{de} a_{dk}$$

$$= \sum_j a^{ij} a_{jk} + \sum_d \sum_f a^{if} \delta_{fd} a_{dk}$$

$$= \sum_j a^{ij} a_{jk} + \sum_d a^{id} a_{dk} = \delta_{ik} .$$

Hence $\bar{c}_{ij} = c_{ij}$ and theorem 4.3 is proved.

Corollary 1 of theorem 4.3. *Let the hypothesis in theorem* 4.3 *be*

(4.62) $$\beta_i^* = \sum_{t=1}^{p} l_{it} \beta_t = 0, \qquad i = 1, \cdots , s \leq p,$$

where the rank of (l_{it}) is s. *Put*

$$\sum_t l_{it} b_t = b_i^* \qquad \textit{and} \qquad \left(\frac{\sigma_{b_i^* b_j^*}}{\sigma^2} \right)^{-1} = c_{ij} .$$

Then

(4.63) $$Q_r - Q_a = \sum_i \sum_j c_{ij} b_i^* b_j^* .$$

Proof: Since the rank of (l_{it}) is s we can add $p - s$ rows to (l_{it}) to obtain a non singular matrix (l_{tv}) with p rows and p columns. The β_t are then also linear functions of $\beta_v^* = \sum_t l_{vt}\beta_t$, $v = 1, \cdots, p$. Clearly $b_v^* = \sum_t l_{vt}b_t$ must minimize Q_a and the corollary follows by applying theorem 4.3.

The most important special case of theorem 4.3 and its corollary is the case where $s = 1$ then

$$Q_r - Q_a = \frac{b_1^2\sigma^2}{\sigma_{b_1}^2}. \tag{4.64}$$

In finding Q_a it is sometimes required to minimize $Q = \sum_\alpha (y_\alpha - \sum_i g_{\alpha i}\beta_i)^2$ under some linear restrictions on the β_j

$$\sum_{j=1}^{p} l_{ij}\beta_j = L_i = 0, \qquad i = 1, \cdots, s, \tag{4.65}$$

$$\text{rank } (l_{ij}) = s < p.$$

Then s of the β_j can be expressed as functions of $p - s$ of them and the regression problem may thus be reduced to a regression problem in $p - s$ of the β_j.

Suppose that all the β's can, by means of (4.65), be presented as linear functions of $\beta_1^*, \cdots, \beta_t^*, \beta_{t+1}^*, \cdots, \beta_{p-s}^*$, where the β_i^* are linear functions of $\beta_1, \cdots, \beta_p$ and that we test the hypothesis $\beta_1^* = \cdots = \beta_t^* = 0$. Then theorem 4.3 also applies to the maximum likelihood estimates $b_1^*, \cdots, b_t^*$, since we can write Q as a function of $\beta_1^*, \cdots, \beta_{p-s}^*$.

Instead of the elimination procedure of the preceding paragraph, it is often more convenient to employ the method of Lagrange operators. This method consists in differentiating the expression

$$Q + \lambda_1 L_1 + \cdots + \lambda_s L_s = Q', \tag{4.66}$$

with respect to $\beta_1, \cdots, \beta_p$ and solving (4.65) together with

$$\frac{\partial Q'}{\partial \beta_i} = 0, \qquad i = 1, \cdots, p \tag{4.67}$$

for the $s + p$ unknown quantities $\beta_1, \cdots, \beta_p$ and $\lambda_1, \cdots, \lambda_s$. The values for $\beta_1, \cdots, \beta_p$ obtained in this way are exactly the maximum likelihood estimates $b_1, \cdots, b_p$ obtained under the restrictions (4.65). A full account of Lagrange's method is given in Hancock "Theory of Maxima and Minima Chapter VI".

The regression coefficient β_p in (4.6) will be termed the general mean if $g_{p\alpha} = 1$ for all α.

THEOREM 4.4: *Let*

$$E(y_\alpha) = \mu_\alpha = \sum_{i=1}^{p} g_{i\alpha}\beta_i .$$

Assume that

1) β_p *is the general mean.*

2) $g_{i\alpha}$ *is either* 0 or 1, $\qquad i = 1, \cdots, s.$

3) $\sum_\alpha g_{i\alpha}g_{j\alpha} = 0 \qquad$ *if* $\qquad i \neq j,\ i, j \leq s.$

4) $\sum_{i=1}^{s} g_{i\alpha}^2 = 1 \qquad \alpha = 1, \cdots, N.$

If

$$Q = \sum \left(y_\alpha - \sum_{i=1}^{p} g_{i\alpha}\beta_i\right)^2$$

is minimized with respect to

$$\beta_1, \cdots, \beta_p \qquad \textit{and} \qquad \sum_{i=1}^{s} t_i\beta_i = 0, \qquad \sum t_i \neq 0$$

is the only restriction on $\beta_1, \cdots, \beta_s, \beta_p$ *and if* λ_1 *is the Lagrange multiplier associated with*

$$\sum_{i=1}^{s} t_i\beta_i \qquad \textit{then} \qquad \lambda_1 = 0.$$

It may be emphasized that any number of restrictions may be imposed on $\beta_{s+1}, \cdots, \beta_{p-1}$. Denoting by $b_1, \cdots, b_p$ the least square estimates of $\beta_1, \cdots, \beta_p$ we obtain the following equations

$$\sum_\alpha y_\alpha g_{i\alpha} - b_i \sum_\alpha g_{i\alpha}^2 - \sum_{d=s+1}^{p} b_d \sum_\alpha g_{d\alpha} g_{i\alpha} - \frac{t_i \lambda_1}{2} = 0,$$

(4.68) $$i = 1, \cdots, s,$$

$$\sum_\alpha y_\alpha - \sum_{i=1}^{s} b_i \sum_\alpha g_{i\alpha} - \sum_{d=s+1}^{p} b_d \sum_\alpha g_{d\alpha} = 0.$$

Because of the conditions 1, 2, 3, 4 we have

(4.69)
$$\sum_\alpha y_\alpha = \sum_\alpha \sum_{i=1}^{s} y_\alpha g_{i\alpha}, \qquad \sum_\alpha g_{i\alpha} = \sum_\alpha g_{i\alpha}^2,$$

$$\sum_{i=1}^{s} \sum_\alpha g_{i\alpha} g_{d\alpha} = \sum_\alpha g_{d\alpha}.$$

If we sum the first of the relations (4.68) from $i = 1, \cdots, s$ we obtain $\lambda_1 = 0$ on account of the relations (4.69).

THEOREM 4.5: Let

$$Q = \sum_\alpha (y_\alpha - \sum_i g_{i\alpha}\beta_i)^2.$$

Let Q_a be the minimum of Q under the restrictions

$$\sum_{i=1}^{s} \beta_i = 0$$

and other restrictions involving $\beta_{s+1}, \cdots, \beta_p$ only. Let $b_1, \cdots, b_s$ be the least square estimates of $\beta_1, \cdots \beta_s$ under these restrictions. Let Q_r be the minimum under the restrictions $\beta_1 = \cdots = \beta_s = 0$ and all other restrictions.

If $Q_r - Q_a$ is a symmetric function of $b_1, \cdots, b_s$ and if the assumptions of theorem 4.4 are satisfied then

(4.70) $$Q_r - Q_a = \frac{s-1}{sc} \sum_{i=1}^{s} b_i^2, \qquad \sigma_{b_i}^2 = c\sigma^2.$$

Proof: $Q_r - Q_a$ is by theorem 4.3 a quadratic form in b_1, $\cdots$, b_s. Since it is symmetric in $b_1, \cdots, b_s$ and since

$$\sum_{i=1}^{s} b_i = 0$$

we must have

$$(4.71)\quad Q_r - Q_a = h \sum_{i=1}^{s} b_i^2 + k \sum_{i,j=1}^{s} b_i b_j = K \sum_{i=1}^{s} b_i^2 .$$

Because of the symmetry, the variances of the b_i must all be equal to each other. $Q_r - Q_a$ has by theorem 4.1 the χ^2 distribution with $(s - 1)$ degrees of freedom. Hence

$$(4.72)\qquad E(Q_r - Q_a) = (s - 1)\sigma^2 = Ksc\sigma^2$$

and theorem 4.5 follows.

We now proceed to present some applications of the principles developed in this chapter.

Example 1. Consider a regression equation

$$(4.74)\qquad E(y) = \beta_1 + \beta_2 x,$$

where the values of y have been observed for certain values of x. For instance y may be the length of a steel rod and x the temperature at which this length is measured. We have then a set of observations

$$y_1, \cdots, y_N$$

of the variable y observed when the variable x had the values $x_1, \cdots, x_N$. We might wish to test whether β_2 has some hypothetical value $\bar{\beta}_2$. We then rewrite (4.74) as

$$(4.75)\qquad E(y - \bar{\beta}_2 x) = \beta_1 + (\beta_2 - \bar{\beta}_2)x.$$

Treating now $y_\alpha - \bar{\beta}_2 x_\alpha = y'_\alpha$ as the independent variable we may apply Theorem 4.3 to the regression coefficient $\beta_2 - \bar{\beta}_2 = \beta_2^*$. If Y'_α is the regression value of y'_α on β_1 and β_2^* and b_2^* the least square estimate of β_2^* and $c\sigma^2$ its variance then we use

$$(4.76)\qquad F = \frac{N - 2}{1} \frac{b_2^{*2}}{c(\sum y_\alpha^2 - \sum Y_\alpha^2)}$$

as a statistic to test the hypothesis $\beta_2^* = 0$. By Theorem 4.1 F has the F distribution with 1 and $N - 2$ degrees of freedom respectively.

From (4.76) we can see the intuitive reason for using the test function F. The total observed sum of squares of deviations

$$\sum_\alpha (y_\alpha - \bar{y})^2 \qquad \text{where} \qquad \bar{y} = \frac{y_1 + \cdots + y_N}{N}$$

has been divided into two components;

$$\sum_\alpha (y_\alpha - Y_\alpha)^2 \qquad \text{and} \qquad \sum_\alpha (Y_\alpha - \bar{y})^2 = \frac{b_2^{*2}}{c} = (Q_r - Q_a).$$

Each of the two quadratic forms in y_α divided by its rank (degrees of freedom) gives us an estimate of the variance σ^2. But whilst the estimate of σ^2 appearing in the denominator of (4.76) is independent of the value of β_2^*, the numerator is an estimate of σ^2 only if $\beta_2^* = 0$. If $\beta_2^* \neq 0$ then the numerator will tend to be larger than σ^2.

Example 2. Suppose now that y is again the length of a steel bar and x its temperature. We wish to test whether the length of a steel bar is a linear function of the temperature, whilst admitting the alternative possibility that the function be of second degree. Our assumption will then be

$$E(y) = \beta_1 + \beta_2 x + \beta_3 x^2, \tag{4.77}$$

where the length y of the steel bar is measured at different temperatures $x_1, \cdots, x_N$. In terms of theorems 4.1 and 4.3 we have

$$g_{1\alpha} = 1, \qquad g_{2\alpha} = x_\alpha, \qquad g_{3\alpha} = x_\alpha^2 .$$

The hypothesis to be tested is $\beta_3 = 0$. The first step is then to estimate $\beta_1, \beta_2, \beta_3$ by least squares. Then if $\sigma_{b_3}^2 = c\sigma^2$, where c can be computed from the $g_{i\alpha}$, and b_3 is the least square estimate of β_3,

$$F = \frac{N-3}{1} \frac{b_3^2}{C\,Q_a}$$

has the F distribution with 1 and $N - 3$ degrees of freedom respectively.

Example 3. We shall consider again the one way classification problem treated in Chapter 3. We assumed that we had taken a sample of $n_1 x$'s from the first classification, n_2 from the second and so on. Denoting by x_{ij} the jth measurement in the ith class we have to consider the following linear hypothesis.

Assumption

$$E(x_{ij}) = \mu_i \qquad \text{for} \qquad i = 1, \cdots, s, \qquad j = 1, \cdots, n_i .$$

The hypothesis to be tested is $\mu_1 = \cdots = \mu_s$. The number of independent linear constraints imposed by the assumption is $n_1 + n_2 + \cdots + n_s - s = n - s$. The number of linear constraints imposed by the hypothesis is $s - 1$. To obtain Q_a we have to minimize

$$\sum_{i=1}^{s} \sum_{j=1}^{n_i} (x_{ij} - \mu_i)^2. \tag{4.78}$$

Let m_i be the least square estimates of μ_i. Then

$$m_i = \frac{1}{n_i} \sum_j x_{ij} = x_{i\cdot}\,, \qquad i = 1, \cdots, s. \tag{4.79}$$

Hence if Y_{ij} is the regression value of x_{ij} on $\mu_1, \cdots, \mu_s$ we have

$$Y_{ij} = x_{i\cdot}\,, \qquad (i = 1, \cdots, s, \qquad j = 1, \cdots, n_i). \tag{4.80}$$

To obtain Q_r we have to minimize $\sum_i \sum_j (x_{ij} - \mu)^2$ which yields as regression value the mean x of all observations. It follows then from Theorem 4.1 and equation 4.1 that

$$F = \frac{n-s}{s-1} \frac{\sum_i n_i x_{i\cdot}^2 - n x^2}{\sum_i \sum_j (x_{ij})^2 - \sum_i n_i x_{i\cdot}^2} \tag{4.81}$$

is the likelihood ratio statistic for testing our hypothesis.

Example 4. We shall now treat the problem of a 2 way classification. As an example suppose that $r \cdot s$ pigs from r different races receive s different diets such that exactly one pig of the ith race ($i = 1, \cdots, r$) receives the jth diet $j = 1, \cdots, s$. The purpose of the experiment is two fold. We want to see if the pig races differ with respect to the weight gains and at the same time we should like to know if the different diets differ in their ability to produce weight gains.

Our observations can be arranged into a matrix

$$\begin{pmatrix} x_{11}, & \cdots, & x_{1s} \\ \cdot & & \cdot \\ \cdot & & \cdot \\ \cdot & & \cdot \\ x_{r1}, & \cdots, & x_{rs} \end{pmatrix},$$

where x_{ij} is the weight gain of the pig from the ith race which receives the jth diet.

We assume now that the weight gain is produced by two factors, race and feed, both of which act independently of each other. Moreover we shall assume that the x_{ij} are normally and independently distributed all with the same variance.

Our linear hypothesis is then the following

$$(4.82) \quad E(x_{ij}) = \mu_{i\cdot} + \mu_{\cdot j} + \mu, \qquad \sum \mu_{i\cdot} = \sum \mu_{\cdot j} = 0,$$

where $\mu_{i\cdot}$ is the "effect" of the ith race $\mu_{\cdot j}$ the "effect" of the jth diet, and μ is a constant independent of i and j.

To find Q_a we have to minimize $\sum_i \sum_j (x_{ij} - \mu_{i\cdot} - \mu_{\cdot j} - \mu)^2$ subject to the restriction of (4.82). The conditions of theorem 4.4 are however obviously satisfied and we may therefore ignore the restrictions. Thus if $m_{i\cdot}$, $m_{\cdot j}$, m are the least square estimates of $\mu_{i\cdot}$, $\mu_{\cdot j}$, μ we have

$$m = \frac{1}{rs} \sum_i \sum_j x_{ij} = x,$$

$$m_i = \frac{1}{s} \sum_j x_{ij} - m = x_{i\cdot} - x,$$

$$m_{\cdot j} = \frac{1}{r} \sum_i x_{ij} - m = x_{\cdot j} - x.$$

Thus the regression value Y_{ij} is given by

$$Y_{ij} = x_{i\cdot} + x_{\cdot j} - x. \tag{4.83}$$

We now apply theorem 4.2 and consider the sequence of hypotheses

$$\begin{aligned} H_1 &: \quad \mu_{ij} = \mu_{i\cdot} + \mu_{\cdot j} + \mu, \\ H_2 &: \quad H_1 \;\&\; \mu_{i\cdot} = 0, \\ H_3 &: \quad H_1 \;\&\; H_2 \;\&\; \mu_{\cdot j} = 0. \end{aligned} \tag{4.84}$$

It is easily seen that the regression values are

$$\begin{aligned} Y_{ij}^{(1)} &= x_{i\cdot} + x_{\cdot j} - x, \\ Y_{ij}^{(2)} &= x_{\cdot j}, \\ Y_{ij}^{(3)} &= x. \end{aligned} \tag{4.85}$$

Hence by theorem 4.2

$$\begin{aligned} Q_a &= \sum_{i,j} (x_{ij} - x_{i\cdot} - x_{\cdot j} + x)^2 \\ &= \sum_{i,j} x_{ij}^2 - s \sum_i (x_{i\cdot} - x)^2 - r \sum_j (x_{\cdot j} - x)^2 - rsx^2. \end{aligned} \tag{4.86}$$

For testing $H_2 : \mu_{i\cdot} = 0$ we have

$$Q_r - Q_a = \sum_{i,j} (Y_{ij}^{(1)} - Y_{ij}^{(2)})^2 = s \sum_i (x_{i\cdot} - x)^2. \tag{4.87}$$

Similarly for testing $H_2' : \mu_{\cdot j} = 0$ we obtain

$$Q_r - Q_a = r \sum_j (x_{\cdot j} - x)^2. \tag{4.88}$$

We can further simplify (4.86), (4.87), (4.88) by means of (3.1) and applying theorem 4.1 we find that

$$\begin{aligned} F_2 &= \frac{(r-1)(s-1)}{r-1} \\ &\cdot \frac{s \sum x_{i\cdot}^2 - rsx^2}{\sum_{i,j} x_{ij}^2 - s \sum x_i^2 - r \sum x_{\cdot j}^2 + rsx^2} \end{aligned} \tag{4.89}$$

and

$$F_2' = \frac{(r-1)(s-1)}{s-1} \tag{4.90}$$

$$\cdot \frac{r \sum x_{\cdot j}^2 - rsx^2}{\sum_i \sum_j x_{ij}^2 - s \sum x_{i\cdot}^2 - r \sum x_{\cdot j}^2 + rsx^2}$$

have both the F distribution and are the likelihood ratio statistics for testing the hypotheses $H_2 : \mu_{i\cdot} = 0$, $H_2' : \mu_{\cdot j} = 0$. The degrees of freedom are $r - 1$ and $(r - 1)(s - 1)$ for F_2 ; $s - 1$ and $(r - 1)(s - 1)$ for F_2' .

Problem 1. Find the proper statistic to test $H_{12} : \mu_{1\cdot} = \mu_{2\cdot}$ and $H_{12}' : \mu_{\cdot 1} = \mu_{\cdot 2}$ in example 4. Hint: apply the corollary to theorem 4.3.

CHAPTER V

Analysis of Variance in an r-way Classification Design

LET US AGAIN CONSIDER example 4 of chapter 4. We had rs quantities x_{ij} ($i = 1, \cdots, r; j = 1, \cdots, s$). The observations could be arranged in classes in two ways and x_{ij} was the value observed in the ith class of the first and in the jth class of the second classification.

This idea can be generalized and we shall in this chapter consider r-way classification designs and their analysis for any r. For practical reasons r will be limited to at most 4 or 5; however, a general treatment of r-way classification designs is just as easy as the treatment of special cases and we shall give it here in all generality.

To give an example of a 3-way classification suppose that we have 10 weather stations. The mean rainfall was recorded by these 10 stations every month in 5 successive years. Every observation is then characterized by 3 numbers, the number of the weather station, the month, and the year in which the observation was made. Thus the observations may be denoted by $x_{a_1a_2a_3}$ ($a_1 = 1, \cdots, 10; a_2 = 1, \cdots, 12; a_3 = 1, \cdots, 5$), where a_1 is the number of the weather station, a_2 the month, and a_3 the year of observation.

We may for instance want to know whether rainfall was different in different locations or in different years. Differences between different months are certain to be present.

These simple questions do not however exhaust the information in which we might be interested. It is of interest to know also whether the combination of a certain location with a certain month has any bearing on the amount of rainfall, or whether rainfall was unusually large in July of a particular year. Accordingly we conceive the mean rainfall in one particular station during one particular month and in one particular year as being made up of the effects of station, month and year as well as of the effect of the interaction of month and year, month and station, year and station and finally one effect due to the interaction of month, year and station. Thus

$$
\begin{aligned}
E(x_{a_1a_2a_3}) &= \mu(1, 2, 3; a_1, a_2, a_3) + \mu(1, 2; a_1, a_2) \\
&\quad + \mu(2, 3; a_2, a_3) + \mu(1, 3; a_1, a_3) \\
&\quad + \mu(1; a_1) + \mu(2; a_2) + \mu(3; a_3) + \mu,
\end{aligned} \tag{5.1}
$$

where

$$
\begin{aligned}
&\sum_{a_1} \mu(1, 2, 3; a_1, a_2, a_3) \\
&\quad = \sum_{a_2} \mu(1, 2, 3; a_1, a_2, a_3) = \sum_{a_3} \mu(1, 2, 3; a_1, a_2, a_3) \\
&\quad = \sum_{a_{i_1}} \mu(i_1, i_2; a_{i_1}, a_{i_2}) = \sum_{a_{i_2}} \mu(i_1, i_2; a_{i_1}, a_{i_2}) \\
&\quad = \sum_{a_{i_1}} \mu(i_1; a_{i_1}) = 0.
\end{aligned}
$$

For instance $\mu(1, 2; 3, 5)$ denotes the effect of the coincidence of station number 3 with month number 5. The assumption can also be written as

$$
\begin{aligned}
x_{a_1a_2a_3} &= \mu(1, 2, 3; a_1, a_2, a_3) + \mu(1, 2; a_1, a_2) \\
&\quad + \mu(2, 3; a_2, a_3) + \mu(1, 3; a_1, a_3) + \mu(1; a_1) \\
&\quad + \mu(2; a_2) + \mu(3; a_3) + \mu + \epsilon_{a_1a_2a_3}.
\end{aligned} \tag{5.2}
$$

We shall assume that the $\epsilon_{a_1a_2a_3}$ are normally and independently distributed all with mean value 0 and the same unknown variance σ^2.

Generally in an r-way classification we shall assume that

$$
\begin{aligned}
&E(x_{a_1, \cdots, a_r}) \\
&\quad = \sum_{\alpha=0}^{r} \sum_{1, 2, \cdots, r} \mu(i_1, \cdots, i_\alpha; a_{i_1}, \cdots, a_{i_\alpha}), \\
&\qquad\qquad (a_i = 1, \cdots, t_i), \\
&\sum_{a_{i_j}=1}^{t_{i_j}} \mu(i_1, \cdots, i_k; a_{i_1}, \cdots, a_{i_k}) = 0,
\end{aligned} \tag{5.3}
$$

where the second summation is defined as a constant μ when $\alpha = 0$ and $\sum_{1,\cdots,r} \mu(i_1, \cdots, i_\alpha; a_{i_1}, \cdots, a_{i_\alpha})$ denotes summation over all combinations $i_1, \cdots, i_\alpha$ chosen from $1, \cdots, r$ with $i_1 < i_2 < \cdots < i_\alpha$. The quantity $\mu(i_1, \cdots, i_\alpha; a_{i_1}, \cdots, a_{i_\alpha})$ is called an $(\alpha - 1)$st order interaction.

We shall denote by $x(i_1, \cdots, i_k; a_1, \cdots, a_k)$ the mean of all observations in class a_1 of classification i_1, class a_2 of classification $i_2, \cdots$, class a_k of classification i_k and by $\sum_{i_1,\cdots,i_k} f(k_1, \cdots, k_\alpha)$. The sum of all $f(k_1, \cdots, k_\alpha)$ for all choices $k_1 < k_2 < \cdots < k_\alpha$ out of $i_1 < i_2 < \cdots < i_k$, $\alpha \leq k$.

We then consider hypotheses $H_{(i_1,\cdots,i_k)}: \mu(i_1, \cdots, i_k; a_1, \cdots, a_k) = 0$ for all $a_1, \cdots, a_k$. We arrange these hypotheses into a sequence as in Theorem 4.2 in such a way that higher order interactions precede lower order interactions. Interactions of the same order may be arranged in any arbitrary way. In computing Q_r we shall first put the term resulting from the Lagrange multipliers equal to 0. It will then be easy to verify that the least square estimates for the μ's obtained in this way always satisfy the restrictions 5.3 and that they are moreover unique solutions of the minimum problem. Minimizing

$$Q = \sum_{a_1} \cdots \sum_{a_r} \left[x_{a_1,\cdots,a_r} - \sum_{\alpha=0}^{r} \sum_{1,\cdots,r} \mu(i_1, \cdots, i_\alpha; a_{i_1}, \cdots, a_{i_\alpha}) \right]^2$$

under the hypotheses considered and denoting by $A(i_1, \cdots, i_\alpha; a_1, \cdots, a_\alpha)$ the maximum likelihood estimate of $\mu(i_1, \cdots, i_\alpha; a_1, \cdots, a_\alpha)$ leads to the equations:

$$x(i_1, \cdots, i_\alpha; a_{i_1}, \cdots, a_{i_\alpha}) = \sum_{\beta=0}^{\alpha} \sum_{i_1,\cdots,i_\alpha} A(k_1, \cdots, k_\beta; a_{k_1}, \cdots, a_{k_\beta}) \tag{5.4}$$

for all $i_1, \cdots, i_\alpha$ for which $\mu(i_1, \cdots, i_\alpha; a_{i_1}, \cdots, a_{i_\alpha})$ is not 0 by hypothesis. For $\alpha = 0$ we have $A = x =$ mean of all observations. For $\alpha = 1$ we have $x(i_1 ; a_{i_1}) = A(i_1 ; a_{i_1}) + A$ and therefore $A(i_1 ; a_{i_1}) = x(i_1 ; a_{i_1}) - x$. We shall prove by induction that

$$A(i_1, \cdots, i_\alpha ; a_{i_1}, \cdots, a_{i_\alpha})$$

(5.5)

$$= \sum_{\beta=0}^{\alpha} (-1)^{\alpha-\beta} \sum_{i_1, \cdots, i_\alpha} x(k_1, \cdots, k_\beta ; a_{k_1}, \cdots, a_{k_\beta}).$$

Assuming that 5.5 is true for all $\alpha' \leq \alpha$ we proceed to prove 5.5 for $\alpha' = \alpha + 1$. We have

$$x(i_1, \cdots, i_{\alpha+1} ; a_{i_1}, \cdots, a_{i_{\alpha+1}})$$

$$= \sum_{\beta=0}^{\alpha+1} \sum_{i_1, \cdots, i_{\alpha+1}} A(k_1, \cdots, k_\beta ; a_{k_1}, \cdots, a_{k_\beta}).$$

Hence

$$A(i_1, \cdots, i_{\alpha+1} ; a_{i_1}, \cdots, a_{i_{\alpha+1}})$$

$$= x(i_1, \cdots, i_{\alpha+1} ; a_{i_1}, \cdots, a_{i_{\alpha+1}})$$

$$- \sum_{\beta=0}^{\alpha} \sum_{i_1, \cdots, i_{\alpha+1}} A(k_1, \cdots, k_\beta ; a_{k_1}, \cdots, a_{k_\beta})$$

(5.6)

$$= x(i_1, \cdots, i_{\alpha+1} ; a_{i_1}, \cdots, a_{i_{\alpha+1}})$$

$$- \sum_{\beta=0}^{\alpha} \sum_{i_1, \cdots, i_{\alpha+1}} \sum_{\gamma=0}^{\beta} (-1)^{\beta-\gamma} \sum_{k_1, \cdots, k_\beta}$$

$$\cdot\, x(b_1, \cdots, b_\gamma ; a_{b_1}, \cdots, a_{b_\gamma}).$$

We compute now in 5.6 the coefficient of $x(b_1, \cdots, b_\gamma ; a_{b_1}, \cdots, a_{b_\gamma})$. The term $x(b_1, \cdots, b_\gamma ; a_{b_1}, \cdots, a_{b_\gamma})$ occurs in the last sum for every choice $k_1, k_2, \cdots, k_\beta$ which contains $b_1, \cdots, b_\gamma$. Out of the $\alpha + 1$ numbers $i_1, \cdots, i_{\alpha+1}$ there are for fixed β exactly

$$\binom{\alpha + 1 - \beta}{\beta - \gamma} = C_{\beta-\gamma}^{\alpha+1-\beta}$$

such choices. Hence the coefficient of $x(b_1, \cdots, b_\gamma; a_{b_1}, \cdots, a_{b_\gamma})$ becomes

$$-\sum_{\beta=\gamma}^{\alpha}(-1)^{\beta-\gamma}\binom{\alpha+1-\gamma}{\beta-\gamma} = \sum_{\beta=0}^{\alpha-\gamma}(-1)^{\beta}\binom{\alpha+1-\gamma}{\beta}$$

$$= (-1)^{\alpha+1-\gamma} - \sum_{\beta=0}^{\alpha+1-\gamma}(-1)^{\beta}\binom{\alpha+1-\gamma}{\beta}$$

$$= (-1)^{\alpha+1-\gamma}.$$

This proves 5.5.

We show next that the solutions in 5.5 satisfy the restrictions in 5.3. This is clear for $A(1; a_1) = x(1; a_1) - x$. We have by 5.6

$$A(1, \cdots, \alpha+1; a_1, \cdots, a_{\alpha+1})$$

$$= x(1, \cdots, \alpha+1; a_1, \cdots, a_{\alpha+1}) \tag{5.6a}$$

$$- \sum_{\beta=0}^{\alpha} \sum_{1, \cdots, \alpha+1} A(k_1, \cdots, k_\beta; a_{k_1}, \cdots, a_{k_\beta}).$$

Summing 5.6a over a_1 and applying mathematical induction we obtain

$$\sum_{a_1} A(1, \cdots, \alpha+1; a_1, \cdots, a_{\alpha+1})$$

$$= t_1\Bigg[x(2, \cdots, \alpha+1; a_2, \cdots, a_{\alpha+1})$$

$$- \sum_{\beta=0}^{\alpha} \sum_{2, \cdots, \alpha+1} A(k_1, \cdots, k_\beta; a_{k_1}, \cdots, a_{k_\beta})\Bigg] = 0.$$

by 5.4.

The following argument now shows that the $A(i_1, \cdots, i_k; a_{i_1}, \cdots, a_{i_k})$ are the unique solutions of the minimum problem.

Suppose we wish to minimize the quadratic form

$$Q' = \sum_{a_{i_1}} \cdots \sum_{a_{i_\alpha}} \Bigg[x(i_1, \cdots, i_\alpha; a_{i_1}, \cdots, a_{i_\alpha})$$

$$- \sum_{\beta=0}^{\alpha} \sum_{i_1, \cdots, i_\alpha} \mu(k_1, \cdots, k_\beta; a_{k_1}, \cdots, a_{k_\beta})\Bigg]^2$$

under the restrictions 5.3 and no further restrictions. The solution to 5.4 which as we have shown satisfy the restrictions are then the uniquely determined values for which $Q' = 0$. Hence if we would write out the least square equations including the terms resulting from the Lagrange operators we should still get the same solutions for the $A(k_1, \cdots, k_\beta; a_{k_1}, \cdots, a_{k_\beta})$ since Q' can take only one minimum value.

We apply now Theorem 4.2 to our sequence of hypotheses. If $H_h = H_1 \& H_2 \& \cdots \& H_{h-1} \& H_{(i_1, \cdots, i_k)}$, then

$$Y^{(h-1)}_{a_1, \cdots, a_r} - Y^{(h)}_{a_1, \cdots, a_r} = A(i_1, \cdots, i_k; a_{i_1}, \cdots, a_{i_k}).$$

In

$$\sum_{b_1} \cdots \sum_{b_r} (Y^{(h-1)}_{b_1, \cdots, b_r} - Y^{(h)}_{b_1, \cdots, b_r})^2$$

each $A(i_1, \cdots, i_k; a_{i_1}, \cdots, a_{i_k})$ occurs $(t_1 \cdots t_r)/(t_{i_1} \cdots t_{i_k})$ times. Thus we have by Theorem 4.2

$$\sum_{a_1} \cdots \sum_{a_r} (x_{a_1, \cdots, a_r})^2$$

$$(5.7) \qquad = \sum_{\alpha=0}^{r} \sum_{1,2,\cdots,r} \frac{t_1 \cdots t_r}{t_{i_1} \cdots t_{i_\alpha}} \sum_{a_{i_1}} \cdots \sum_{a_{i_\alpha}} \cdot [A(i_1, \cdots, i_\alpha; a_{i_1}, \cdots, a_{i_\alpha})]^2.$$

We replace now in the identity 5.7 $x_{a_1 \cdots a_r}$ by

$$x'_{a_1, \cdots, a_r}$$

$$= x_{a_1, \cdots, a_r} - \sum_{\alpha=0}^{r} \sum_{1, \cdots, r} \mu(i_1, \cdots, i_\alpha; a_{i_1}, \cdots, a_{i_\alpha})$$

$$(5.8) \qquad = \sum_{\alpha=0}^{r} \sum_{1, \cdots, r} [A(i_1, \cdots, i_\alpha; a_{i_1}, \cdots, a_{i_\alpha}) - \mu(i_1, \cdots, i_\alpha; a_{i_1}, \cdots, a_{i_\alpha})].$$

But

$$A'(i_1, \cdots, i_\alpha; a_1, \cdots, a_\alpha) = [A(i_1, \cdots, i_\alpha; a_1, \cdots, a_\alpha) - \mu(i_1, \cdots, i_\alpha; a_1, \cdots, a_\alpha)]$$

are the uniquely determined values for which

$$x'_{a_1,\cdots,a_r} = \sum_{\alpha=0}^{r} \sum_{1,\cdots,r} A'(i_1\,,\ \cdots\ ,\ i_\alpha\ ;\ a_{i_1}\,,\ \cdots\ ,\ a_{i_\alpha}).$$

Hence from 5.7 we obtain

$$Q = \sum_{a_1} \cdots \sum_{a_r} \Big[x_{a_1,\cdots,a_r} - \sum_{\alpha} \sum_{1,\cdots,r} \mu(i_1\,,\ \cdots\ ,\ i_\alpha\ ;\ a_{i_1}\,,\ \cdots\ ,\ a_{i_\alpha}) \Big]^2$$

(5.9)

$$= \sum_{\alpha=0}^{r} \sum_{1,\cdots,r} \sum_{a_{i_1}} \cdots \sum_{a_{i_\alpha}} \frac{t_1 \cdots t_r}{t_{i_1} \cdots t_{i_\alpha}} \cdot [A(i_1\,,\ \cdots\ ,\ i_\alpha\ ;\ a_{i_1}\,,\ \cdots\ ,\ a_{i_\alpha}) - \mu(i_1\,,\ \cdots\ ,\ i_\alpha\ ;\ a_{i_1}\,,\ \cdots\ ,\ a_{i_\alpha})]^2.$$

Besides testing hypotheses concerning sets of interactions $\mu(i_1, \cdots, i_\alpha; a_1, \cdots, a_\alpha)$ for all $a_1, \cdots, a_\alpha$ we may also wish to test hypotheses which concern individual interactions. In such cases certain sets of interactions $\mu(i_1, \cdots, i_\alpha; a_1, \cdots, a_\alpha)$ will be assumed to be equal to 0 for all $a_1, \cdots, a_\alpha$.

We shall refer to such interactions as interactions of type 1. Other interactions $\mu(i_1, \cdots, i_\alpha; a_1, \cdots, a_\alpha)$ will be unknown for all $a_1, \cdots, a_\alpha$. These we shall call interactions of type II.

In one such set of interactions, however, we may wish to test hypotheses concerning individual values of the set and we shall call those interactions of type III. Equation 5.9 shows that for finding Q_a and Q_r we must put $\mu(i_1, \cdots, i_\alpha; a_1, \cdots, a_\alpha) = 0$ for interactions of type I and $\mu(i_1, \cdots, i_\alpha; a_1, \cdots, a_\alpha) = A(i_1, \cdots, i_\alpha; a_1, \cdots, a_\alpha)$ for interactions of type II. We then have to minimize for a particular choice $j_1, \cdots, j_k$

$$\sum_{a_1} \cdots \sum_{a_k} [A(j_1\,,\ \cdots\ ,\ j_k\ ;\ a_1\,,\ \cdots\ ,\ a_k) - \mu(j_1\,,\ \cdots\ ,\ j_k\ ;\ a_1\,,\ \cdots\ ,\ a_k)]^2$$

with respect to $\mu(j_1, \cdots, j_k; a_1, \cdots, a_k)$ under the restrictions

$$\sum_{a_e} \mu(j_1, \cdots, j_e, \cdots, j_k; a_1, \cdots, a_e, \cdots, a_k) = 0$$

and certain other restrictions imposed by assumption and hypothesis.

As an example consider a three way classification and assume that all 2nd order interactions are 0. We wish to test the hypothesis that all interactions between the first and second classification are 0. The assumption then is

$$\mu(1, 2, 3; a_1, a_2, a_3) = 0,$$
$$(a_1 = 1, \cdots, t_1; a_2 = 1, \cdots, t_2; a_3 = 1, \cdots, t_3).$$

The hypothesis to be tested is $\mu(1, 2; a_1, a_2) = 0$, $(a_1 = 1, \cdots, t_1; a_2 = 1, \cdots, t_2)$. The number of linear restrictions imposed by the hypothesis is $(t_1 - 1)(t_2 - 1)$. Clearly Q is minimized under the assumption if we put $\mu(i_1, \cdots, i_\alpha; a_{i_1}, \cdots, a_{i_\alpha}) = A(i_1, \cdots, i_\alpha; a_1, \cdots, a_\alpha)$ for $\alpha \leq 2$ and this solution also must satisfy the conditions of 5.3. Similarly to obtain Q_r we put $\mu(i_1, \cdots, i_\alpha; a_1, \cdots, a_\alpha) = A(i_1, \cdots, i_\alpha; a_1, \cdots, a_\alpha)$ for all $\mu(i_1, \cdots, i_\alpha; a_1, \cdots, a_\alpha)$ which are not 0 under the hypothesis. This solution likewise satisfies 5.3. Therefore

$$Q_a = \sum_{a_1} \sum_{a_2} \sum_{a_3} [A(1, 2, 3; a_1, a_2, a_3)]^2,$$

$$Q_r = Q_a + t_3 \sum_{a_1} \sum_{a_2} [A(1, 2; a_1, a_2)]^2.$$

The F statistic for testing the hypothesis is therefore:

$$F = \frac{(t_1 - 1)(t_2 - 1)(t_3 - 1)}{(t_1 - 1)(t_2 - 1)} \cdot \frac{t_3 \sum_{a_1} \sum_{a_2} [A(1, 2; a_1, a_2)]^2}{\sum_{a_1} \sum_{a_2} \sum_{a_3} [A(1, 2, 3; a_1, a_2, a_3)]^2}.$$

Suppose now that under the same assumptions as before we wish to test the hypothesis $\mu(1, 2; 1, 1) = \mu(1, 2; 1, 2)$. To find Q_r in this case we would have to minimize

$$[A(1, 2; 1, 1) - \mu(1, 2; 1, 1)]^2$$

$$+ [A(1, 2; 1, 2) - \mu(1, 2; 1, 1)]^2$$

$$+ \sum_{a_1=2}^{t_1} \sum_{a_2=1}^{t_2} [A(1, 2; a_1, a_2) - \mu(1, 2; a_1, a_2)]^2$$

$$+ \sum_{a_2=3}^{t_2} [A(1, 2; 1, a_2) - \mu(1, 2; 1, a_2)]^2$$

under the restrictions

$$\sum_{a_1} \mu(1, 2; a_1, a_2) = 0, \qquad (a_2 = 1, \cdots, t_2);$$

$$\sum_{a_2} \mu(1, 2; a_1, a_2) = 0, \qquad (a_1 = 1, \cdots, t_1)$$

where $\mu(1, 2; 1, 1) = \mu(1, 2; 1, 2)$.

It is easier to apply the corollary to Theorem 4.3 to the linear form $\mu(1, 2; 1, 1) - \mu(1, 2; 1, 2)$. We then have to find the variance of $A(1, 2; 1, 1) - A(1, 2; 1, 2)$. We have

$$A(1, 2; 1, 1)$$

$$= x(1, 2; 1, 1) - x(1; 1) - x(2; 1) + x,$$

$$A(1, 2; 1, 2)$$

$$= x(1, 2; 1, 2) - x(1; 1) - x(2; 2) + x,$$

$$A(1, 2; 1, 1) - A(1, 2; 1, 2)$$

$$= x(1, 2; 1, 1) - x(1, 2; 1, 2) + x(2; 2) - x(2; 1).$$

Remembering that the covariance between two independent quantities is 0 we obtain

$$\sigma^2_{[A(1,2;1,1)-A(1,2;1,2)]} = \sigma^2_{x(1,2;1,1)} - 2\sigma_{x(1,2;1,1)x(2;1)} + \sigma^2_{x(1,2;1,2)} - 2\sigma_{x(1,2;1,2)x(2;2)} + \sigma^2_{x(2;2)} + \sigma^2_{x(2;1)},$$

$$\sigma^2_{[A(1,2;1,1)-A(1,2;1,2)]} = 2\sigma^2 \frac{(t_1 - 1)}{t_1 t_3}.$$

Thus by Theorem 4.1 and 4.3 the F statistic to test the hypothesis $\mu(1, 2; 1, 1) = \mu(1, 2; 1, 2)$ is

$$F = \frac{(t_1 - 1)(t_2 - 1)(t_3 - 1)}{1} \frac{t_1 t_3}{2(t_1 - 1)} \cdot \frac{[A(1, 2; 1, 1) - A(1, 2; 1, 2)]^2}{\sum_{a_1} \sum_{a_2} \sum_{a_3} [A(1, 2, 3; a_1, a_2, a_3)]^2}.$$

The identity 5.7 can be generalized to yield

$$\sum_{a_1} \cdots \sum_{a_\alpha} [x(i_1, \cdots, i_\alpha; a_{i_1}, \cdots, a_{i_\alpha})]^2$$

$$(5.10) \qquad = \sum_{\beta=0}^{\alpha} \sum_{i_1, \cdots, i_\alpha} \frac{t_1 \cdots t_\alpha}{t_{k_1} \cdots t_{k_\beta}} \sum_{a_{k_1}} \cdots \sum_{a_{k_\beta}} \cdot [A(k_1, \cdots, k_\beta; a_{k_1}, \cdots, a_{k_\beta})]^2.$$

To prove 5.10 we note that $x(i_{k_1}, \cdots, i_{k_\beta}; a_{k_1}, \cdots, a_{k_\beta})$ may be regarded as the mean of all $x(i_1, \cdots, i_\alpha; a_{i_1}, \cdots, a_{i_\alpha})$ with fixed $a_{k_1}, \cdots, a_{k_\beta}$. Applying then the identity 5.9 to the quantities $x(i_1, \cdots, i_\alpha; a_1, \cdots, a_\alpha)$ yields 5.10, since the quantities $A(k_1, \cdots, k_\beta; a_{k_1}, \cdots, a_{k_\beta})$ in 5.10 are defined in terms of the $x(i_1, \cdots, i_\alpha; a_{i_1}, \cdots, a_{i_\alpha})$.

To facilitate the computation of sums of squares of interactions we shall prove

$$\sum_{a_1} \cdots \sum_{a_k} [A(i_1, \cdots, i_k; a_{i_1}, \cdots, a_{i_k})]^2$$

(5.11)
$$= \sum_{\alpha=0}^{k} (-1)^{k-\alpha} \sum_{i_1, \cdots, i_k} \sum_{a_{j_1}} \cdots \sum_{a_{j_\alpha}} \frac{t_{i_1} \cdots t_{i_k}}{t_{j_1} \cdots t_{j_\alpha}} \cdot [x(j_1, \cdots, j_\alpha; a_{i_1}, \cdots, a_{j_\alpha})]^2.$$

For instance

$$\sum_{a_1} \cdots \sum_{a_3} [A(1, 2, 3; a_1, a_2, a_3)]^2$$
$$= \sum_{a_1} \sum_{a_2} \sum_{a_3} [x(1, 2, 3; a_1, a_2, a_3)]^2 - t_1 \sum_{a_2} \sum_{a_3} [x(2, 3; a_2, a_3)]^2 - t_2 \sum_{a_1} \sum_{a_3} [x(1, 3; a_1, a_3)]^2 - t_3 \sum_{a_1} \sum_{a_2} [x(1, 2; a_1, a_2)]^2 + t_1 t_2 \sum_{a_3} [x(3; a_3)]^2 + t_1 t_3 \sum_{a_2} [x(2; a_2)]^2 + t_2 t_3 \sum_{a_1} [x(1; a_1)]^2 - t_1 t_2 t_3 x^2.$$

We shall prove 5.11 by induction. We have

$$A^2 = x^2, \qquad \sum_{a_1} [A(i_1; a_1)]^2 = \sum_{a_1} [x(i_1; a_1) - x]^2 = \sum_{a_1} [x(i_1; a_1)]^2 - t_1 x^2.$$

Suppose that 5.11 is true for $k' < k$. From 5.10 we have

$$\sum_{a_{i_1}} \cdots \sum_{a_{i_k}} [A(i_1, \cdots, i_k; a_{i_1}, \cdots, a_{i_k})]^2$$

(5.12)
$$= \sum_{a_{i_1}} \cdots \sum_{a_{i_k}} [x(i_1, \cdots, i_k; a_{i_1}, \cdots, a_{i_k})]^2 - \sum_{\alpha=0}^{k-1} \sum_{i_1, \cdots, i_k} \frac{t_{i_1} \cdots t_{i_k}}{t_{k_1} \cdots t_{k_\alpha}} \sum_{a_{k_1}} \cdots \sum_{a_{k_\alpha}} \cdot [A(k_1, \cdots, k_\alpha; a_{k_1}, \cdots, a_{k_\alpha})]^2.$$

Applying 5.11 to 5.12 for $\alpha < k$ we find

$$\sum_{a_{i_1}} \cdots \sum_{a_{i_k}} [A(i_1, \cdots, i_k; a_{i_1}, \cdots, a_{i_k})]^2$$

$$= \sum_{a_{i_1}} \cdots \sum_{a_{i_k}} [x(i_1, \cdots, i_k; a_{i_1}, \cdots, a_{i_k})]^2$$

$$(5.13) \qquad - \sum_{\alpha=0}^{k-1} \sum_{i_1, \cdots, i_k} \frac{t_{i_1} \cdots t_{i_k}}{t_{k_1} \cdots t_{k_\alpha}} \sum_{\beta=0}^{\alpha} (-1)^{\alpha-\beta}$$

$$\cdot \sum_{k_1, \cdots, k_\alpha} \sum_{a_{j_1}} \cdots \sum_{a_{j_\beta}} \frac{t_{k_1} \cdots t_{k_\alpha}}{t_{j_1} \cdots t_{j_\beta}}$$

$$\cdot [x(j_1, \cdots, j_\beta; a_{j_1}, \cdots, a_{j_\beta})]^2.$$

The term

$$[x(j_1, \cdots, j_\beta; a_{j_1}, \cdots, a_{j_\beta})]^2 \frac{t_{i_1} \cdots t_{i_k}}{t_{j_1} \cdots t_{j_\beta}}$$

occurs in this expansion as often as we can make a choice of the indices $j_1, \cdots, j_\beta$ out of indices $k_1, \cdots, k_\alpha$ with $\beta \leq \alpha < k$. Since the indices $j_1, \cdots, j_\beta$ are fixed, there remain $k - \beta$ indices to choose from. With α fixed there are then $\alpha - \beta$ indices to choose out of $k - \beta$ indices. Hence for the fixed α the term

$$x(j_1, \cdots, j_\beta; a_{j_1}, \cdots, a_{j_\beta}) \frac{t_{i_1} \cdots t_{i_\alpha}}{t_{j_1} \cdots t_{j_\beta}}$$

occurs

$$\binom{k-\beta}{\alpha-\beta} = C_{\alpha-\beta}^{k-\beta}$$

times. Hence its coefficient becomes

$$- \sum_{\alpha=\beta}^{k-1} (-1)^{\alpha-\beta} \binom{k-\beta}{\alpha-\beta} = - \sum_{l=0}^{k-\beta-1} (-1)^l \binom{k-\beta}{l}$$

$$= - \sum_{l=0}^{k-\beta} (-1)^l \binom{k-\beta}{l} + (-1)^{k-\beta}$$

$$= (1-1)^{k-\beta} + (-1)^{k-\beta}.$$

Substituting this result in 5.13 we obtain 5.11.

An important special case arises if in an r-way classification design we do not take one but several observations in every one of the multiple classifications. Such a design may be treated as an $(r + 1)$ way classification design by simply numbering the variables in every subclass in an arbitrary manner. We shall then be justified in assuming that the $(r + 1)$st classification has no effect on the mean value. Or $\mu(i_1, \cdots, i_k, r + 1; a_{i_1}, \cdots, a_{i_k}, a_{r+1}) = 0$ for all choices $i_1 < \cdots < i_k < r + 1$. We then have from 5.9

$$Q_a = \sum_{\alpha=0}^{r} \sum_{1,\cdots,r} \frac{t_1 \cdots t_r t_{r+1}}{t_{j_1} \cdots t_{j_\alpha}} \sum_{a_{j_1}} \cdots \sum_{a_{j_\alpha}} \sum_{a_{r+1}}$$

$$\cdot [A(j_1, \cdots, j_{\alpha, r+1}; a_{j_1}, \cdots, a_{j_\alpha} a_{r+1})]^2$$

$$= \sum_{a_1} \cdots \sum_{a_{r+1}} [x(1, \cdots, r + 1; a_1, \cdots, a_{r+1})]^2$$

$$(5.14) \qquad - t_{r+1} \sum_{\alpha} \sum_{1,\cdots,r} \frac{t_1 \cdots t_r}{t_{j_1} \cdots t_{j_r}} \sum_{a_{j_1}} \cdots \sum_{a_{j_\alpha}}$$

$$\cdot [A(j_1, \cdots, j_\alpha; a_{j_1}, \cdots, a_{j_\alpha})]^2$$

$$= \sum_{a_1} \cdots \sum_{a_{r+1}} [x(1, \cdots, r + 1; a_1, \cdots, a_{r+1})]^2$$

$$- t_{r+1} \sum_{a_1} \cdots \sum_{a_r} [x(1, \cdots, r; a_1, \cdots, a_r)]^2$$

$$= \sum_{a_1} \cdots \sum_{a_{r+1}} [x(1, \cdots, r, r + 1; a_1, \cdots, a_r, a_{r+1})$$

$$- x(1, \cdots, r; a_1, \cdots, a_r)]^2.$$

Formula 5.14 is easy to interpret. Since the distribution of $x_{a_1 \cdots a_r a_{r+1}}$ is independent of a_{r+1} by assumption we obtain an estimate of the common variance from the sums of squares of deviations from the means of the observations in each subclass. The number of degrees of freedom of this estimate is

$t_1 \cdots t_r(t_{r+1} - 1)$. The number of restrictions in our assumption is easily seen to be the same number.

Problem 1. Under the assumptions leading to 5.14 derive the F statistic for testing the following hypotheses.

$$H_1: \quad \mu(1, 2; a_1, a_2) = 0 \qquad \text{for all } a_1, a_2.$$

$$H_2: \quad \mu(1, 2; a_1, a_2) + \mu(1; a_1) = 0 \qquad \text{for all } a_1, a_2.$$

CHAPTER VI

The Power of the Analysis of Variance Test

WE ARE CONSIDERING a situation in which we know apriori that the cumulative distribution function of the random variables $x_1, \cdots, x_n$ is given by a function

$$f(x_1, \cdots, x_n, \theta_1, \cdots, \theta_r). \tag{6.1}$$

We wish to test the hypothesis that certain of the parameters θ have certain specified values which for convenience we may assume to be 0.

The hypothesis may then be formulated as follows

$$H: \quad \theta_1 = \cdots = \theta_s = 0. \tag{6.2}$$

We test this hypothesis in the following way. Suppose it is possible to determine a region W in the n dimensional space R_n in such a way that the probability that a sample $x_1, \cdots, x_n$ will fall into W is a fixed constant α provided the hypothesis H is true, in symbols $P(x_1, \cdots, x_n \subset W \mid H) = \alpha$. The number α is called the level of significance of the test or the size of W. We then decide to take a sample $x_1, \cdots, x_n$ and to reject the hypothesis H if the point $x_1, \cdots, x_n$ lies in W.

If the point $x_1, \cdots, x_n$ does not lie in W we either accept H as true or make further investigations. These investigations may consist in taking a larger sample if the distribution in the larger sample depends also on $\theta_1, \cdots, \theta_s$. The fact that the region W has a fixed size if H is true assures us that, provided H is true, we shall in the long run make a wrong decision only in α of the cases, where we draw a sample. This alone is however quite insufficient to make the test valuable. An example will illustrate this. Suppose $\alpha = .05$ and we put numbers from 1 to 20 into an urn and test every hypothesis by drawing a number from our urn. We reject the hypothesis H whenever the number 1 is drawn. Otherwise we do not reject it. Obviously the probability of rejecting H when H is true is $\alpha = .05$.

Nevertheless the test is obviously of no value. The reason for this is that the probability of rejecting H when H is false is also only .05. Thus the test does not discriminate between H and situations different from H.

We shall denote by $P(E \mid H)$ the probability that E will happen computed under the assumption that H is true. Let us consider another alternative situation H' and denote the point $x_1, \cdots, x_n$ by x. Then

$$P(x \subset W \mid H) = \alpha \tag{6.3}$$

is called the size of the critical region W and

$$P(x \subset W \mid H') \tag{6.4}$$

is called the power of the critical region W with respect to the alternative situation H'. The power $P(x \subset W \mid H')$ is the probability of discovering that H is not true provided that H' is true. It is thus a function of the alternative H'. If

$$P(x \subset W \mid H') \geq P(x \subset W' \mid H') \tag{6.5}$$

for all regions W' for which

$$P(x \subset W' \mid H) = \alpha \tag{6.6}$$

then W is called a most powerful region of size α with respect to the alternative H'. If there exists a region which is most powerful with respect to all alternatives then it is clear that this region is superior to all other regions.

Unfortunately most powerful regions with respect to all alternatives do rarely exist. Thus the choice of the critical region has to be made on the basis of some compromise principle. It seems for instance reasonable to require that

$$I: \quad P(x \subset W \mid H') \geq \alpha$$

for all H'. A region which fulfills (6.3) and I is called an unbiased critical region of size α. If it also fulfills (6.5) for all regions W' which satisfy (6.3) and I, then it is called a most powerful unbiased region of size α. Most powerful unbiased regions do also rarely exist.

It may be seen from the foregoing discussion that a knowledge of the power function $P(x \subset W \mid H') = f(H')$ is indispensable if we want to know what a test really accomplishes and we shall, therefore, in this chapter derive the power function of the analysis of variance tests.

In chapter one we have shown that the statistic F is computed from the ratio of two chi square expressions.

$$\chi_1^2 = \frac{x_1^2 + \cdots + x_{n_1}^2}{\sigma^2},$$

$$\chi_2^2 = \frac{y_1^2 + \cdots + y_{n_2}^2}{\sigma^2},$$

where $x_1, \cdots, x_{n_1}; y_1, \cdots, y_{n_2}$ were assumed to be independently and normally distributed variables with means 0 and variance σ^2. If $x_1, \cdots, x_{n_1}$ have variance σ_1^2 and $y_1, \cdots, y_{n_2}$ variance σ_2^2 there are two essentially different hypotheses that may be tested by means of the F statistic: the hypothesis $H_1 : \sigma_1^2 = \sigma_2^2$ under the assumption $E(x_i) = E(y_i) = 0$ and the hypothesis $H_2 : E(y_i) = 0$ under the assumption $\sigma_1^2 = \sigma_2^2$ and $E(x_i) = 0$. We shall be chiefly concerned with the hypothesis H_2.

In chapter IV we discussed tests of linear hypotheses. In proving theorem 4.1 we have shown that the F ratio was given by

$$F = \frac{n_1}{n_2}\frac{\chi_2^2}{\chi_1^2}, \quad \chi_2^2 = \frac{y_1^2 + \cdots + y_{n_2}^2}{\sigma^2}, \quad \chi_1^2 = \frac{x_1^2 + \cdots + x_{n_1}^2}{\sigma^2},$$

where the assumption stated that

$$E(x_i) = 0, \qquad (i = 1, \cdots, n_1). \tag{6.7}$$

The hypothesis to be tested was

$$E(y_i) = 0, \qquad (i = 1, \cdots, n_2). \tag{6.8}$$

Thus the alternatives to be considered are of the form

$$H' : \quad E(y_i) = \theta_i. \tag{6.9}$$

The critical region W for testing H was given by $F \geq \bar{F}$. To find the power of the test it is therefore necessary to compute the distribution of

$$(6.10) \qquad \chi'^2 = \frac{y_1^2 + \cdots + y_{n_2}^2}{\sigma^2}$$

under the assumption that the y_i are normally distributed with mean value θ_i and common variance σ^2. We then have to derive the distribution of

$$(6.11) \qquad F' = \frac{\chi'^2}{\chi_1^2}.$$

The power of the test will then be given by $P(F' \geq n_2/n_1 \bar{F})$. Our problem will be solved if we find the distribution of F'. For our evaluation of (6.11) it is necessary to bring the linear hypothesis first into the form (6.7) and (6.8) by applying the transformations discussed in the proof of Theorem (4.1).

In the derivation of the distribution of χ'^2 we shall need the function $\Gamma(z)$ as defined in chapter one and the function

$$(6.12) \qquad \mathrm{B}(n, m) = \int_0^1 x^{n-1}(1 - x)^{m-1}\, dx.$$

The Γ function satisfies the relations $\Gamma(n) = (n - 1)\Gamma(n - 1)$, $\Gamma(1) = 1$, and $\Gamma(\frac{1}{2}) = \pi^{\frac{1}{2}}$. Between the Γ and the β function the following relation holds

$$(6.13) \qquad \mathrm{B}(n, m) = \frac{\Gamma(m)\Gamma(n)}{\Gamma(n + m)}.$$

To prove this relation we compute

$$\Gamma(m)\Gamma(n) = \int_0^\infty x^{n-1}e^{-x}\, dx \int_0^\infty y^{m-1}e^{-y}\, dy$$

$$= \int_0^\infty \int_0^\infty e^{-(x+y)}x^{n-1}y^{m-1}\, dx\, dy.$$

We make the substitution

$$y = u(1 - z), \qquad x = uz. \tag{6.14}$$

Its Jacobian is u. The region $0 \leq x < \infty$, $0 \leq y < \infty$ is transformed into $0 \leq u < \infty$, $0 \leq z < 1$. Hence

$$\Gamma(m)\Gamma(n) = \int_0^\infty e^{-u}u^{n+m-1}\,du \int_0^1 z^{n-1}(1-z)^{m-1}\,dz$$

$$= \Gamma(m+n)\mathrm{B}(n, m).$$

This proves (6.13).

We proceed to derive the distribution of χ'^2. We know that χ'^2 is the sum of, say, r squares of random variable $z_1, \cdots, z_r$ which are independently and normally distributed with common variance σ^2 and means $d_1, \cdots, d_r$. The joint distribution of $z_1, \cdots, z_r$ is thus given by

$$p(z_1, \cdots, z_r) = \frac{1}{(2\pi)^{r/2}\sigma^r} \exp\left[-\frac{1}{2\sigma^2}\sum_i (z_i - d_i)^2\right]. \tag{6.15}$$

Putting

$$\lambda = \frac{1}{2\sigma^2}\sum_i d_i^2 \tag{6.16}$$

equation (6.15) may be written as

$$\begin{aligned} &p(z_1, \cdots, z_r) \\ &= \frac{e^{-\lambda}}{(2\pi)^{r/2}\sigma^r} \exp\left(-\frac{1}{2\sigma^2}\left[\sum_i z_i^2 - 2\sum_i z_i d_i\right]\right). \end{aligned} \tag{6.17}$$

We now put

$$\begin{aligned} W_1 &= \left(\sum_i d_i^2\right)^{-\frac{1}{2}} \sum_i z_i d_i = \sum_i z_i d_i', \\ W_i &= \sum_{j=1}^r a_{ij} z_j, \qquad (i = 2, \cdots, r), \end{aligned} \tag{6.18}$$

where the matrix

$$T = \begin{pmatrix} d_1' & \cdots & d_r' \\ a_{21} & \cdots & a_{2r} \\ \cdot & & \cdot \\ \cdot & & \cdot \\ \cdot & & \cdot \\ a_{r1} & \cdots & a_{rr} \end{pmatrix}$$

is orthogonal and assume $r > 1$. We then have

$$\begin{aligned} E(W_1) &= (\sum_i d_i^2)^{\frac{1}{2}}, \\ E(W_i) &= 0, \qquad (i = 2, \cdots, r) \end{aligned} \tag{6.19}$$

because of the orthogonality of T. Furthermore

$$\chi'^2 = \frac{1}{\sigma^2} \sum_i z_i^2 = \frac{1}{\sigma^2} \sum_i W_i^2 .$$

Since T is orthogonal the W_i are independently and normally distributed with common variance σ^2 and

$$\frac{1}{\sigma^2} \sum_{i=z}^{r} W_i^2 = \chi^2 \tag{6.20}$$

has the χ^2 distribution with $(r - 1)$ degrees of freedom given by (1.2). The joint distribution of χ^2 and W_1 is therefore given by the density function

$$\begin{aligned} P(\chi^2, W_1) &= \frac{e^{-\lambda}}{(2\pi)^{1/2} 2^{(r-1)/2} \Gamma([r - 1]/2)\sigma} (\chi^2)^{(r-3)/2} \\ &\quad \cdot \exp\left(-\frac{1}{2\sigma^2} [\sigma^2\chi^2 + W_1^2 - 2\sigma W_1(2\lambda)^{1/2}]\right). \end{aligned} \tag{6.21}$$

To obtain the distribution of

$$\chi'^2 = \frac{W_1^2}{\sigma^2} + \chi^2 \tag{6.22}$$

we put

$$\chi^2 = \chi'^2 \cos^2 \theta, \qquad \frac{W_1}{\sigma} = \chi' \sin \theta. \tag{6.23}$$

The Jacobian of this transformation becomes

$$\begin{vmatrix} \cos^2\theta & -\chi'^2 \sin 2\theta \\ \dfrac{\chi'\sigma \sin\theta}{2} & \sigma\chi' \cos\theta \end{vmatrix} = \sigma\chi' \cos\theta$$

and to the region $0 \leq \chi^2 < \infty$, $-\infty \leq W_1 < \infty$ corresponds the region $0 \leq \chi'^2 < \infty$, $-\pi/2 \leq \theta \leq \pi/2$. Thus the joint distribution of χ'^2 and θ is given by the density function

$$Q(\chi'^2, \theta) = \frac{e^{-\lambda}}{\pi^{1/2} 2^{r/2} \Gamma([r-1]/2)} (\chi'^2)^{(r-2)/2} (\cos\theta)^{r-2} \cdot \exp\left[-\tfrac{1}{2}(\chi'^2 - 2(2\lambda)^{1/2}\chi' \sin\theta)\right]. \tag{6.24}$$

If we integrate this expression with respect to θ from $-\pi/2$ to $\pi/2$ we shall obtain the distribution of (χ'^2). To perform this integration we expand $\exp[+(2\lambda\chi'^2)^{\frac{1}{2}} \operatorname{Sin}\theta]$ into a series. Since for m odd

$$\int_{-\pi/2}^{\pi/2} \cos^{r-2}\theta \sin^m \theta \, d\theta = 0$$

we obtain

$$\int_{-\pi/2}^{\pi/2} \cos^{r-2}\theta \exp[(2\lambda\chi'^2)^{1/2} \sin\theta] \, d\theta = \sum_{m=0}^{\infty} \frac{(2\lambda\chi'^2)^m}{(2m)!} \int_{-\pi/2}^{\pi/2} \cos^{r-2}\theta \sin^{2m}\theta \, d\theta. \tag{6.25}$$

We have

$$\begin{aligned} \int_{-\pi/2}^{\pi/2} \cos^{r-2}\theta \sin^{2m}\theta \, d\theta &= \int_{-1}^{1} (1-u^2)^{(r-3)/2} (u^2)^m \, du \\ &= \int_0^1 (1-v)^{(r-3)/2} v^{m-(1/2)} \, dv \\ &= \mathrm{B}\left(\frac{r-1}{2}, m + \frac{1}{2}\right) \\ &= \frac{\Gamma([r-1]/2)\Gamma(m+1/2)}{\Gamma(r/2+m)}. \end{aligned} \tag{6.26}$$

On the other hand

$$(2m)! = (2m)(2m-1)\cdots 3\cdot 2\cdot 1$$
$$= 2^m m!(2m-1)(2m-3)\cdots 5\cdot 3\cdot 1$$
$$= \frac{2^{2m}m!}{\Gamma(\frac{1}{2})}\left(\frac{2m-1}{2}\cdot\frac{2m-3}{2}\cdots\frac{5}{2}\cdot\frac{3}{2}\cdot\Gamma\left(\frac{1}{2}\right)\right)$$
$$= \frac{2^{2m}m!}{\pi^{1/2}}\Gamma\left(m+\frac{1}{2}\right).$$

Hence

$$\int_{-\pi/2}^{\pi/2}\cos^{r-2}\theta\exp\left[(2\lambda\chi'^2)^{1/2}\sin\theta\right]d\theta$$
$$= \sum_{m=0}^{\infty}\left(\frac{\lambda\chi'^2}{2}\right)^m\frac{\Gamma([r-1]/2)\pi^{1/2}}{m!\Gamma(r/2+m)}$$
$$= \pi^{1/2}\Gamma\left(\frac{r-1}{2}\right)\sum_{m=0}^{\infty}\frac{(\lambda\chi'^2/2)^m}{m!\Gamma(r/2+m)}.$$

Thus the distribution of χ'^2 is given by its density function

$$Q(\chi'^2) = \frac{e^{-\lambda}}{2}\left(\frac{1}{2}\chi'^2\right)^{(r-2)/2}\exp\left(-\frac{1}{2}\chi'^2\right)\sum_{m=0}^{\infty}\frac{(\lambda\chi'^2/2)^m}{m!\Gamma(r/2+m)}. \tag{6.27}$$

For $\lambda = 0$ equation (6.27) reduces to the χ^2 distribution 1.2 as it should. It is not difficult to verify that 6.27 also holds for $r = 1$.

We now proceed to derive the distribution of $G = \chi'^2/\chi^2$ where χ'^2 and χ^2 are independent and χ^2 has the χ^2 distribution with s degrees of freedom. The joint probability density of χ^2 and χ'^2 is given by

$$P(\chi^2, \chi'^2) = \frac{e^{-\lambda}}{4\Gamma(s/2)}\left(\frac{\chi'^2}{2}\right)^{(r-2)/2}\left(\frac{\chi^2}{2}\right)^{(s-2)/2}$$
$$\cdot\exp\left(-\frac{1}{2}(\chi'^2+\chi^2)\right)\sum_{m=0}^{\infty}\frac{\lambda^m(\chi'^2/2)^m}{m!\Gamma(r/2+m)}.$$

We make the substitution

$$\chi'^2 = \frac{Gz}{1+G}, \qquad \chi^2 = \frac{z}{1+G}.$$

The Jacobian of this substitution is $z/(1 + G)^2$. Thus the joint distribution of $z/2$ and G is given by its density function:

$$q\left(\frac{z}{2}, G\right) = e^{-\lambda}\left(\frac{G}{1+G}\right)^{(r-2)/2}\left(\frac{1}{1+G}\right)^{(s+2)/2} e^{-(z/2)}$$

(6.28)

$$\cdot \sum_{m=0}^{\infty}\left(\frac{G}{1+G}\right)^m \frac{\lambda^m (z/2)^{(r+s+2m-2)/2}}{m!\Gamma(r/2+m)\Gamma(s/2)}.$$

Integrating out with respect to z we obtain the density of the distribution of G.

$$P(G) = \sum_{m=0}^{\infty} e^{-\lambda}\left(\frac{G}{1+G}\right)^{(r+2m-2)/2}\left(\frac{1}{1+G}\right)^{(s+2)/2}$$

(6.29)

$$\cdot \frac{\lambda^m \Gamma([r+s]/2+m)}{m!\Gamma(r/2+m)\Gamma(s/2)}$$

or on account of (6.13)

$$P(G) = \sum_{m=0}^{\infty} e^{-\lambda}\left(\frac{G}{1+G}\right)^{(r+2m-2)/2}\left(\frac{1}{1+G}\right)^{(s+2)/2} \frac{\lambda^m}{m!}$$

(6.30)

$$\cdot\left[B\left(\frac{r}{2}+m, \frac{s}{2}\right)\right]^{-1}.$$

Let $\bar{F}_\alpha$ be the critical value of F for the level of significance α so that $P(F \geq \bar{F}_\alpha \mid \lambda = 0) = \alpha$. Put $r/s\, \bar{F}_\alpha = \bar{G}_\alpha$. P. C. Tang (Statistical Research Memoirs V.2, 1938) has tabulated the integrals

(6.31) $$\int_0^{\bar{G}_{.01}} P(G)\, dG, \qquad \int_0^{\bar{G}_{.05}} P(G)\, dG$$

for various values of $\Phi = [2\lambda/(r+1)]^{\frac{1}{2}}$ and various degrees of freedom. This integral represents the probability P_{II} that we shall fail to reject the hypothesis $\theta_{s+1} = \cdots = \theta_{s+r} = 0$ although it is false and some alternative $\theta_{s+1} = d_1, \cdots, \theta_{s+r} = d_r$ is true for which

$$\lambda = \frac{\sum d_i^2}{2\sigma^2}$$

Thus one obtains an excellent picture of what the F test will accomplish. Tang's tables must also be consulted if it is desired to find the sample size necessary to discover alternatives with specified values of λ with a given probability.

The evaluation of (6.30) and (6.31) requires the knowledge of λ and σ^2 but we may use $\overline{\sigma}^2 = (Q_a)/s$ as an estimate of σ^2.

The assumptions of a linear hypothesis state that the given normally and independently distributed random variables $x_1, \cdots, x_n$ have the same variance and means $\mu_1, \cdots, \mu_n$ satisfying the relations

$$(6.32) \qquad \sum_{j=1}^{n} c_{ij}\mu_j = 0, \qquad (i = 1, \cdots, s), \qquad \text{rank } (c_{ij}) = s.$$

The hypothesis then states that

$$(6.33) \quad \sum_j c_{s+i,j}\mu_j = 0, \; (i = 1, \cdots, r), \; \text{rank} \begin{pmatrix} c_{ij} \\ c_{s+i,j} \end{pmatrix} = s + r.$$

Lemma 4.1 shows that we may assume that the c_{ij} are the first $r + s$ rows of an orthogonal matrix. Hence

$$(6.34) \qquad \sum_{i=1}^{n} (x_i - \mu_i)^2 = \sum_{i=1}^{n} \left[\sum_{j=1}^{n} c_{ij}(x_j - \mu_j) \right]^2$$

and therefore

$$(6.35) \qquad Q_r - Q_a = \sum_{i=s+1}^{s+r} \left[\sum_{j=1}^{n} c_{ij}x_j \right]^2.$$

Suppose now that the alternative H' states that $E(x_i) = \overline{\mu}_i$ where the $\overline{\mu}_i$ fulfill the relations (6.32) but

$$(6.36) \quad \sum_j c_{s+i,j}\overline{\mu}_j = d_i, \qquad (i = 1, \cdots, r), \qquad \sum_i d_i^2 > 0.$$

Then

$$(6.37) \qquad 2\sigma^2\lambda = \sum_i d_i^2 = \sum_{i=s+1}^{r+s} \left[\sum_{j=1}^{n} c_{ij}\bar{\mu}_j \right]^2 .$$

Comparing (6.35) and (6.37) we see that we may obtain $2\sigma^2\lambda$ simply by substituting into the expression for $Q_r - Q_a$ the values $\bar{\mu}_j$ for x_j . This simple rule is particularly useful since the alternative is mostly stated in terms of the mean values of x_j and not in terms of the linear functions (6.33) of these mean values.

To illustrate the use of Tang's tables we consider testing the row effects in a k by m two way classification design (example 4 of Chapter 4). The assumption was formulated in the form

$$(6.38) \qquad E(x_{ij}) = \mu_{i\cdot} + \mu_{\cdot j} + \mu$$

with $\sum_i \mu_{i\cdot} = \sum_j \mu_{\cdot j} = 0$. The hypothesis to be tested was

$$(6.39) \qquad H: \quad \mu_{i\cdot} = 0, \qquad (i = 1, \cdots, k).$$

We obtained

$$(6.40) \quad Q_r - Q_a = m \sum_i (x_{i\cdot} - x)^2, \qquad x_{i\cdot} = \frac{1}{m} \sum_j x_{ij} .$$

Consider now the alternative H':

$$(6.41) \quad E(x_{ij}) = \theta_i + \mu_{ij} + \mu, \quad \sum_i \theta_i = 0, \quad \sum_i \theta_i^2 > 0.$$

Then $E(x_{i\cdot}) = \theta_i + \mu$, $E(x) = \mu$.

Applying our rule we have to substitute in (6.40) for x_{ij} the expression $\theta_i + \mu_{\cdot j} + \mu$. Hence for $x_{i\cdot}$ we have to substitute $\theta_i + \mu$. Thus

$$(6.42) \qquad 2\sigma^2\lambda = m \sum_i \theta_i^2 .$$

The quantity

$$\frac{1}{m} \Phi^2 = \frac{\sum_i \theta_i^2}{k\sigma^2}$$

can be interpreted as the mean square of the row effects expressed as a multiple of the variance. Suppose for instance that this mean square is $.8\ \sigma^2$ and that $m = 5$; then $\Phi = 2$. If $k = 4$ then the degrees of freedom for Q_a are $(k - 1)(m - 1) = 12$. In Tang's tables* we find that for 3 and 12 degrees of freedom respectively and for $\Phi = 2$ the probability P_{II} of not rejecting the null hypothesis is .463 if a 1% level of significance is used and .178 if a 5% level of significance is used. That is to say: If we use a 5% level of significance, we shall, in more than 82 cases out of 100 reject the hypothesis $\theta_i = 0$ $(i = 1, 2, 3, 4)$ if the mean square of the row effects is at least .8 times the variance.

Tang's tables do not only give us very valuable information about the results to be expected from analysis of variance tests but enable us also to find the number of experiments necessary to achieve certain results. Suppose for instance that we plan a two way classification design with, if necessary, more than 1 experiment in each subclass. We wish to test on a 1% level of significance whether the interaction between the two classifications is 0. We are interested in alternatives for which the mean square of the interactions is at least .16 times the variance and we want to take a large enough sample to uncover such alternatives in at least 50% of the experiments.

Our assumption then is

$$\mu(1, 2, 3; i, j, k) = \mu(1, 3; i, k)$$
$$= \mu(2, 3; j, k) = \mu(3; k) = 0$$

for $i = 1, \cdots, t_1$; $j = 1, \cdots, t_2$; $k = 1, \cdots, t_3$. By (5.14) $Q_a = \sum_i \sum_j \sum_k [x(1, 2, 3; i, j, k) - x(1, 2; i, j)]^2$ with $t_1 t_2 (t_3 - 1)$ degrees of freedom. From (5.9) we find $Q_r - Q_2 = t_3 \sum_i \sum_j [A(1, 2; i, j)]^2$ with $(t_1 - 1)(t_2 - 1)$ degrees of freedom. Thus if $\mu(1, 2; i, j) = d_{ij}$ we obtain

$$2\sigma^2\lambda = t_3 \sum_i \sum_j (d_{ij})^2$$

*The degrees of freedom of the numerator are, in Tang's tables, denoted by f_1; those of the denominator by f_2. The quantity $E^2{}_\alpha = G_\alpha/(1 + G_\alpha)$.

and

$$\Phi^2 = \frac{2\lambda}{(t_1 - 1)(t_2 - 1) + 1}$$

$$= \frac{t_1 t_2 t_3}{(t_1 - 1)(t_2 - 1) + 1} \frac{\sum_i \sum_j (d_{ij})^2}{\sigma^2 t_1 t_2} .$$

We are interested only in alternatives for which

$$\frac{\sum_i \sum_j (d_{ij})^2}{\sigma^2 t_1 t_2} \geq .16 \qquad \text{or} \qquad \Phi^2 \geq .16 \frac{t_1 t_2 t_3}{(t_1 - 1)(t_2 - 1) + 1} .$$

Suppose now that $t_1 = 2$, $t_2 = 5$ then $\Phi^2 \geq .32\, t_3$. We reproduce below the relevant part of Tang's table for $f_1 = 4$ and a 1% level of significance. We find P_{II} as follows

f_2 \ Φ	1.5	2.0	2.5
30	.570	.225	.044
60	.509	.165	.024 .

For $t_3 = 6$ we have $\Phi^2 = 1.92$, $f_2 = 50$ and this would not be enough to insure that $1 - P_{II} \geq 50\%$. For $t_3 = 7$ we have $\Phi^2 = 2.24$, $f_2 = 60$ and P_{II} is approximately .51.

Although Tang's results give a good picture of the discriminating power of analysis of variance tests, the question arises whether other tests could not accomplish more than the analysis of variance test does. Generally one does not know the alternatives and it is not possible to maximize the power with respect to every possible alternative. Therefore it will be the aim of the investigator to maximize some average of the power. A. Wald has shown that the analysis of variance test has such an optimum property. (Ann. Math. Stat. Vol.13 #4).

In Chapter four it was shown that tests of linear hypotheses can be brought into the following form. The variables

$$x_1, \cdots, x_r; \qquad y_1, \cdots, y_s, y_{s+1}, \cdots, y_p$$

are normally and independently distributed with common variance σ^2. It is known that $E(x_i) = 0$, $(i = 1, \cdots, r)$. The hypothesis to be tested is

$$(6.43) \qquad E(y_i) = 0, \qquad (i = 1, \cdots, s).$$

The critical region W_0 in the analysis of variance test is defined by

$$(6.44) \qquad G = \frac{n_2}{n_1} F = \frac{y_1^2 + \cdots + y_s^2}{x_1^2 + \cdots + x_s^2} \geq C.$$

That is to say the hypothesis (4.43) will be rejected if $G \geq C$. From (6.29) we see that the distribution of G depends only on

$$\lambda = \frac{1}{2\sigma^2} \sum_{i=1}^{s} \theta_i^2$$

where $E(y_i) = \theta_i$. Hence we may denote the power of the region (6.44) with respect to the alternative

$$E(y_i) = \theta_i, \quad (i = 1, \cdots, s); \quad E[(y_i - \theta_i)^2] = E[(x_i)^2] = \sigma^2$$

by $P_0(\lambda)$.

Let W be another critical region and denote its power function by

$$P(\theta_1, \cdots, \theta_p, \sigma).$$

Consider now in the p-dimensional space $z_1, \cdots, z_p$ the surface S defined by

$$(6.45) \quad 2\lambda\sigma^2 = z_1^2 + \cdots + z_s^2, z_i = \theta_i, (i = s + 1, \cdots, p).$$

Let $\overline{P}(\lambda, \sigma, \theta_{s+1}, \cdots, \theta_p)$ denote the average power on the surface defined by (6.45). That is to say

$$\begin{aligned} &\overline{P}(\lambda, \sigma, \theta_{s+1}, \cdots, \theta_p) \\ (6.46) \qquad &= \left(\int_S dA\right)^{-1} \int_S P(z_1, \cdots, z_s, \theta_{s+1}, \cdots, \theta_p, \sigma) \, dA. \end{aligned}$$

Wald proved that for all W of the same size as W_0

$$(6.47) \qquad \overline{P}(\lambda, \sigma, \theta_{s+1}, \cdots, \theta_p) \leq P_0(\lambda).$$

Thus the power of the analysis of variance test is higher than or equal to the mean power over the surface (6.45) of any other test on the same level of significance.

Clearly if $P(\theta_1, \cdots, \theta_s, \sigma)$ depends only on λ then $\bar{P}(\lambda) = P(\lambda)$ and it follows from (6.47) that

$$P(\lambda) \leq P_0(\lambda). \tag{6.48}$$

The inequality (6.48) had been previously obtained by P. L. Hsu (Biometrika, Jan. 1941).

The proof of Wald's theorem is beyond the scope of this book. Wald's and Hsu's results however may be taken as a full justification for the use of the analysis of variance in testing a linear hypothesis.

CHAPTER VII

Latin Squares and Incomplete Balanced Block Designs

SUPPOSE THAT m VARIETIES of wheat are to be compared as to their mean yield on a certain type of soil. We have at our disposal a rectangular field subdivided into m^2 plots. However, even if we are careful in the selection of our field, differences in soil fertility will occur on it. Thus if all the plots of the first row are occupied by the first variety, it may very well be that the first row is of high fertility and we might obtain a high yield for the first variety although it is not superior to the other varieties. We shall be less likely to vitiate our comparisons, if we replicate every variety once in every row and at the same time randomize the position of the varieties within the rows. We might for instance take m cards with the numbers $1, \cdots, m$ on them, shuffle them well and then lay them out in a row to determine the position of the varieties in the first row. Repetition of this process will yield the position of the varieties in the second row and so forth. An arrangement of this type is called a randomized block arrangement. A mathematically rigorous treatment of this arrangement is at present not yet available. An approximate test of varietal effects is possible by treating the arrangement as a two-way classification design ignoring the variation of soil fertility within the rows. We shall discuss this design in detail in Chapter XII. A better plan will be the systematic elimination of soil fertility differences, which is preferable to randomization and should be applied whenever it is possible. It yields in most cases more efficient estimates of the varietal effects and has the great advantage that a mathematically rigorous treatment is available.

The line of attack in our particular example is as follows. We conceive of the mean yield $E(y_{ijk})$ of the kth variety on the plot in the ith row and jth column of the field as given by

$$(7.1) \qquad \begin{gathered} E(y_{ijk}) = \mu_i + \nu_j + \rho_k + \rho, \\ \sum_i \mu_i = \sum_j \nu_j = \sum_k \rho_k = 0. \end{gathered}$$

This assumption is for instance always satisfied if the soil fertility is a linear function of the coordinates, an assumption which is likely to be true if the field is not too large and is homogeneous in appearance. The quantities μ_i , ν_j , ρ_k are called the row, column, and varietal effects respectively. The design is called a Latin square if every variety is planted once in every row and once in every column. The expected value of the mean yield of the kth variety in our experiment is then by (7.1) equal to

$$\frac{1}{m} \sum_{i,j} E(y_{ijk}) = \rho_k + \rho$$

where the summation runs over all pairs i, j for which y_{ijk} is defined. Thus

$$y_{\cdot\cdot k} = \frac{1}{m} \sum_{i,j} y_{ijk}$$

provides an unbiased estimate of $\rho_k + \rho$. Since every variety occurs once in every row and once in every column, the mean y of all yields provides an estimate of ρ so that the varietal effects ρ_k , $(k = 1, \cdots, m)$ can be estimated.

The assumption of our linear hypothesis is therefore that the y_{ijk} are normally and independently distributed all with the same but unknown variance σ^2 and that their expectations are given by (7.1). Note that as soon as i and j are fixed k is determined by our design. The parameters $\mu_{ijk} = E(y_{ijk})$ are expressed by the $3m + 1$ parameters ν_j , μ_i , ρ_k , $(i, j, k = 1, \cdots, m)$ and ρ. However, these parameters are not independent since

$$\sum_i \mu_i = \sum_j \nu_j = \sum_k \rho_k = 0.$$

Hence there are $3m - 2$ independent parameters and Q_a will therefore have $m^2 - 3m + 2$ degrees of freedom. The hypotheses to be tested are manifold. In the first place, we might wish to test whether the varieties differ at all from each other, we shall then test the hypothesis $\rho_i = 0$ $(i = 1, \cdots, m)$. Or we may wish to test the difference between two varieties, say ρ_1 and ρ_2. The hypothesis to be tested is then $\rho_1 = \rho_2$. Also we might wish to test whether the rows (or columns) have any effect. We then test the hypothesis $\mu_i = 0$ (or $\nu_i = 0$), $(i = 1, \cdots, m)$ and so forth. We shall first derive Q_a. The design obviously satisfies the conditions of Theorem 4.4 with respect to each of the three sets of variables μ_i, ν_j, ρ_k. Hence in finding Q_a we may by virtue of theorem 4.4 ignore the restrictions in (7.1). Minimizing

$$Q = \sum_i \sum_j (y_{ijk} - \mu_i - \nu_j - \rho_k - \rho)^2$$

with respect to μ_i, ν_j, ρ_k, ρ and denoting our estimates of these quantities by $\hat{\mu}_i$, $\hat{\nu}_j$, $\hat{\rho}_k$, $\hat{\rho}$ we obtain

$$\hat{\rho} = \frac{1}{m^2} \sum_i \sum_j y_{ijk} = y,$$

$$\hat{\mu}_i = \frac{1}{m} \sum_{j,k} y_{ijk} - y = y_{i\cdot\cdot} - y,$$

(7.2)

$$\hat{\nu}_j = \frac{1}{m} \sum_{i,k} y_{ijk} - y = y_{\cdot j \cdot} - y,$$

$$\hat{\rho}_k = \frac{1}{m} \sum_{i,j} y_{ijk} - y = y_{\cdot\cdot k} - y.$$

Because for instance the ith row contains every variety and every column exactly once so that the varietal and the column effects will cancel out. Thus

$$(7.3) \qquad Q_a = \sum_i \sum_j (y_{ijk} - y_{i\cdot\cdot} - y_{\cdot j\cdot} - y_{\cdot\cdot k} + 2y)^2.$$

We now apply theorem 4.2 taking H_1 equal to the assumption,

$$H_2: \quad \mu_i = 0 \ (i = 1, \cdots, m),$$

$$H_3: \quad \nu_j = 0 \ (j = 1, \cdots, m),$$

$$H_4: \quad \rho_k = 0 \ (k = 1, \cdots, m).$$

Then

$$\sum y_{ijk}^2 = \sum (y_{ijk} - y_{i\cdot\cdot} - y_{\cdot j\cdot} - y_{\cdot\cdot k} + 2y)^2 + m \sum (y_{i\cdot\cdot} - y)^2 + m \sum (y_{\cdot j\cdot} - y)^2 + m \sum (y_{\cdot\cdot k} - y)^2 + m^2 y^2.$$

The same decomposition is also obtained, however, if we renumber the hypotheses H_2, H_3, H_4. Thus the hypothesis $H_4 : \rho_k = 0$ is to be tested by

$$F = \frac{m^2 - 3m + 2}{m - 1} \cdot \frac{m \sum y_{\cdot\cdot k}^2 - m^2 y^2}{\sum_i \sum_j y_{ijk}^2 - m[\sum_i y_{i\cdot\cdot}^2 + \sum_j y_{\cdot j\cdot}^2 + \sum_k y_{\cdot\cdot k}^2] + 2m^2 y^2} \cdot \tag{7.4}$$

The expressions for testing row and column effects are entirely analogous. To test the hypothesis $\rho_1 = \rho_2$ we apply formula (4.64). We have $\hat{\rho}_1 - \hat{\rho}_2 = y_{\cdot\cdot 1} - y_{\cdot\cdot 2}$. Now $y_{\cdot\cdot 1}$ and $y_{\cdot\cdot 2}$ are independent quantities each a mean of m independent observations, thus

$$\sigma_{y_{\cdot\cdot 1}}^2 = \sigma_{y_{\cdot\cdot 2}}^2 = \frac{\sigma^2}{m}$$

and therefore

$$\sigma_{(y_{\cdot\cdot 1} - y_{\cdot\cdot 2})}^2 = \frac{2\sigma^2}{m}.$$

Hence to test $H: \rho_1 = \rho_2$ we have to use

$$F = \frac{m^2 - 3m + 2}{1} \cdot \frac{m(y_{\cdot\cdot 1} - y_{\cdot\cdot 2})^2}{2Q_a}. \tag{7.5}$$

Similarly if we test H: $\rho_1 = 0$ we have first to compute the variance of $\hat{\rho}_1 = y_{\cdot\cdot 1} - y$. We have

$$\sigma^2_{(y_{\cdot\cdot 1}-y)} = \sigma^2_{y_{\cdot\cdot 1}} - 2\sigma_{y_{\cdot\cdot 1}y} + \sigma^2_y$$
$$= \sigma^2\left(\frac{1}{m} - \frac{2}{m^2} + \frac{1}{m^2}\right) = \frac{\sigma^2}{m} \cdot \frac{m-1}{m} .$$

Hence

$$(7.6) \qquad F = \frac{m^3 - 3m + 2}{1} \cdot \frac{m^2}{m-1} \cdot \frac{(y_{\cdot\cdot 1} - y)^2}{Q_a}$$

is the likelihood ratio statistic for testing H: $\rho_1 = 0$.

The treatment of experiments set out in several, say r, replications each of which constitutes a Latin square does not offer any particular difficulty. The observations may be denoted by $y^{(l)}_{ijk}$ where l is the replication number. The assumption states

$$(7.7) \qquad \begin{gathered} E(y^{(l)}_{ijk}) = \mu^{(l)}_i + \nu^{(l)}_j + \rho_k + \alpha_{(l)} + \mu, \\ \sum_i \mu^{(l)}_i = \sum_j \nu^{(l)}_j = \sum_k \rho_k = \sum_l \alpha_{(l)} = 0. \end{gathered}$$

The number of independent parameters is

$r(m-1)$	for row effects,
$r(m-1)$	for column effects,
$(m-1)$	for varietal effects,
$(r-1)$	for replicates,
1	for mean.

Hence the number of degrees of freedom for Q_a becomes $(m-1)$ $(rm - r - 1)$.

It is often possible to test at the same time other effects on the yield, for instance we might be able to apply m different fertilizers and to construct a design which forms a Latin square with respect to fertilizers and varieties each and has in addition to this the property that every fertilizer is applied exactly once to every variety. For $m = 4$ one could use for instance the design

$$\begin{array}{cccc} v_1f_1 & v_2f_2 & v_3f_3 & v_4f_4 \\ v_2f_3 & v_1f_4 & v_4f_1 & v_3f_2 \\ v_3f_4 & v_4f_3 & v_1f_2 & v_2f_1 \\ v_4f_2 & v_3f_1 & v_2f_4 & v_1f_3 \end{array}$$

where v_1, v_2, v_3, v_4 denote the 4 varieties, f_1, f_2, f_3, f_4 denote the 4 fertilizers.

This idea can be generalized to test the effects of r different categories of conditions for each of which there are m possibilities. We then need designs with the following properties. There are r different letters. Each of these letters occurs m times with each of the indices $1, \cdots, m$. They are to be arranged into a square, divided into m^2 subsquares, in such a way that the indices on each letter form a Latin square and so that each pair of letters occurs with each pair of indices exactly once in one of the subsquares. A design of this type is called a set of r orthogonal Latin squares.

The analysis of these designs is entirely analogous to that of the Latin square design. The required F statistics can easily be obtained by applying Theorem 4.1.

If the assumptions made for the analysis of the Latin square are justified then the Latin square is the best design for field experiments, which is at present available. However, it is necessary in a Latin square that the number of experiments on each variety be equal to the total number of varieties investigated. Thus if the number of varieties is large the number of replications becomes likewise large. This means not only an unduly large expense for the experiment but also necessitates the use of large blocks, so that the assumption (7.1) which underlies the analysis of the Latin square is not even approximately fulfilled. We shall therefore discuss other designs which take care of this situation.

If we plant the varieties in relatively small blocks we may assume that the soil fertility is the same for each plot in the same block.

Thus again making the assumption that the mean yield is a linear function of varietal effect and block effect we have

$$(7.8) \qquad E(y_{ij}) = v_i + b_j + \mu, \qquad \sum_i v_i = \sum_j b_j = 0,$$

where y_{ij} is the yield of the experiment which consists in planting the ith variety on a plot of the jth block. Applying the likelihood ratio principle to the linear hypothesis (7.8) we have to minimize

$$(7.9) \qquad Q = \sum_{i,j} (y_{ij} - v_i - b_j - \mu)^2,$$

where $\sum_{i,j}$ runs over all pairs i, j for which the ith variety occurs in the jth block, with respect to v_i, b_j and μ under the restriction $\sum_i v_i = \sum_j b_j = 0$. Minimizing Q and denoting least square estimates by carets leads to the equations

$$\sum_{i,j} y_{ij} = \sum_i r_i\hat{v}_i + \sum_j k_j\hat{b}_j + N\hat{\mu},$$

$$(7.10) \qquad V_i = r_i\hat{v}_i + \sum_{(i)} \hat{b}_j + r_i\hat{\mu},$$

$$B_j = \sum^{(j)} \hat{v}_i + k_j\hat{b}_j + k_j\hat{\mu}$$

since by Theorem 4.4 the restrictions $\sum v_i = \sum b_j = 0$ may be ignored. In (7.10)

V_i denotes the sum of the yields of the ith variety,
B_j denotes the sum of the yields in the jth block,
r_i denotes the number of replicates of the ith variety,
k_j denotes the number of plots in the jth block,
$\sum_{(i)} b_j$ denotes the sum of the effects of all blocks, which contain a plot with the ith variety.
$\sum^{(j)} v_i$ denotes the sum of the varietal effects of all varieties that occur in the jth block.
N is the number of experiments.

In order that such a design be really useful, the following requirements must be fulfilled:

1.) The solution to the system 7.10 must exist and must be unique.

2.) It must be possible to compute the solutions to 7.10 within a reasonable time.

3.) The estimates of the varietal effects should be reasonably accurate.

The $\hat{v}_i$ and $\hat{b}_j$ are linear functions of the observations. Hence if the y_{ij} are normally distributed, then each $\hat{v}_i$, $\hat{b}_j$, $\hat{\mu}$ will be normally distributed.

The size of the resulting confidence interval for v_i is then exactly proportional to its standard deviation. The requirement 3 is somewhat vague. Suppose every variety occurs the same number of times and it would be possible to carry out an experiment in a two by two classification according to blocks and varieties with a complete replication in every block. In such a design the estimate $\hat{v}_i$ would then have a certain variance σ^2/h. Suppose the variance of $\hat{v}_i$ as computed from (7.10) is σ^2/c_i . Then

$$e = \frac{c_i}{h} \tag{7.11}$$

is called the efficiency factor of the design leading to (7.10) with respect to the estimate $\hat{v}_i$. The efficiency factors with respect to varietal differences are defined similarly. Clearly if there is a choice between two designs one of which is more efficient than the other whilst both justify the assumption 7.8, then the experimenter will choose the more efficient design.

Various designs have been constructed which satisfy the requirements 1 and 2 and the requirement 3 to a fairly satisfactory extent. The best of these are the incomplete balanced block designs. These are available for certain combinations of the number of varieties and number of replications.

A balanced block design is an arrangement of v varieties into b blocks of k plots each such that

1.) No block contains the same variety twice.

2.) Every variety is replicated r times.

3.) Every variety v_i occurs with every other variety v_j exactly λ times together in the same block.

The total number of experiments is bk on the one hand and rv on the other hand so that

$$b \cdot k = r \cdot v. \tag{7.12}$$

Every variety v_j occurs in r blocks. These r blocks contain $r(k - 1)$ varieties different from v_j. Since every $v_i \neq v_j$ occurs among them exactly λ times

$$r(k - 1) = \lambda(v - 1). \tag{7.13}$$

Equations 12 and 13 are necessary conditions for the existence of a block with the parameters b, v, r, k, λ. Another necessary condition for a design in which not every variety is repeated in every block is

$$b \geq v. \tag{7.14}$$

The condition (7.14) was first proved by R. A. Fisher, Ann. of Eugenics (1940) 10 pp. 52-75, and will be derived later. The conditions (7.12), (7.13) and (7.14) are not sufficient for the existence of the design. Thus for instance the design $v = b = 43$, $r = k = 7$, $\lambda = 1$ is known to be impossible. In fact necessary and sufficient conditions are at the present time not yet known. Various methods for the construction of incomplete balanced block designs will be given in the next chapter.

We proceed to discuss the analysis of balanced incomplete block designs and note first that in 7.10 $r_i = r$, $k_j = k$. Hence on account of $\sum_i v_i = \sum_j b_j = 0$ 7.10 reduces to

$$\sum_{i,j} y_{ij} = rv\hat{\mu},$$

$$V_i = r\hat{v}_i + \sum_{(i)} \hat{b}_j + r\hat{\mu}, \tag{7.15}$$

$$B_j = \sum^{(j)} \hat{v}_i + k_j\hat{b} + k\hat{\mu}.$$

We put $T_i = \sum_{(i)} B_j$ = sum of the totals of all the blocks which contain the ith variety. Summing the third equation in (7.15) over all blocks containing the ith variety we obtain

$$T_i = k \sum_{(i)} \hat{b}_j + (r - \lambda)\hat{v}_i + rk\hat{\mu} \tag{7.16}$$

since $\sum_i \hat{v}_i = 0$ and since every variety different from v_i occurs in the sum λ times whilst v_i occurs r times. Multiplying the second of the equations (7.15) by k we obtain

$$kV_i = k \sum_{(i)} \hat{b}_j + rk\hat{v}_i + rk\hat{\mu}. \tag{7.17}$$

Subtracting (7.16) from (7.17) we get

$$(rk - r + \lambda)\hat{v}_i = kV_i - T_i . \tag{7.18}$$

Substituting from (7.12) and (7.13)

$$rk - r + \lambda = r(k - 1) + \lambda = \lambda(v - 1) + \lambda = \lambda v.$$

Hence

$$\hat{\mu} = y,$$

$$\hat{v}_i = \frac{1}{\lambda v}(kV_i - T_i), \tag{7.19}$$

$$\hat{b}_j = \frac{1}{k} B_j - \frac{1}{\lambda k v} \sum^{(j)} (kV_i - T_i) - y.$$

We observe that $(k - 1)V_i$ and $T_i - V_i$ are independent quantities and therefore

$$\begin{aligned} \frac{\sigma^2_{\hat{v}_i}}{\sigma^2} &= \frac{1}{\lambda^2 v^2}[(k - 1)^2 r + r(k - 1)] \\ &= \frac{rk(k - 1)}{\lambda^2 v^2} = \frac{k(v - 1)}{\lambda v^2} . \end{aligned} \tag{7.20}$$

We now apply Theorem 4.2 to the sequence of hypotheses

$$H_1: \quad E(y_{ij}) = v_i + b_j + \mu, \qquad H_2: \quad v_i = 0 \ (i = 1, \cdots, v),$$

$$H_3: \quad b_j = 0 \ (j = 1, \cdots b).$$

Then

$$\begin{aligned} Q_a &= \sum_{i,j} y_{ij}^2 - \frac{1}{k} \sum_j B_j^2 - \sum_{i,j} \left(\hat{v}_i - \frac{1}{k} \sum^{(j)} v_i\right)^2, \\ Q_r &= \sum_{i,j} y_{ij}^2 - \frac{1}{k} \sum_j B_j^2 . \end{aligned} \tag{7.21}$$

On account of the conditions of an incomplete block design the expression for $Q_r - Q_a$ is symmetric in the v_i, $(i = 1, \cdots, v)$. Hence by Theorem 4.5 and on account of 7.20

$$(7.22)\qquad \begin{aligned} Q_r - Q_a &= \frac{\lambda v}{k} \sum_i \hat{v}_i^2 , \\ Q_a &= \sum_{i,j} y_{ij}^2 - \frac{1}{k} \sum_j B_j^2 - \frac{\lambda v}{k} \sum_i \hat{v}_i^2 . \end{aligned}$$

To carry out tests of significance for the hypothesis $v_i = v_j$ it is necessary to know the variance of $\hat{v}_i - \hat{v}_j$. We have

$$(7.23)\qquad \sigma^2_{\hat{v}_i - \hat{v}_j} = \sigma^2_{\hat{v}_i} + \sigma^2_{\hat{v}_j} - 2\sigma_{\hat{v}_i \hat{v}_j} .$$

Now $\hat{v}_i$ and $\hat{v}_j$ are given by (7.19). Counting the observations common to the terms in (7.19), we find no common observation in V_i and V_j, λ common observations in V_i and T_j or V_j and T_i and $k\lambda$ observations occurring in T_i as well as in T_j. Thus

$$\lambda^2 v^2 \sigma_{\hat{v}_i \hat{v}_j} = (-k\lambda - k\lambda + k\lambda)\sigma^2 = -k\lambda\sigma^2$$

and therefore

$$(7.24)\qquad \frac{\sigma^2_{\hat{v}_i - \hat{v}_j}}{\sigma^2} = \frac{2k(v - 1)}{\lambda v^2} + \frac{2k}{\lambda v^2} = \frac{2k}{\lambda v} .$$

Application of the corollary to Theorem 4.3 then yields the proper test statistic for testing the hypothesis $v_i = v_j$.

To find the efficiency factors with respect to $\hat{v}_i$ and $\hat{v}_i - \hat{v}_j$ we have to compute the variance of the estimates $\hat{v}_i$, $\hat{v}_i - \hat{v}_j$ in a two-way classification design with r replications and these are easily found to be $v - 1/rv$ and $2/r$ respectively so that in both cases the efficiency factor is $\lambda v/rk$. This is mostly quite satisfactory, as for instance in the designs

$$(v, b, r, k, \lambda) = (16, 24, 9, 6, 3), (8, 14, 7, 4, 3),$$

$$(11, 11, 5, 5, 2) \quad \text{or} \quad (21, 21, 5, 5, 1).$$

CHAPTER VIII

Galois Fields and Orthogonal Latin Squares

IT WAS SEEN IN CHAPTER VII that the analysis of sets of orthogonal Latin squares and of incomplete balanced block designs offers no particular difficulty. The construction of these designs however leads to very interesting combinatorial problems, some of which are not yet completely solved.

A Latin square of side m is an arrangement of m letters into m^2 subsquares of a square in such a way that every row and every column contains every letter exactly once. Two Latin squares are termed orthogonal if, when one is superimposed upon the other, every ordered pair of symbols occurs exactly once in the resulting square. Thus the Latin squares

$$\begin{matrix} A & B & C \\ B & C & A \\ C & A & B \end{matrix} \qquad \begin{matrix} \alpha & \beta & \gamma \\ \gamma & \alpha & \beta \\ \beta & \gamma & \alpha \end{matrix}$$

are orthogonal. The problem of constructing, for instance, a set of r orthogonal Latin squares of side m could be regarded as solved if we either can give a method by which such a design can be constructed or are able to prove that the design cannot exist. This problem is at present still unsolved for many combinations of r and m. Various methods have been discovered however for obtaining solutions in a great many cases. In fact, within the range useful in the design of experiments, the solution has been obtained for most cases with only a few exceptions. The experimenter will usually not go beyond m = 13. The problem of the construction of orthogonal Latin squares within this range is solved for m = 2, 3, 4, 5, 6, 7, 8, 9, 11, 13. That is to say, $(m - 1)$ orthogonal Latin squares of side m can be constructed for m = 2, 3, 4, 5, 7, 8, 9, 11, 13 while it is proved that no six-sided orthogonal pair exists nor more than $(m - 1)$ orthogonal Latin squares of side m. An orthogonal pair of side 12 can be constructed, but it is not known whether a pair of orthogonal 10 sided squares or a triple of orthogonal 12 sided squares exists.

To understand the methods by which orthogonal Latin squares have been constructed we need certain elementary concepts of algebra and of the theory of numbers which will be developed presently.

Let a, b, m be integers. We shall write

$$a \equiv b(m) \tag{8.1}$$

in words, a congruent to b modulo m, if m divides $a - b$. Such congruences can be treated like equations. For instance if $a \equiv b(m)$, then $a \pm c \equiv b \pm c(m)$, $ac \equiv bc(m)$. The proof of these two propositions is left to the reader. If also $c \equiv d(m)$, then $ac \equiv bd(m)$, $a \pm c \equiv b \pm d(m)$.

Proof: According to our definition we have

$$a - b = \lambda_1 m, \qquad c - d = \lambda_2 m, \qquad \lambda_1, \lambda_2 \text{ integers.}$$

Hence $ac = bd + m(\lambda_2 b + \lambda_1 d) + \lambda_1\lambda_2 m^2$ and therefore

$$ac \equiv bd(m). \tag{8.2}$$

The relation $a \pm c \equiv b \pm d(m)$ follows in a similar manner.

The rules for division of congruences are not so simple. We shall prove however the following rule:

If $ac \equiv bc(m)$ *and* $t = (m, c)$ *is the greatest common divisor* (g.c.d.) *of m and c then*

$$a \equiv b\left(\frac{m}{t}\right). \tag{8.3}$$

Proof: $ac - bc = \lambda m$, λ integral. Hence

$$a - b = \frac{\lambda m}{c} = \frac{\lambda}{c/t} \cdot \frac{m}{t}. \tag{8.4}$$

The left side of (8.4) is an integer. Since m/t and c/t are integers and c/t is prime to m/t, it follows that λ is divisible by c/t.

Hence $\lambda/(c/t)$ is an integer and m/t divides $a - b$. In particular it follows that we may divide a congruence by any number which is prime to the modulus. If m is a prime number p then we may divide congruences mod p by any number a such that $a \not\equiv 0(p)$.

In the following we shall always calculate mod p. That is to say, we shall replace every number by its smallest positive residue mod p. For instance $4 + 2 \equiv 1(5)$, $2.8 \equiv 1(5)$ and so forth.

Let p be a prime number and form the following design.

$$
(8.5)\quad L_j = \begin{matrix} 0 & 1 \cdots p-1 \\ j & 1+j \cdots p-1+j \\ 2j & 1+2j \cdots p-1+2j \\ \cdot & \cdot \qquad \cdot \\ \cdot & \cdot \qquad \cdot \\ \cdot & \cdot \qquad \cdot \\ (p-1)j & 1+(p-1)j \cdots (p-1)+(p-1)j. \end{matrix} \qquad j=1,\cdots,p-1
$$

All numbers in L_j are reduced mod p. We shall show that L_j is a Latin square. If this were not true, then since only the symbols $0, 1, \cdots, p - 1$ occur in L_j, we would have some row or column in which one of the symbols occurs twice. If the ith row contains the same number in the kth column and in the rth column we should have

$$k + ij \equiv r + ij(p),$$

$$k \equiv r(p).$$

A similar argument shows that every column contains every number exactly once. Thus L_j, $(j = 1, \cdots, p - 1)$ is a Latin square. We shall show now that L_i is orthogonal to L_j if $i \neq j$. If this were not the case, we should have the same ordered pair of numbers occurring in two different boxes of the square which results from superimposition of L_i on L_j. Let mn be a pair which occurs twice and assume that it occurs in the αth row and βth column and in the γth row and δth column. Then

$$\beta + \alpha j \equiv \delta + \gamma j \equiv m(p),$$

$$\beta + \alpha i \equiv \delta + \gamma i \equiv n(p).$$

Hence

$$\alpha(i - j) \equiv \gamma(i - j)(p).$$

But $-p < (i - j) < p$ and $(i - j)$ is therefore prime to p. We may therefore divide by $i - j$ and obtain $\alpha \equiv \gamma(p)$, $\beta \equiv \delta(p)$.

As an example we present a set of 4 orthogonal 5 sided squares.

L_1	L_2	L_3	L_4
0 1 2 3 4	0 1 2 3 4	0 1 2 3 4	0 1 2 3 4
1 2 3 4 0	2 3 4 0 1	3 4 0 1 2	4 0 1 2 3
2 3 4 0 1	4 0 1 2 3	1 2 3 4 0	3 4 0 1 2
3 4 0 1 2	1 2 3 4 0	4 0 1 2 3	2 3 4 0 1
4 0 1 2 3	3 4 0 1 2	2 3 4 0 1	1 2 3 4 0

If we consider the properties of the system of residues mod p which were used in constructing the L_i we note that, particularly, the uniqueness of the division was necessary. Because of the uniqueness of the division the residues $a, 2a, \cdots, (p-1)a$ are $(p - 1)$ different residues all different from 0 provided $a \not\equiv 0(p)$. Hence one of them must be the residue 1. Thus to every residue $a \not\equiv 0(p)$ there exists a residue a^{-1} called the inverse of a such that $a \cdot a^{-1} \equiv 1(p)$.

From our method of constructing $m - 1$ orthogonal squares if m is a prime number, it may be surmised that we can always construct $m - 1$ orthogonal Latin squares if we have a system $\mathfrak{F}$ of m elements satisfying the following conditions.

To every pair of elements a, b in $\mathfrak{F}$ there exist two uniquely determined elements $a + b$ and $a \cdot b$ in $\mathfrak{F}$. The "addition" and "multiplication" satisfy the following conditions:

I. $a + b = b + a$, $ab = ba$, The commutative law.

II. $(a + b) + c = a + (b + c)$, $(ab)c = a(bc)$, The associative law.

III. *There exist two elements* 0, 1 *in* $\mathfrak{F}$ *such that*

$$a + 0 = a \qquad a \cdot 1 = a$$

for every a in $\mathfrak{F}$.

IV. *To every* $a \neq 0$ *there exists an element* $(-a)$ *and an element* a^{-1} *such that*

$$a + (-a) = 0, \qquad a \cdot a^{-1} = 1.$$

The element a^{-1} *is called the inverse of a.*

V. $c(a + b) = ca + cb$, The distributive law.

A system satisfying the postulates $I - V$ is called a field. If the number of elements, which we shall call the marks of the field, is finite, then it is called a finite field or a Galois field. It may be remarked that the commutative law of addition, and, if the field is finite, also the commutative law of multiplication need not be postulated.

Let $g_0 = 0, g_1 = 1, g_2, \cdots, g_{m-1}$ be the elements of the finite field $\mathfrak{F}$ and form the designs:

$$(8.6)\quad L_i = \begin{matrix} 0 & 1 & \cdots & g_{m-1} \\ g_i & g_i+1 & \cdots & g_i+g_{m-1} \\ g_ig_2 & g_ig_2+1 & \cdots & g_ig_2+g_{m-1} \\ \cdot & \cdot & & \cdot \\ \cdot & \cdot & & \cdot \\ \cdot & \cdot & & \cdot \\ g_ig_{m-1} & g_ig_{m-1}+1 & \cdots & g_ig_{m-1}+g_{m-1} \end{matrix} \qquad (i = 1, \cdots, m-1)$$

Then by exactly the same argument that was applied in the case of the field of residues mod m we can show that $L_1, \cdots, L_{m-1}$ is a set of $m - 1$ orthogonal Latin squares. Hence we have

THEOREM 8.1: *If* $g_0 = 0$, $g_1 = 1$, $g_2, \cdots, g_{m-1}$ *are the marks of a finite field, then the designs* L_i *of* (8.6) *form a set of* $m - 1$ *orthogonal Latin squares.*

In a field $\mathfrak{F}$ the following propositions hold:

Proposition 1: $a \cdot 0 = 0$ *for every* a.

Proof: $a = a(1 + 0) = a + a \cdot 0$; adding $(-a)$ to both sides of this equation we obtain Proposition 1.

Proposition 2: $ab = 0$, $a \neq 0$ *implies* $b = 0$.

Proof: This follows by multiplying $ab = 0$ with a^{-1}.

We denote by $m \cdot x$ where m is an integer and x a mark of $\mathfrak{F}$ the sum of mx's. We then have

Proposition 3: *If* m *is an integer such that* $m \cdot 1 = 0$ *then* $m \cdot x = 0$ *for every* x. *If* $mx = 0$ *for one* $x \neq 0$, *then* $my = 0$ *for all* y *in* $\mathfrak{F}$.

Proof: If $m \cdot 1 = 0$ then $mx = (m \cdot 1)x = 0x = 0$. Also if $mx = 0$ then $mx = (m \cdot 1)x = 0$ if $x \neq 0$ then by Proposition 1 $m \cdot 1 = 0$ and therefore $m \cdot y = 0$ for every y.

Proposition 4: *Let* p *be the smallest positive integer for which* $p \cdot 1 = 0$ *then* p *is a prime.* (Such an integer need, of course, not exist.)

Proof: Suppose $p = mn$, $m < p$, $n < p$ then $mn \cdot 1 = (m \cdot 1)(n \cdot 1) = 0$. Hence either $m \cdot 1 = 0$ or $n \cdot 1 = 0$ contradicting the significance of p.

The number p is called the characteristic of the field. If there is no integer p for which $p \cdot 1 = 0$ then the field is called a field of characteristic 0 and is necessarily infinite because the elements $n \cdot 1$, $n = 0, 1, \cdots$ ad. inf. are then all different.

THEOREM 8.2: *The number of elements in a Galois field* $\mathfrak{F}$ *is a power of its characteristic* p.

Proof: Put $w_1 = 1$. If there is a mark $w_2 \neq a \cdot 1$ for $a = 0, \cdots, p - 1$ form all marks $a_1 w_1 + a_2 w_2$, $a_1 = 0, 1, \cdots, p - 1$;

$a_2 = 0, 1, \cdots, p - 1$. These are p^2 different marks. If they do not yet exhaust all the marks of $\mathfrak{F}$ then take a mark w_3 different from $a_1w_1 + a_2w_2$ and form all marks $a_1w_1 + a_2w_2 + a_3w_3$. Continue the process until all marks of $\mathfrak{F}$ are exhausted. If $w_1, \cdots, w_m$ are obtained in this way, then $a_1w_1 + \cdots + a_mw_m$ $(a_i = 0, 1, \cdots, p - 1)$ represent all the marks of $\mathfrak{F}$. If

$$(8.7) \qquad a_1w_1 + \cdots + a_mw_m = b_1w_1 + \cdots + b_mw_m$$

then $(a_1 - b_1)w_1 + \cdots + (a_m - b_m)w_m = 0$. Let k be the largest number for which $a_k - b_k = -c_k \neq 0$. Then

$$c_kw_k = (a_1 - b_1)w_1 + \cdots + (a_{k-1} - b_{k-1})w_{k-1}.$$

Let c_k^{-1} be the inverse to c_k in the field of residues mod p then

$$w_k = c_k^{-1}(a_1 - b_1)w_1 + \cdots + c_k^{-1}(a_{k-1} - b_{k-1})w_{k-1}$$
$$= d_1w_1 + \cdots + d_{k-1}w_{k-1}$$

where $d_1, \cdots, d_{k-1}$ are residues mod p. But this contradicts the significance of w_k. Hence $\mathfrak{F}$ contains p^m elements.

Let α be any mark of a Galois field, G.F.(p^m), and form $1, \alpha, \alpha^2, \cdots, \alpha^k, \cdots$. Since the number of marks is finite we must have for some $k > j$

$$\alpha^k = \alpha^j, \qquad \alpha^{k-j} = 1.$$

Definition: *If t is the smallest positive integer such that $\alpha^t = 1$, then t is called the order of α.*

Let $x_1, \cdots, x_{p^m-1}$, be all the non-zero elements of G.F.(p^m) then

$$\alpha x_1 \alpha x_2 \cdots \alpha x_{p^m-1} = x_1 \cdots x_{p^m-1} \qquad \text{if } \alpha \neq 0.$$

Hence

$$(8.8) \qquad \alpha^{p^m-1} = 1 \qquad \text{for all } \alpha \neq 0.$$

We shall prove now several propositions on the order of elements of a finite field $\mathfrak{F}$.

Proposition 5: *If s is the order of α and $\alpha^n = 1$, then $n \equiv 0(s)$.* For we can find an integer λ such that $n = \lambda s + r$, $0 \leq r < s$, and $\alpha^n = 1$ implies $\alpha^r = 1$, hence $r = 0$, since s is the order of α.

Corollary: *If s is the order of* α *then* $p^m - 1 \equiv 0(s)$.

Proposition 6: *If* α *has the order s and* β *the order t and* $(s, t) = 1$ *then* $\alpha \cdot \beta$ *has the order st.*

Proof: $(\alpha\beta)^r = 1$ implies $\beta^{sr} = 1$ and $sr \equiv 0(t)$ by Proposition 5. Hence $r \equiv 0(t)$ and similarly $r \equiv 0(s)$. Thus $r \equiv 0(st)$. But $(\alpha\beta)^{st} = 1$ and st is therefore the order of $\alpha \cdot \beta$.

Proposition 7: *If* α *has the order* $\lambda\mu$ *then* α^λ *has the order* μ.

The proof is left to the reader.

Proposition 8: *If s is the largest order occurring in a Galois field* $\mathfrak{F}$ *and if t is any order then* $s \equiv 0(t)$.

Proof: If $s \not\equiv 0(t)$ then for some prime p we should have $s = p^e r$, $t = p^f r'$, $(p, r) = (p, r') = 1$, $f > e$. If α has the order s and β the order t, then by propositions 6 and 7 $\alpha^{p^e}\beta^{r'}$ has the order $p^f \cdot r > s$, but this contradicts the significance of s.

Definition: *A mark of order* $p^m - 1$ *in the Galois field of order* p^m *is called a primitive root. We are now prepared to prove*

THEOREM 8.3: *A Galois field* G.F. (p^m) *of order* p^m, *has* $\phi(p^m - 1)$ *primitive roots, where* $\phi(n)$ *denotes the number of residues* mod n *which are prime to* n.

Lemma 8.1: *A polynomial* $P(x) = x^n + a_1x^{n-1} + \cdots + a_n$ *of degree n with coefficients in* G.F.(p^m) *has at most n roots.*

Let α be a root of $P(x)$. Then $P(\alpha) = 0$. Hence

$$P(x) = P(x) - P(\alpha)$$

$$= x^n - \alpha^n + \cdots + a_{n-1}(x - \alpha) = (x - \alpha)Q(x)$$

where $Q(x)$ is a polynomial of degree $(n - 1)$ with coefficients in G.F. (p^m). If β is a root of $P(x)$, then by Proposition 2 either $\beta = \alpha$ or $Q(\beta) = 0$. Lemma 8.1 then follows easily by induction.

Proof of Theorem 8.3: Let s be the largest order occurring in G.F.(p^m). Then since every order divides s we must have for every α in G.F.(p^m)

$$\alpha^s = 1. \tag{8.11}$$

By lemma 8.1 it follows from (8.11) that $s \geq p^m - 1$ but also $p^m - 1 \equiv 0(s)$ and therefore $p^m - 1 = s$. Thus there exists at least one primitive root. Let w be this primitive root, then w^i where i is prime to $p^m - 1$ is also a primitive root. Hence there are $\phi(p^m - 1)$ primitive roots.

If a primitive root is known then the construction of a set of $(m - 1)$ orthogonal Latin squares can be simplified considerably. Let w be a primitive root and $0, 1, x_3, \cdots, x_n$ be the elements of a finite field of order n then

$$
\begin{array}{llll}
 & 0 & 1 & \cdots\ x_n \\
 & w^{0+i} & 1+w^{0+i} & \cdots\ x_n+w^{0+i} \\
(8.12)\quad \overline{L_i} = & w^{1+i} & 1+w^{1+i} & \cdots\ x_n+w^{1+i} \qquad (i=0,1,\cdots,n-2) \\
 & \cdot & \cdot & \cdot \\
 & \cdot & \cdot & \cdot \\
 & \cdot & \cdot & \cdot \\
 & w^{n-2+i} & 1+w^{n-2+i} & \cdots\ x_n+w^{n-2+i}
\end{array}
$$

are $n - 1$ orthogonal Latin squares. It should be observed that $\overline{L}_{i+1}$ is obtained from $\overline{L}_i$ by cyclically permuting the last $n - 1$ rows.

We now proceed to construct a G.F.(p^m) for every m and every p. If $m = 1$ then the residues mod p form a G.F.(p).

We consider polynomials

$$p(x) = x^n + a_1x^{n-1} + \cdots + a_n$$

whose coefficients $a_1, \cdots, a_n$ are elements of a field. We shall prove:

THEOREM 8.4: *If $p(x)$, $q(x)$ are polynomials with coefficients in a field $\mathfrak{F}$ then there exists a polynomial $d(x)$ such that*

$$(8.13)\qquad p(x) \equiv 0(d(x)), \qquad q(x) \equiv 0(d(x))$$

and such that $p(x) \equiv 0(h(x))$, $q(x) \equiv 0(h(x))$ implies *$d(x) \equiv 0(h(x))$. Further there exist polynomials $a(x)$ and $b(x)$ such that*

$$(8.14)\qquad a(x)p(x) + b(x)q(x) = d(x).$$

If $d(x)$ has the first coefficient 1 then $d(x)$ is called the greatest common divisor of $p(x)$ and $q(x)$ and we shall write

$$(8.15)\qquad (p(x), q(x)) = d(x).$$

If $d(x)$ fulfills the conditions of Theorem 8.4 then $a \cdot d(x)$ also fulfills these conditions for every non-zero mark a of $\mathfrak{F}$. Hence if b is the first coefficient of $d(x)$ then $b^{-1}d(x)$ also fulfills the conditions of Theorem 8.4 and has first coefficient 1. It also follows that the greatest common divisor is uniquely determined.

Proof of Theorem 8.4: Consider all expressions of the form

$$a(x)p(x) + b(x)q(x) = d(x) \tag{8.16}$$

for all $a(x)$ and $b(x)$. Let $d(x)$ in 8.16 have the lowest possible degree whereby the polynomial 0 is not considered to have a degree. We shall prove that $d(x)$ satisfies the conditions of Theorem 8.4. By long division we can obtain a polynomial $h(x)$ such that

$$p(x) - h(x)d(x) = r(x) \tag{8.17}$$

is either 0 or has a smaller degree than $d(x)$. Multiplying 8.16 by $h(x)$ we have

$$h(x)a(x)p(x) + h(x)b(x)q(x) = p(x) - r(x)$$

Putting

$$\bar{a}(x) = -[h(x)a(x) - 1], \qquad \bar{b}(x) = -[h(x)b(x)]$$

we have

$$\bar{a}(x)p(x) + \bar{b}(x)q(x) = r(x).$$

Since $d(x)$ has the lowest degree of all polynomials 8.16 it follows that $r(x) = 0$. Thus $p(x) \equiv 0(d(x))$. Similarly $q(x) \equiv 0(d(x))$. From 8.16 it is obvious that $d(x)$ also fulfills all the other conditions of Theorem 8.4.

Definition: *If $g(x)$ with coefficients in a field $\mathfrak{F}$ has no divisor except a and $a \cdot g(x)$ with $a \subset \mathfrak{F}$, then $g(x)$ is called irreducible in $\mathfrak{F}$.*

We now define congruences modulo a polynomial $m(x)$ in exactly the same way as congruences in the system of all integers. We then calculate mod $m(x)$ by adding, subtracting, and multiplying in the ordinary manner and by always replacing every polynomial $f(x)$ by the residue of smallest degree obtained in dividing $f(x)$ by $m(x)$.

THEOREM 8.5: *If $g(x)$ is irreducible in $\mathfrak{F}$ then the residues* mod *$g(x)$ in the system $\mathfrak{F}(x)$ of all polynomials with coefficients in $\mathfrak{F}$ form a field.*

That the field postulates are satisfied by the system of residues mod $g(x)$ is obvious except for the existence of an inverse. Hence Theorem 8.5 is proved if we can prove: To every $f(x) \not\equiv 0(g(x))$ there exists a $q(x)$ such that $f(x)q(x) \equiv 1(g(x))$. This is equivalent to stating that there exists a $\lambda(x)$ such that

$$f(x)q(x) - 1 = \lambda(x)g(x). \tag{8.18}$$

Since $g(x)$ is irreducible and $f(x) \not\equiv 0(g(x))$ we have $(f(x), g(x)) = 1$ and Theorem 8.5 follows from 8.16.

We now take $\mathfrak{F}$ to be the finite field, G.F.(p) of residues mod p, then we have

Corollary to Theorem 8.5: *If $g(x)$ of degree n with coefficients in* G.F.(p) *is irreducible in* G.F.(p) *then the residues* mod $g(x)$ *form a Galois field with p^n elements.*

Every polynomial with coefficients in G.F.(p) is, mod $g(x)$, congruent to one of the p^n polynomials

$$a_0 + a_1x + \cdots + a_{n-1}x^{n-1}, \tag{8.19}$$

where $a_0, a_1, \cdots, a_{n-1}$ may be any of the residues mod p.

Hence to construct a G.F. (p^n) we have to find an irreducible polynomial of degree n with coefficients in G.F.(p).

For instance the polynomial $x^2 + x + 1$ is irreducible mod 2. Hence the residue 0, 1, x, $x + 1$ form a G.F.(2^2). Also

$$x^0 \equiv 1(x^2 + x + 1),$$

$$x^1 \equiv x(x^2 + x + 1),$$

$$x^2 \equiv x + 1(x^2 + x + 1).$$

Hence x is a primitive root of this Galois field. Writing the addition and multiplication tables for the marks 0, 1, x, $x + 1$ we have

Addition

	0	1	x	$x+1$
0	0	1	x	$x+1$
1	1	0	$x+1$	x
x	x	$x+1$	0	1
$x+1$	$x+1$	x	1	0

Multiplication

	0	1	x	$x+1$
0	0	0	0	0
1	0	1	x	$x+1$
x	0	x	$x+1$	1
$x+1$	0	$x+1$	1	x .

From the addition table we obtain, since x is a primitive root, 3 orthogonal Latin squares of side 4 by cyclically permuting the last 3 rows. We shall however replace x by 2 and $x + 1$ by 3. This yields the following 3 orthogonal Latin squares.

$$\begin{matrix} 0&1&2&3 \\ 1&0&3&2 \\ 2&3&0&1 \\ 3&2&0&1 \end{matrix} \qquad \begin{matrix} 0&1&2&3 \\ 2&3&0&1 \\ 3&2&1&0 \\ 1&0&3&2 \end{matrix} \qquad \begin{matrix} 0&1&2&3 \\ 3&2&1&0 \\ 1&0&3&2 \\ 2&3&0&1 \end{matrix} .$$

The polynomial $x^2 + x - 1$ is irreducible mod 3 since

$$0^2 + 0 - 1 \equiv -1(3), \qquad 1^2 + 1 - 1 \equiv 1(3),$$

$$(-1)^2 + (-1) - 1 \equiv (-1)(3).$$

The mark x is a primitive root for

$$\begin{aligned} x^0 &= 1, & x^4 &= -1, \\ x^1 &= x, & x^5 &= -x, \\ x^2 &= -x + 1, & x^6 &= x - 1, \\ x^3 &= -x - 1, & x^7 &= x + 1. \end{aligned}$$

We leave it to the reader to obtain, using this Galois field, 8 orthogonal Latin squares of side 9.

THEOREM 8.6: *There is a Galois field of order p^r to every prime p and every r.*

The proof requires several steps.

Lemma 8.2: *Every modulo p irreducible polynomial of degree r is,* mod p, *a divisor of* $x^{p^r-1} - 1$.

We shall write $a(x) \equiv b(x) \bmod (f(x), p)$ (in words $a(x)$ congruent $b(x)$ modulis $f(x)$ and p) if $a(x) - b(x)$ is divisible by $f(x)$ mod p. The residues mod $(f(x), p)$ form a Galois field of order p^r. Hence

$$x^{p^r-1} \equiv 1(f(x), p),$$

(8.20)

$$x^{p^r-1} - 1 \equiv 0(f(x), p)$$

and this is Lemma 8.2.

Lemma 8.3: *If $f(x)$ is irreducible* mod p and of degree $s > r$ then $f(x)$ is mod p not a divisor of $x^{p^r-1} - 1$.

Assume that $x^{p^r-1} - 1 \equiv 0(f(x), p)$ and consider the Galois field of residues mod $(f(x), p)$. The order of this Galois field is p^s. Every element of this Galois field is of the form $a_0 + a_1x + \cdots + a_kx^k$, $k < s$ where $a_0, a_1, \cdots, a_k$ are residues mod p. Now

$$(8.21)\qquad (a_0 + a_1x + \cdots + a_kx^k)^{p^r} \equiv a_0 + a_1x + \cdots + a_kx^k(f(x), p)$$

since $x^{p^r} \equiv x(f(x), p)$ by assumption. Hence $p^r - 1$ is an upper bound for the order in our Galois field, but this contradicts Theorem 8.3 since $s > r$.

Lemma 8.4: *The polynomial* $x^m - 1$ *has no double roots* mod p *if* $m \not\equiv 0(p)$.

We can define the differential quotient for polynomials mod p by the same formal rules as in ordinary calculus. It is easy to prove then that a polynomial has, mod p, a double root only if $f(x)$ and df/dx have a common factor. But obviously $x^m - 1$ and mx^{m-1} have, mod p, no factor in common if m is prime to p.

We can now prove Theorem 8.6: The polynomial $x^{p^r-1} - 1$ has, mod p, no irreducible factor of degree larger than r. All the irreducible polynomials of degree $f < r$ are, mod p, factors of $x^{p^f-1} - 1$. Since $x^{p^r-1} - 1$ has no double roots, the sum of the degrees of all irreducible factors of degree f together is thus at most $p^f - 1$. Hence the sum of the degrees of all factors of degree $<r$ is at most

$$\sum_{f=1}^{r-1} p^f < \frac{p^r - 1}{p - 1}.$$

Hence there must be at least one irreducible factor of degree r. Let $f(x)$ be this polynomial. Then the expressions

$$(8.22)\qquad a_0 + a_1x + \cdots + a_{r-1}x^{r-1}$$

mod $(p, f(x))$ form a Galois field of order p^r.

Definition: *Two fields* $\mathfrak{F}$ *and* $\mathfrak{F}'$ *are called isomorphic if there exists a bi-unique correspondence* $a \leftrightarrow a'$, $a \subset \mathfrak{F}$, $a' \subset \mathfrak{F}'$ *such that* $a \leftrightarrow a'$, $b \leftrightarrow b'$ *implies* $a + b \leftrightarrow a' + b'$, $ab \leftrightarrow a'b'$.

THEOREM 8.7: *Any two Galois fields with* p^r *marks are isomorphic.*

It is easy to see that every G.F.(p) is isomorphic with the system of residues mod p. We know that there exists a mod p irreducible polynomial $g(x)$ of degree r. Let $\mathfrak{F}$ be any Galois field with p^r marks $\alpha_0 = 0, \alpha_1 = 1, \alpha_2, \cdots, \alpha_{p^r-1}$. Then $x^{p^r-1} - 1 = (x - \alpha_1) \cdots (x - \alpha_{p^r-1})$. Since $g(x)$ mod p is a divisor of $x^{p^r-1} - 1$ it follows that for some i we must have $g(\alpha_i) = 0$. Since g is irreducible mod p, the expressions

$$(8.23) \qquad a_0 + a_1\alpha_i + \cdots + a_{r-1}\alpha_i^{r-1}$$

where the a_i are multiples of the unit element of $\mathfrak{F}$ must all be different from 0 and thus also different from each other. Otherwise $g(x)$ mod p would have a factor in common with a polynomial of degree $<r$. Thus 8.23 presents p^r different elements of $\mathfrak{F}$ and hence every element of $\mathfrak{F}$. But the correspondence $f(\alpha_i) \leftrightarrow f(x)$ where $f(\alpha_i) \subset \mathfrak{F}$ and $f(x)$ is in the field $\overline{\mathfrak{F}}$ of residues mod $(g(x), p)$ is clearly an isomorphism. Thus any two fields $\mathfrak{F}$, $\mathfrak{F}'$ are isomorphic to $\overline{\mathfrak{F}}$ and hence isomorphic to each other.

In an abstract sense we have therefore only one Galois field with p^r marks. We shall denote this Galois field by G.F.(p^r).

If x in the field of residues mod $(f(x), p)$ does not satisfy any equation $x^m - 1 \equiv 0(f(x), p)$ with $m < p^{r-1}$, then x is a primitive root. On the other hand if α is a primitive root of G.F.(p^r) then α must satisfy an irreducible equation of degree r. Thus if we wish for convenience to have G.F.(p^r) presented by the residues mod $(f(x), p)$ in such a way that x is a primitive root, then we have to remove from $x^{p^r-1} - 1$ all factors which are factors of $x^m - 1$ for any $m < p^r - 1$. The remaining polynomial has as its roots all the primitive roots of G.F.(p^r) and must therefore have by Theorem 8.3 the degree $\phi(p^r - 1)$. We shall call it the cyclotomic polynomial of order $p^r - 1$.

To construct, for instance, G.F.(2^3) we first form the cyclotomic polynomial of order $2^3 - 1 = 7$. Its degree is $\phi(7) = 6$. Removing the root 1 from $x^7 - 1$ we obtain

$$x^6 + x^5 + x^4 + x^3 + x^2 + x + 1.$$

This polynomial must mod 2 decompose into 2 factors of degree 3 each. Thus

$$(x^6 + x^5 + x^4 + x^3 + x^2 + x + 1)$$

$$\equiv (x^3 + ax^2 + bx + c)(x^3 + \bar{a}x^2 + \bar{b}x + \bar{c})(2)$$

Hence

$$c\bar{c} \equiv 1(2), c \equiv \bar{c} \equiv 1(2), b + \bar{b} \equiv 1(2). \text{ Let } b \equiv 0, \bar{b} \equiv 1(2).$$

Then

$$\bar{a}c + a\bar{c} + b\bar{b} \equiv a + \bar{a} \equiv 1(2) \quad c + \bar{c} + a\bar{b} + b\bar{a} \equiv a \equiv 1(2).$$

Hence $a \equiv 1(2)$, $\bar{a} \equiv 0(2)$ and

$$x^6 + x^5 + x^4 + x^3 + x^2 + x + 1$$

$$\equiv (x^3 + x^2 + 1)(x^3 + x + 1)(2).$$

It is left to the reader to construct G.F.(2^3) and 7 orthogonal Latin squares of side 8.

For higher values of $p^r - 1$ it is rather laborious to find mod p irreducible polynomials of degree r by decomposing the cyclotomic polynomial of order $p^r - 1$. It is however easy to find irreducible polynomials in other ways, if we are willing to forego the advantage of having x as a primitive root. For instance, if p is odd then there always exist residues a for which $x^2 \equiv a(p)$ is not solvable. Then $x^2 - a$ is irreducible mod p. The polynomial $x^3 - x$ is identically 0 mod 3; thus $x^3 - x - 1$ is irreducible mod 3 since it otherwise would have a linear factor mod 3. The polynomial $x^4 + x + 1$ is irreducible mod 2. Obviously it does not have the root 0 or 1, thus the only possible decomposition would be of the form

$$x^4 + x + 1 \equiv (x^2 + bx + 1)(x^2 + b'x + 1)(2).$$

From which it would follow that $b + b' \equiv 1(2)$ and $b + b' \equiv 0(2)$ which is impossible. With these and similar considerations one easily obtains the following irreducible polynomials:

mod 2 $\quad x^2 + x + 1,\ x^3 + x + 1,\ x^4 + x + 1,\ x^5 + x^2 + 1,$

mod 3 $\quad x^2 + x - 1,\ x^3 - x + 1,$

mod 5 $\quad x^2 + 2,$

mod 7 $\quad x^2 + 1.$

These polynomials take care of all Galois fields with less than 63 elements and these satisfy all needs that have arisen so far in the design of experiments.

From Theorem 8.6 and Theorem 8.1 we see that a set of $m - 1$ orthogonal Latin squares of side m can always be constructed, if m is the power of a prime. If m is not the power of a prime then m may be decomposed into prime powers.

$$m = p_1^{e_1} \cdots p_s^{e_s} \qquad (p_i \neq p_j).$$

We then construct the following system. We consider "points".

$$\gamma = (g^{(1)}, g^{(2)}, \cdots, g^{(s)}), \qquad g^{(i)} \subset G.F.(p_i^{(e_i)}).$$

We define addition and multiplication by the rules

$$\gamma_1 \overset{+}{\times} \gamma_2 = (g_1^{(1)}, \cdots, g_1^{(s)}) \overset{+}{\times} (g_2^{(1)}, \cdots, g_2^{(s)})$$

$$= (g_1^{(1)} \overset{+}{\times} g_2^{(1)}, \cdots, g_1^{(s)} \overset{+}{\times} g_2^{(s)}).$$

The system thus constructed is not a field since, for instance, the element $(0, 1, \cdots, 1)$ has no inverse in multiplication. However, the postulates I-IV for addition and I-III for multiplication and postulate V are fulfilled. All the "points" which have no 0 among their coordinates possess inverses.

Let

$$0, \qquad g_1^{(i)} = 1, \qquad g_2^{(i)}, \cdots, g_{p_i^{e_i}-1}^{(i)}$$

be the marks of G.F.$(p_i^{e_i})$, then if $r = \min_i(p_i^{e_i} - 1)$ the "points"

$$\text{(8.24)} \qquad \gamma_j = (g_j^{(1)}, g_j^{(2)}, \cdots, g_j^{(s)}), \qquad 0 < j \leq r$$

possess inverses and also $\gamma_j - \gamma_i$ does if $i \neq j$. Now we number the points γ in such a way, that the first r elements are given by 8.24 and form the r arrays.

$$
(8.25) \qquad L_j = \begin{array}{cccc}
0 & 1 & \cdots & \gamma_{m-1} \\
\gamma_j & \gamma_j + 1 & \cdots & \gamma_j + \gamma_{m-1} \\
\gamma_j\gamma_2 & \gamma_j\gamma_2 + 1 & \cdots & \gamma_j\gamma_2 + \gamma_{m-1} \\
\cdot & \cdot & & \cdot \\
\cdot & \cdot & & \cdot \\
\cdot & \cdot & & \cdot \\
\gamma_j\gamma_{m-1} & \gamma_j\gamma_{m-1} + 1 & \cdots & \gamma_j\gamma_{m-1} + \gamma_{m-1} .
\end{array}
$$

We prove first that L_j is a Latin square. Suppose the αth row would contain an element twice then

$$\gamma_j\gamma_\alpha + \gamma_k = \gamma_j\gamma_\alpha + \gamma_l$$

from which $\gamma_k = \gamma_l$, $k = l$ follows. Suppose that the ith column contains the same element twice, then

$$\gamma_i + \gamma_j\gamma_\alpha = \gamma_i + \gamma_j\gamma_\beta \qquad j \leq r$$

and since γ_j possesses an inverse this implies $\gamma_\alpha = \gamma_\beta$.

We shall now prove that L_i is orthogonal to L_j if $i \neq j$. Assume that they were not orthogonal. Then in superimposing L_i on L_j we should have two compartments in the resulting square containing the same pair of "points". If this pair occurs in the αth row and the βth column and in the σth row and the τth column, we should have

$$\gamma_j\gamma_\alpha + \gamma_\beta = \gamma_j\gamma_\sigma + \gamma_\tau ,$$

$$\gamma_i\gamma_\alpha + \gamma_\beta = \gamma_i\gamma_\sigma + \gamma_\tau .$$

Hence

$$(8.26) \qquad (\gamma_i - \gamma_j)\gamma_\alpha = (\gamma_i - \gamma_j)\gamma_\sigma$$

and since $\gamma_i - \gamma_j$ possesses an inverse 8.26 implies $\gamma_\alpha = \gamma_\sigma$ and consequently $\gamma_\beta = \gamma_\tau$. Thus we have

THEOREM 8.8: *Let* $g^1_{i_1}$, $g^{(2)}_{i_2}$, $\cdots$, $g^{(s)}_{i_s}$ *denote the elements of* G.F.$(p_1^{e_1})$, $\cdots$, G.F.$(p_s^{e_s})$ *respectively where* $g_0^{(i)}$ *is the* 0 *element and* $g_1^{(i)}$ *the unit element of* G.F.$(p_i^{e_1})$. *Form the points*

$$\gamma = (g^{(1)}_{i_1}, g^{(2)}_{i_2}, \cdots , g^{(s)}_{i_s})$$

which are multiplied and added by multiplying and adding their coordinates. Let further

$$\gamma_j = (g_j^{(1)}, \cdots , g_j^{(s)}), \qquad 0 < j \leq r = \min_i (p_i^{ei} - 1)$$

and number the remaining points in any arbitrary way from $r + 1$ *to* $m = p_1^{e_1} \cdots p_s^{e_s}$ *in such a way that* $\gamma_m = 0 = (g_0^{(1)}, \cdots , g_0^{(s)})$. *Then the arrays*

$$L_j = \begin{array}{llll} 0 & 1 & \cdots & \gamma_{m-1} \\ \gamma_j & \gamma_j + 1 & \cdots & \gamma_j\, \gamma_{m-1} \\ \gamma_j\gamma_2 & \gamma_j\gamma_2 + 1 & \cdots & \gamma_j\gamma_2 + \gamma_{m-1} \\ \cdot & \cdot & & \cdot \\ \cdot & \cdot & & \cdot \\ \cdot & \cdot & & \cdot \\ \gamma_j\gamma_{m-1} & \gamma_j\gamma_{m-1} + 1 & \cdots & \gamma_j\gamma_{m-1} + \gamma_{m-1} \end{array} \qquad (j = 1, \cdots , r)$$

form a set of r orthogonal Latin squares.

This result is the best that has been obtained so far. No case of more than $r = \min_i (p_i^{ei} - 1)$ orthogonal squares is known to date. Tarry (Le Probleme de 36 Officiers. Comptes Rendus de'l Association Francaise pour L'avancement des Sciences II (1901) pp. 170-203) found by a skillful tactical enumeration that no 6 sided orthogonal pair exists. For numbers larger than 6 which are not powers of a prime the problem is completely unsolved[1] although it has been considered by mathematicians

[1]After completion of this manuscript R. H. Bruck and H. J. Ryser (Canad. J. of Math. Vol. 1, pp. 88-93) proved the non-existence of $m - 1$ orthogonal squares of side m if $m \equiv 1, 2$ (4) and the square free part of m is divisible by a prime of the form $4k + 3$.

long before Latin squares were applied in designing experiments.

It can readily be shown that no more than $m - 1$ orthogonal Latin squares of side m can be constructed. For we may always arrange the numbering in the Latin squares in such a way that the first row is $1, 2, \cdots, m$. Then in the remaining compartments different Latin squares must contain different numbers which must also be different from the column number. Thus at most $(m - 1)$ Latin squares of side m can occur in a set of orthogonal Latin squares.

Historically it may be remarked that the first proof of the existence of $(m - 1)$ orthogonal Latin squares if m is a prime power seems to have been given by McNeish. (Annals of Mathematics, Vol. XIII, pp. 221-227.) The methods for the construction of orthogonal Latin squares presented in this book are due to R. C. Bose. (Sankhya 1939).

CHAPTER IX

The Construction of Incomplete Balanced Block Designs

IN THE CONSTRUCTION of incomplete balanced block designs finite projective geometries have been utilized and yield whole series of these designs. For our purposes it will be sufficient to consider finite analytic geometries. The points of these geometries are defined as follows. We consider G.F.(p^n). A point in the m dimensional finite geometry P.G.(m, p^n) is an ordered set of $m + 1$ elements of G.F.(p^n), not all of which are equal to 0. Two sets $(g_1, \cdots, g_{m+1})$, $(g_1', \cdots, g_{m+1}')$ represent the same point if $g_i = \lambda g_i'$, $i = 1, \cdots, m + 1$, $0 \neq \lambda \subset$ G.F.(p^n). For any two distinct points $p_1 = (g_1, \cdots, g_{m+1})$, $p_2 = (g_1', \cdots, g_{m+1}')$ we define as the line joining them the set of all points of the form

$$\text{(9.1)} \qquad \begin{gathered} \lambda_1 p_1 + \lambda_2 p_2 = (\lambda_1 g_1 + \lambda_2 g_2', \cdots, \lambda_1 g_{m+1} + \lambda_2 g_{m+1}'), \\ \lambda_1, \lambda_2 \subset \text{G.F.}(p^n), \end{gathered}$$

where at least one of the λ's is different from 0.

The system of points and lines obtained in this manner is called the analytic projective geometry of G.F.(p^n) of m dimensions and is denoted by P.G.(m, p^n).

We first compute the number of points in P.G.(m, p^n). There are $p^{n(m+1)}$ ordered sets of $m + 1$ marks of G.F.(p^n). Since we excluded the set $(0 \cdots 0)$ there remain $p^{n(m+1)} - 1$ ordered sets at least one of whose elements is different from 0. These may be arranged in groups of $p^n - 1$ sets all of whose elements represent the same points, since $(g_1, \cdots, g_{m+1}) = (\lambda g_1, \cdots, \lambda g_{m+1})$ for every $\lambda \neq 0$ in G.F.(p^n). Hence there are

$$\text{(9.2)} \qquad \frac{p^{n(m+1)} - 1}{p^n - 1} = 1 + p^n + \cdots + p^{nm}$$

distinct points. The lines are given in the form $\lambda_1 p_1 + \lambda_2 p_2$ where p_1 and p_2 are distinct points. The points of this line are given by their line coordinates λ_1, λ_2. Two points λ_1, λ_2; μ_1, μ_2 will be distinct if $(\lambda_1, \lambda_2) \neq \nu(\mu_1, \mu_2)$ for all ν in G.F.(p^n). Hence the points of a line form an analytic one dimensional geometry and the line has therefore $1 + p^n$ points.

We now consider the k dimensional subspaces of P.G.(m, p^n). Let $p_1, \cdots, p_{k+1}$ be $k + 1$ linearly independent points. That is to say

$$\lambda_1 p_1 + \cdots + \lambda_{k+1} p_{k+1} = (0, \cdots, 0) \tag{9.3}$$

implies $\lambda_1 = \cdots = \lambda_{k+1} = 0$. We consider then all the points of the form $\lambda_1 p_1 + \cdots + \lambda_{k+1} p_{k+1}$. Assume that two of these points are equal. Then

$$\lambda_1 p_1 + \cdots + \lambda_{k+1} p_{k+1} = \nu(\mu_1 p_1 + \cdots + \mu_{k+1} p_{k+1}),$$

$$(\lambda_1 - \nu\mu_1)p_1 + \cdots + (\lambda_{k+1} - \nu\mu_{k+1})p_{k+1} = (0, \cdots, 0).$$

Since $p_1, \cdots, p_{k+1}$ are independent this implies

$$\lambda_1 = \nu\mu_1, \cdots, \lambda_{k+1} = \nu\mu_{k+1}.$$

We can now introduce coordinates $\lambda_1, \cdots, \lambda_{k+1}$ in the k dimensional subspaces. Clearly for $k \geq 1$ the subspaces contain for every two points also the line joining them. Hence every k dimensional subspace of a P.G.(m, p^n) is itself a P.G.(k, p^n) and has therefore $1 + p^n + \cdots + p^{kn}$ points. We now compute the number of P.G.(k, p^n) contained in a P.G.(m, p^n). Every P.G.(k, p^n) is determined by a set of $(k + 1)$ independent points. The first of these, p_1, may be chosen in $1 + p^n + \cdots + p^{nm}$ ways. For p_2 we have then $p^n + \cdots + p^{nm}$ choices. For the third p_3 we may choose any point not on the line through p_1 and p_2 which leaves us $p^{2n} + \cdots p^{nm}$ choices. After the lth point $(l < k + 1)$ has been chosen, we may choose for the $(l + 1)$th point any point not in the P.G.$(l - 1, p^n)$ determined by $p_1, \cdots, p_l$. Thus $1 + p^n + \cdots + p^{n(l-1)}$ points are excluded and $p^{ln} + \cdots + p^{mn}$ are left to choose from. Thus the number of distinct ordered sets of $k + 1$ independent points in P.G.(m, p^n) is

(9.4) $$(1 + \cdots + p^{mn}) \cdots (p^{kn} + \cdots + p^{mn}).$$

The number of ordered sets of $(k + 1)$ independent points in P.G.(k, p^n) is by 9.4

$$(1 + \cdots + p^{kn}) \cdots (p^{(k-1)n} + p^{kn})p^{kn}.$$

Hence the number of P.G.(k, p^n) contained in P.G.(m, p^n) becomes

(9.5) $$\frac{(1 + \cdots + p^{mn})(p^n + \cdots + p^{mn})\cdots(p^{kn} + \cdots + p^{mn})}{(1 + \cdots + p^{kn}) \cdots (p^{(k-1)n} + p^{kn})p^{kn}}.$$

We finally want to find the number of P.G.(s, p^n) in P.G. (m, p^n) which contain a given P.G.(k, p^n). We first choose a point p_{k+2} not contained in the given P.G.(k, p^n). This point p_{k+2} may be chosen out of $p^{(k+1)n} + \cdots + p^{mn}$ points. We then choose p_{k+3} out of the $p^{(k+2)n} + \cdots + p^{mn}$ points not contained in the P.G.$(k + 1, p^n)$ which contains p_{k+2} and the given P.G. (k, p^n). Continuing in this manner we can obtain a P.G.(s, p^n) containing the given P.G.(k, p^n) in $(p^{(k+1)n} + \cdots + p^{mn}) \cdots (p^{sn} + \cdots + p^{mn})$ ways. Putting $m = s$ we see that every P.G.(s, p^n) is obtained in this manner in $(p^{(k+1)n} + \cdots + p^{sn}) \cdots (p^{(s-1)n} + p^{sn})p^{sn}$ ways. Hence for $s > k$ we must have

$$\frac{(p^{(k+1)n} + \cdots + p^{mn}) \cdots (p^{sn} + \cdots + p^{mn})}{(p^{(k+1)n} + \cdots + p^{sn}) \cdots (p^{(s-1)n} + p^{sn})p^{sn}}$$

different P.G.(s, p^n) in P.G.(m, p^n) which contain a given P.G. (k, p^n).

Summarizing we have:

1. *Every* P.G.(m, p^n) *contains exactly* $1 + p^n + \cdots + p^{mn}$ *points.*

2. *Every* P.G.(m, p^n) *contains exactly*

$$\frac{(1 + p^n + \cdots + p^{mn}) \cdots (p^{kn} + \cdots + p^{mn})}{(1 + p^n + \cdots + p^{kn}) \cdots (p^{(k-1)n} + p^{kn})p^{kn}} \quad \text{P.G.}(k, p^n).$$

3. *Every* P.G.(k, p^n) *in* P.G.(m, p^n) *is contained in*

$$\frac{(p^{(k+1)n} + \cdots + p^{mn}) \cdots (p^{sn} + \cdots + p^{mn})}{(p^{(k+1)n} + \cdots + p^{sn}) \cdots (p^{(s-1)n} + p^{sn})p^{sn}}$$

P.G.(s, p^n)'s for $s > k$.

For $k = 0, 1$ *one obtains in particular:*

A. *Every point is contained in*

$$r = \frac{(p^n + \cdots + p^{mn}) \cdots (p^{sn} + \cdots + p^{mn})}{(p^n + \cdots + p^{sn}) \cdots (p^{(s-1)n} + p^{sn})p^{sn}}$$

P.G.(s, p^n) *of a* P.G.(m, p^n) $\quad m \geq s > 0.$

B. *Every line is contained in*

$$\lambda = \frac{(p^{2n} + \cdots + p^{mn}) \cdots (p^{sn} + \cdots + p^{mn})}{(p^{2n} + \cdots + p^{sn}) \cdots (p^{sn})}$$

P.G.(s, p^n) *for* $m \geq s > 1.$

Every P.G.(s, p^n) contains with every pair of points also the whole line joining them. Thus every pair of points is contained in λ different P.G.(s, p^n).

We may now identify the points with varieties and the P.G. (s, p^n) with blocks. Then we have the following theorem.

THEOREM 9.1: *The* P.G.(s, p^n) *contained in a* P.G.(m, p^n) *form a balanced incomplete block design with the parameters*

$$(9.6) \quad b = \frac{(1 + p^n + \cdots + p^{mn}) \cdots (p^{sn} + \cdots + p^{mn})}{(1 + \cdots + p^{sn}) \cdots (p^{(s-1)n} + p^{sn})p^{sn}}$$

$$= b(s, m, p^n),$$

$$v = 1 + p^n + \cdots + p^{mn} = v(m, p^n),$$

$$k = 1 + p^n + \cdots + p^{sn} = k(s, p^n),$$

$$r = \frac{(p^n + \cdots + p^{mn}) \cdots (p^{sn} + \cdots + p^{mn})}{(p^n + \cdots + p^{sn}) \cdots (p^{(s-1)n} + p^{sn})p}$$

$$= r(s, m, p^n),$$

$$\lambda = \begin{cases} 1 & \text{if } s = 1 \\ \dfrac{(p^{2n} + \cdots + p^{mn}) \cdots (p^{sn} + \cdots + p^{mn})}{(p^{2n} + \cdots + p^{sn}) \cdots (p^{(s-1)n} + p^{sn})p^{sn}} & \\ \quad = \lambda(s, m, p^n) & \text{if } s > 1. \end{cases}$$

We next consider the points in P.G.(m, p^n) common to a given P.G.$(m - 1, p^n)$ and a given P.G.(s, p^n) not contained in it. Let p_1 be a point in the P.G.(s, p^n) which is not contained in the P.G.$(m - 1, p^n)$. Let $q_1, \cdots, q_m$ be m linearly independent points in the P.G.$(m - 1, p^n)$. Then $p_1, q_1, \cdots, q_m$ are $m + 1$ linearly independent points and hence every point of P.G.(m, p^n) is of the form

$$\lambda_1 p_1 + \lambda_2 q_1 + \cdots + \lambda_{m+1} q_m .$$

Now let $p_1, p_2, \cdots, p_{s+1}$ be $s + 1$ linearly independent points of the given P.G.(s, p^n). Then for every i we must have an equation

$$p_i = \lambda_1^{(i)} p_1 + \lambda_2^{(i)} q_1 + \cdots + \lambda_{m+1}^{(i)} q_m . \tag{9.7}$$

Therefore $p_i' = p_i - \lambda_1^{(i)} p_1$, $i = 2, \cdots, s + 1$, is contained in the P.G.$(m - 1, p^n)$. The points $p_2', \cdots, p_{s+1}'$ are obviously linearly independent. Hence the P.G.$(s - 1, p^n)$ of points of the form $\lambda_2 p_2' + \cdots + \lambda_{s+1} p_{s+1}'$ is contained in the P.G.$(m - 1, p^n)$. But these are all the points of the given P.G.(s, p^n) which are contained in the P.G.$(m - 1, p^n)$. If there were another point p_1' of the P.G.(s, p^n) contained in the P.G.$(m - 1, p^n)$ and linearly independent of $p_2', \cdots, p_{s+1}'$, then $\lambda_1 p_1' + \cdots + \lambda_{s+1} p_{s+1}'$ would present every element in the P.G.(s, p^n), contrary to the hypothesis that not all its points are contained in the P.G.$(m - 1, p^n)$.

Now by deleting from a P.G.(m, p^n) any given P.G. $(m-1, p^n)$ and all its points one obtains another system of points and lines which is termed the finite analytic Euclidean Geometry E.G.(m, p^n) of m dimensions. Every P.G.(s, p^n) contained in P.G.(m, p^n) but not in the P.G.$(m-1, p^n)$ becomes an E.G.(s, p^n), since by deleting a P.G.$(m-1, p^n)$ from P.G.(m, p^n) we also delete a P.G.$(s-1, p^n)$ from each of these P.G.(s, p^n) contained in P.G.(m, p^n). The number of points of an E.G. (m, p^n) is

$$v(m, p^n) - v(m-1, p^n) = p^{mn}.$$

The number of E.G.(s, p^n) contained in E.G.(m, p^n) is

$$b(s, m, p^n) - b(s, m-1, p^n).$$

The number of E.G.(s, p^n) containing a given E.G.(k, p^n) is the same as the number of P.G.(s, p^n) containing a given P.G.(k, p^n). Hence we have

THEOREM 9.2: *The* E.G.(s, p^n) *contained in an* E.G.(m, p^n) *form a balanced incomplete block design with the parameters*

$$\begin{aligned} b &= b(s, m, p^n) - b(s, m-1, p^n), \\ v &= p^{mn}, \\ k &= p^{sn}, \qquad (9.8) \\ r &= r(s, m, p^n), \\ \lambda &= \lambda(s, m, p^n). \end{aligned}$$

As an example we construct the lines of the P.G.(3, 2) and the E.G.(3, 2). Applying 9.6 and 9.8 we see that we have in the P.G.(3, 2) exactly 35 lines and 15 points and in the E.G. (3, 2) exactly 28 lines and 8 points. Every point must occur in 7 lines. Every line of the P.G.(3, 2) contains 3 points and every line of the E.G.(3, 2) contains 2 points. Hence the balanced block designs which we shall obtain have the parameters

$$b = 35, \quad v = 15, \quad r = 7, \quad k = 3, \quad \lambda = 1;$$

$$b = 28, \quad v = 8, \quad r = 7, \quad k = 2, \quad \lambda = 1.$$

The second design consists simply of all pairs of points and can easily be obtained directly. G.F.(2) consists of the two elements 0, 1 with the rules of composition $0 + 0 = 0, 0 + 1 = 1 + 0 = 1, 1 + 1 = 0$.

The points are then given by

$$p_1 = 1000, \quad p_5 = 1100, \quad p_9 = 0101, \quad p_{13} = 1011,$$
$$p_2 = 0100, \quad p_6 = 1010, \quad p_{10} = 0011, \quad p_{14} = 0111,$$
$$p_3 = 0010, \quad p_7 = 1001, \quad p_{11} = 1110, \quad p_{15} = 1111.$$
$$p_4 = 0001, \quad p_8 = 0110, \quad p_{12} = 1101,$$

The lines can be obtained by taking pairs of points, for instance, p_1 and p_2 and forming $\lambda_1 p_1 + \lambda_2 p_2$ for $(\lambda_1, \lambda_2) = (0, 1), (1, 0), (1, 1)$. Thus for instance the points in the line p_1, p_2 are p_1, p_2 and $p_1 + p_2 = p_5$. The lines through p_1, p_5 and p_2, p_5 need not be constructed if the line through p_1, p_2 has already been written down. Proceeding systematically in this way one obtains 35 lines.

$$p_1p_2p_5, \quad p_2p_3p_8, \quad p_3p_5p_{11}, \quad p_4p_{11}p_{15}, \quad p_6p_{12}p_{14},$$
$$p_1p_3p_6, \quad p_2p_4p_9, \quad p_3p_7p_{13}, \quad p_5p_6p_8, \quad p_7p_8p_{15},$$
$$p_1p_4p_7, \quad p_2p_6p_{11}, \quad p_3p_9p_{14}, \quad p_5p_7p_9, \quad p_7p_{11}p_{14},$$
$$p_1p_8p_{11}, \quad p_2p_7p_{12}, \quad p_3p_{12}p_{15}, \quad p_5p_{10}p_{15}, \quad p_8p_9p_{10},$$
$$p_1p_9p_{12}, \quad p_2p_{10}p_{14}, \quad p_4p_5p_{12}, \quad p_5p_{13}p_{14}, \quad p_8p_{12}p_{13},$$
$$p_1p_{10}p_{13}, \quad p_2p_{13}p_{15}, \quad p_4p_6p_{13}, \quad p_6p_7p_{10}, \quad p_9p_{11}p_{13},$$
$$p_1p_{14}p_{15}, \quad p_3p_4p_{10}, \quad p_4p_8p_{14}, \quad p_6p_9p_{15}, \quad p_{10}p_{11}p_{12}.$$

If we delete from this design all the points with last coördinate 0, that is to say, the plane $\lambda_1 p_1 + \lambda_2 p_2 + \lambda_3 p_3$ then we must obtain the E.G.(3, 2). The deleted points are $p_1, p_2, p_3, p_5,$

p_6, p_8, p_{11}. The reader may verify that the remaining sets consist of all possible pairs of the remaining 28 points. To give also a non-trivial example of a finite Euclidean geometry we shall construct the E.G.(2, 3). The P.G.(2, 3) has $3^2 + 3 + 1 = 13$ points; the E.G.(2, 3) has 9 points. G.F.(3) consists of the marks 0, 1, -1 considered mod 3. The points of P.G.(2, 3) are:

$$\begin{array}{llll} p_1 = 1,0,0, & p_5 = 1,0,1, & p_9 = 1,0,-1, & p_{13} = 0,-1,1. \\ p_2 = 0,1,0, & p_6 = 0,1,1, & p_{10} = -1,1,1, & \\ p_3 = 0,0,1, & p_7 = 1,1,1, & p_{11} = 1,-1,1, & \\ p_4 = 1,1,0, & p_8 = 1,-1,0, & p_{12} = 1,1,-1, & \end{array}$$

The line through p_1 and p_2 consists of the points p_1, p_2, $p_1 + p_2 = p_4$, $p_1 - p_2 = p_8$. Systematically proceeding as before one obtains the lines:

$$\begin{array}{llll} p_1p_2\,p_4\,p_8\,, & p_2p_3p_6\,p_{13}\,, & p_3p_8p_{10}p_{11}\,, & p_7p_8p_9p_{13}\,, \\ p_1p_3\,p_5\,p_9\,, & p_2p_5p_7\,p_{11}\,, & p_4p_5p_{10}p_{13}\,, & \\ p_1p_6\,p_7\,p_{10}\,, & p_2p_9p_{10}p_{12}\,, & p_4p_6p_9\,p_{11}\,, & \\ p_1p_{11}p_{12}p_{13}\,, & p_3p_4p_7\,p_{12}\,, & p_5p_6p_8\,p_{12}\,, & \end{array}$$

Now we delete one line, say the first and all the points on it and obtain

$$\begin{array}{llll} p_3\,p_5\,p_9\,, & p_3p_6\,p_{12}\,, & p_3p_7\,p_{12}\,, & p_6p_9p_{11}\,, \\ p_6\,p_7\,p_{10}\,, & p_5p_7\,p_{11}\,, & p_3p_{10}p_{11}\,, & p_5p_6p_{12}\,, \\ p_{11}p_{12}p_{13}\,, & p_9p_{10}p_{12}\,, & p_5p_{10}p_{13}\,, & p_7p_9p_{13}\,. \end{array}$$

This is the E.G.(2, 3).

The E.G.(2, p^n) can also easily be obtained from a set of

$p^n - 1$ orthogonal Latin squares of side p^n which were constructed from a Galois field. We take as points the compartments of the Latin square numbered from 1 to p^{2n}. The lines are then given by the columns, the rows, and by the sets of compartments whose ith number is α, $(\alpha = 1, \cdots, p^n)$, $(i = 1, \cdots, p^n - 1)$. These lines are arranged in $m + 1$ sets of m parallel lines each. Thus for instance the rows are parallel to each other. To obtain the P.G.(2, p^n) one adds additional points, the same point to each line of a set of parallel lines and different points to intersecting lines, and takes these additional points into one additional line.

Finite geometries furnish whole series of balanced incomplete block designs. However, only a few of these are at present of practical interest since the number of replications should in most practical cases not exceed 10.

Other series of these designs can be obtained by applying two theorems first proved by R. C. Bose. (Annals of Eugenics, 9 (1939) pp. 358-399.) To formulate these two theorems we need the concept of a module. A module is a system of elements such that to each pair of elements a, b there is uniquely defined a sum $a + b$ satisfying the postulates I, II, III, IV for the addition in a field. For instance the residues mod m form a module for every m. A module with a finite number of elements is called a finite module. If $\mathfrak{M}$ has n elements then $\mathfrak{M}$ is called a module of order n.

Let $\mathfrak{M}$ now be a module of order n and let m varieties $A_1^{(i)}$, $\cdots$, $A_m^{(i)}$ correspond to every element $A^{(i)}$ of the module. We may form blocks of these varieties.

$$(9.9) \qquad (A_{i_1}^{(\alpha_1)}, \cdots, A_{i_k}^{(\alpha_k)}), \qquad (A_{j_1}^{(\beta_1)}, \cdots, A_{j_k}^{(\beta_k)}).$$

From every block of k varieties we may write $k(k - 1)$ expressions of the form $A_\gamma - B_\delta = (A - B)_{\gamma\delta}$. This expression is called a difference of type $\gamma\delta$.

Taking for instance as our module the residues mod 5 we could form the blocks

$$(0_1, 1_2, 2_1), \qquad (0_2, 3_1, 4_2).$$

Then the differences are 1_{21}, 2_{11}, 4_{12}, 1_{12}, 3_{11}, 4_{21} from the first block, 3_{12}, 4_{22}, 2_{21}, 1_{21}, 1_{22}, 4_{12} from the second block. The differences of type $\alpha\beta$ are called pure if $\alpha = \beta$ and mixed if $\alpha \neq \beta$.

If in t blocks every pure difference except 0 is repeated λ times and every mixed difference the same number λ of times, then the differences are termed symmetrically repeated.

We shall now prove the following theorem.

THEOREM 9.3: *Let $\mathfrak{M}$ be a module containing the elements $v^{(0)}, \cdots, v^{(n-1)}$ and let m varieties $v_1^{(i)}, \cdots, v_m^{(i)}$ correspond to every element $v^{(i)}$. The variety $v_j^{(\alpha)}$ is said to belong to the jth class. Suppose that there exist t blocks of elements $B_1, \cdots, B_t$ such that*

1. *The varieties in each block are different from each other.*
2. *Among the elements in $B_1, B_2, \cdots, B_t$ exactly r varieties belong to each of the m classes.*
3. *The differences arising from $B_1, \cdots, B_t$ are symmetrically repeated, each occurring λ times.*

If

$$B = (v_{\alpha_1}^{(i_1)}, \cdots, v_{\alpha_k}^{(i_k)})$$

and $v^{i_e} + \theta = v^{i_e}$ let

$$B_\theta = (v_{\alpha_1}^{(i_1)}, \cdots, v_{\alpha_k}^{(i_k)}). \tag{9.10}$$

Form the blocks $B_{i\theta}$ for all i and all $\theta \subset \mathfrak{M}$, then:

1. *In the blocks $B_{i\theta}$ every variety occurs r times.*
2. *Any two varieties occur together in the same block exactly λ times.*

Corollary: *If each block B_i contains the same number of varieties the blocks $B_{i\theta}$ form an incomplete balanced block design.*

Proof of Theorem 9.3: To every pair of elements v, v' of $\mathfrak{M}$ there is exactly one θ such that $v + \theta = v'$. Hence since r of the varieties in $B_1, \cdots, B_t$ belong to the ith class, the variety v_i' will occur exactly r times. In order that a pair u_α, v_β of varieties occurs exactly μ times in the blocks $B_{i\theta}$ it is necessary and sufficient that exactly μ times for u'_α and v'_β in the same block

$$(9.11)\quad \begin{aligned} u' + \theta &= u, \\ v' + \theta &= v. \end{aligned}$$

Hence $u' - v' = u - v = d$. Then $\theta = u - u' = v - v'$. Hence the pair u_α , v_β occurs exactly as many times as the difference d arises as a difference of type $\alpha\beta$ in the initial blocks $B_1, \cdots, B_t$, that is to say $\mu = \lambda$ times. This proves the theorem.

As an example consider the group of residues mod $2t + 1$ and the pairs

$$(1, 2t), (2, 2t - 1), \cdots, (t, t + 1).$$

Every residue different from 0 arises from these pairs just once. Now consider the blocks

$$(1_1, (2t)_1, 0_2), (2_1, (2t - 1)_1, 0_2), \cdots, (t_1, (t + 1)_1, 0_2);$$

$$(1_2, (2t)_2, 0_3), (2_2, (2t - 1)_2, 0_3), \cdots, (t_2, (t + 1)_2, 0_3);$$

$$(1_3, (2t)_3, 0_1), (2_3, (2t - 1)_3, 0_1), \cdots, (t_3, (t + 1)_3, 0_1);$$

$$(0_1, 0_2, 0_3).$$

All pure differences arise exactly once from the first two elements of the first $3t$ blocks. All non 0 mixed differences of type 1,2 and type 2,1 arise from the first set of blocks, those of type 2,3 and type 3,2 from the second set and those of type 1,3 and 3,1 from the 3rd set. The mixed differences 0 arise from $(0_1, 0_2, 0_3)$. Since each block contains 3 varieties, we obtain by applying Theorem 9.3 an incomplete balanced block design with $v = 6t + 3$, $b = (3t + 1)(2t + 1)$, $r = 3t + 1$, $k = 3$, $\lambda = 1$.

For instance let $t = 2$, then $2t + 1 = 5$ and the initial blocks are $(1_1, 4_1, 0_2)$, $(2_1, 3_1, 0_2)$, $(1_2, 4_2, 0_3)$, $(2_2, 3_2, 0_3)$, $(1_3, 4_3, 0_1)$, $(2_3, 3_3, 0_1)$, $(0_1, 0_2, 0_3)$. We leave the construction of this design to the reader.

Let us now adjoin to the module $\mathfrak{M}$ the symbol ∞ with the rule of operation $\infty + a = \infty$. We shall now prove the following theorem.

THEOREM 9.4: *Let $\mathfrak{M}$ be a module with n elements $u^{(0)}, \cdots, u^{(n-1)}$. To every element $u^{(\alpha)}$ let there correspond m varieties $u_1^{(\alpha)}, \cdots, u_m^{(\alpha)}$, whilst one variety corresponds to the symbol ∞. The variety $u_i^{(\alpha)}$ is said to belong to the ith class and the varieties $u_i^{(\alpha)}$ are called finite varieties. Suppose there exist $t + s$ blocks $B_1, \cdots, B_t, B_1', \cdots, B_s'$, such that:*

1. *The varieties in each block are different from each other.*
2. *The blocks $B_1, \cdots, B_t$ contain exactly k finite varieties each while $B_1', \cdots, B_s'$ contain exactly $(k - 1)$ finite varieties and ∞.*
3. *Among the varieties in $B_1, \cdots, B_t$ exactly $ns - \lambda$ belong to each class, while among the varieties in $B_1', \cdots, B_s'$ exactly λ belong to each class.*
4. *The differences arising from the finite varieties are symmetrically repeated, each occurring λ times.*

We define the blocks $B_{i\theta}, B_{i\theta}'$ as in Theorem 9.3.

Then the blocks $B_{i\theta}, B_{i\theta}'$ form an incomplete balanced block design with the parameters $v = mn + 1, b = n(t + s), r = ns, k, \lambda$.

From Theorem 9.3 it follows that every finite variety is repeated $r = ns$ times and each pair of finite varieties occurs λ times. The variety ∞ occurs in each of the ns blocks $B_{i\theta}'$ hence ∞ occurs also ns times. Also each finite variety occurs in the $B_{i\theta}'$ because of 3 exactly λ times. Hence ∞ occurs with every finite variety λ times together in the same block.

As an application we shall construct designs with $v = 12t + 4$, $b = (3t + 1)(4t + 1)$, $r = 4t + 1$, $k = 4$, $\lambda = 1$ where $4t + 1$ is a power of a prime.

We take the elements of G.F.$(4t + 1)$ with respect to addition as composition as our module $\mathfrak{M}$. Let x be a primitive root. We shall first show that there exist odd numbers α and q such that $(x^\alpha + 1)/(x^\alpha - 1) = x^q$.

The non 0 elements of G.F.$(4t + 1)$ are given by $x^0, x^1, \cdots,$

x^{4t-1}. We form for every $\alpha \neq 0$ $(x^\alpha + 1)/(x^\alpha - 1)$. This is a non 0 mark of G.F.$(4t + 1)$ if $\alpha \neq 2t$, since x is a primitive root $x^{2t} \neq 1$ and hence $x^{2t} = -1$. Hence for all values $\alpha \neq 0$, $2t$ we have

$$(9.12) \qquad \frac{x^\alpha + 1}{x^\alpha - 1} = x^q.$$

Clearly $x^\alpha = (x^q + 1)/(x^q - 1)$. Hence to every $\alpha \neq 0$, $2t$ belongs a unique value $q \neq 0$, $2t$ but among the residues mod $4t$ $1, 2, \cdots, 2t - 1, 2t + 1, \cdots, 4t - 1$ there are $2t$ odd residues but only $2t - 2$ even residues. Hence to at least 2 odd residues there must belong an odd residue.

Now let 3 varieties correspond to each mark of G.F.$(4t + 1)$. We form the $(3t + 1)$ blocks

$$\begin{aligned} &(x_1^{2i}, \; x_1^{2t+2i}, \; x_2^{2i+\alpha}, \; x_2^{2t+2i+\alpha}); \\ &(x_2^{2i}, \; x_2^{2t+2i}, \; x_3^{2i+\alpha}, \; x_3^{2t+2i+\alpha}); \qquad i = 0, 1, \cdots, t-1 \\ &(x_3^{2i}, \; x_3^{2t+2i}, \; x_1^{2i+\alpha}, \; x_1^{2t+2i+\alpha}); \\ &(\infty, 0_1, 0_2, 0_3). \end{aligned}$$

We observe first that $x^{2t} = -1$. We further put $x^\alpha + 1 = x^u$, $x^\alpha - 1 = x^v$, $x^{2t} - 1 = x^\beta$. Then we may choose α so that

$$(9.13) \qquad u - v \equiv 1(2).$$

Every class of varieties occurs $4t$ times in the first $3t$ blocks and once in the last block. The differences of type (1, 1) arise from the first and 3rd set of blocks and may be written as

$$(9.14) \; x^{2i+\epsilon_1 2t+\epsilon_2\alpha}(x^{2t} - 1) = x^{2i+2t\epsilon_1+\epsilon_2\alpha+\beta}, \; (i = 0, \cdots, t-1),$$

where ϵ_1, ϵ_2 are either 1 or 0. These are $4t$ differences. We shall show that no two of them are equal. Suppose that

$$(9.15) \qquad x^{2i+\epsilon_1 2t+\epsilon_2\alpha+\beta} = x^{2j+\epsilon'_1 2t+\epsilon'_2\alpha+\beta}.$$

Then

$$x^{2(i-j)+2t(\epsilon_1-\epsilon'_1)+\alpha(\epsilon_2-\epsilon'_2)} = 1.$$

Hence

$$(9.16) \qquad 2(i - j) + 2t(\epsilon_1 - \epsilon_1') \equiv -\alpha(\epsilon_2 - \epsilon_2')(4t).$$

Since α is odd it follows that $\epsilon_2 \equiv \epsilon_2'(2)$ and therefore $\epsilon_2 = \epsilon_2'$. Thus $i - j \equiv t(\epsilon_1 - \epsilon_1')(2t)$. Hence either $i - j \equiv 0(2t)$ or $i - j \equiv t(2t)$. Both of these congruences are impossible for $i \neq j$ since $i, j \leq t - 1$. Hence the $4t$ differences of type 1, 1 are distinct and different from 0 and therefore must contain each of the $4t$ non 0 marks exactly once. Similarly, it may be shown that every mark of G.F.$(4t + 1)$ occurs exactly once among the differences of type 2, 2 and 3, 3. Let us now consider the mixed differences of type 1, 2. These arise from the first set of blocks and from the last block only. Those from the first set of blocks may be written as

$$(9.17) \quad x^{2i+\epsilon_1 2t} - x^{2i+\alpha+\epsilon_2 2t} = x^{2i}\left(\pm 1 - \begin{pmatrix} + - \\ - + \end{pmatrix} x^{\alpha}\right).$$

Hence one obtains one of the four expressions

$$-x^{2i}(x^{\alpha} - 1) = x^{2i+2t+v}, \qquad x^{2i}(x^{\alpha} - 1) = x^{2i+v},$$

$$x^{2i}(x^{\alpha} + 1) = x^{2i+u}, \qquad -x^{2i}(x^{\alpha} + 1) = x^{2i+2t+u},$$

hence either

$$x^{2i+\epsilon 2t+u} \qquad \text{or} \qquad x^{2i+\epsilon 2t+v}.$$

We obtain thus $4t$ non zero marks of G.F.$(4t + 1)$. We shall prove that they are all different. We first observe that

$$(9.18) \qquad x^{2i+\epsilon 2t+u} = x^{2j+\epsilon' 2t+u}$$

implies $i - j \equiv t(\epsilon' - \epsilon)(2t)$, which was already shown to be impossible. But

$$(9.19) \qquad x^{2i+\epsilon 2t+u} = x^{2j+\epsilon' 2t+v}$$

implies $u - v \equiv 0(2)$ which contradicts 9.13. Thus each of the $4t$ non 0 marks of G.F.$(4t + 1)$ occurs excatly once among the differences of type 1, 2. The proof for the other mixed differences is analogous. The 0 differences of mixed type all arise from the last block. Thus all the conditions of Theorem 9.4 are satisfied.

As an example let $4t + 1 = 9$. G.F.(9) may be presented as the field of residues mod 3, $y^2 + 1$. G.F.(9) then consists of the 9 marks; $0, 1, -1, y, y + 1, y - 1, -y, -y + 1, -y - 1$. $x = (-y + 1)$ is a primitive root.

$$x^2 = (-y + 1)^2 = y^2 + y + 1 = y,$$

$$x^3 = (-y + 1)^3 = y + 1, \qquad x^4 = -1,$$

(9.20)

$$x^5 = y - 1, \quad x^6 = -y, \quad x^7 = -1 - y, \quad x^8 = 1.$$

$$\frac{x + 1}{x - 1} = \frac{-y - 1}{-y} = \frac{x^3}{x^2} = x.$$

Hence we may take $\alpha = 1$. The first set of initial blocks is then

$$(1_1\,,\,(-1)_1\,,\,x_2\,,\,-x_2), \qquad (x_1^2\,,\,-x_1^2\,,\,x_2^3\,-\,x_2^3).$$

Thus the initial blocks are

$$[(1)_1\,;\,(-1)_1\,;\,(-y + 1)_2\,;\,(y - 1)_2],$$

$$[y_1\,;\,-y_1\,;\,(y + 1)_2\,;\,(-y - 1)_2];$$

$$[(1)_2\,;\,(-1)_2\,;\,(-y + 1)_3\,;\,(y - 1)_3],$$

$$[y_2\,;\,-y_2\,;\,(y + 1)_3\,;\,(-y - 1)_3];$$

$$[(1)_3\,;\,(-1)_3\,;\,(-y + 1)_1\,;\,(y - 1)_1],$$

$$[y_3\,;\,-y_3\,;\,(y + 1)_1\,;\,(-y - 1)_1];$$

$$(\infty\,;\,0_1\,;\,0_2\,;\,0_3).$$

The completion of the design is left to the reader. The designs constructed from Theorem 9.3 have for $m = 1$ the property that every variety occurs exactly t times in every position in the blocks. This is of importance if the position in the block has an effect on the yield. The analysis of variance of such designs, when the block position has an effect on the yield, is straight forward and is left to the reader.

Of particular interest are the so-called symmetrical designs with $v = b$, $r = k$. From any symmetrical design two other designs can be obtained. The derived design obtained by retaining in the blocks $B_2, \cdots, B_b$ only those varieties which are in B_1 and the residual design which is obtained by deleting from the design all the varieties in B_1. In order to show that these configurations are really incomplete balanced block designs we shall show that every block has exactly λ varieties in common with B_1. From this result it follows that the derived and residual designs are incomplete balanced block designs with the parameters: $k, v - 1, k - 1, \lambda, \lambda - 1$ and $v - k, v - 1, k, k - \lambda, \lambda$ respectively.

As an example for the processes of residuation and derivation we shall consider the design 25, 25, 9, 9, 3. This design was constructed by Bhattacharya (Bull. Calcutta Math. Soc. 36 (1945) pp. 91-96) and is not yet incorporated in the statistical tables of Fisher and Yates, which listed all incomplete balanced block designs with $r \leq 10$ which were known up to 1943. Bhattacharya's design is as follows:

(9.20)

1, 2, 5, 6, 11, 12, 17, 20, 23;	1, 3, 5, 7, 10, 12, 18, 21, 24;
1, 2, 9, 10, 15, 16, 17, 21, 25;	1, 3, 9, 11, 14, 16, 18, 22, 23;
1, 2, 7, 8, 13, 14, 17, 22, 24;	1, 3, 6, 8, 13, 15, 18, 20, 25;
3, 4, 7, 8, 9, 10, 17, 20, 23;	2, 4, 6, 8, 9, 11, 18, 21, 24;
3, 4, 11, 12, 13, 14, 17, 21, 25;	2, 4, 10, 12, 13, 15, 18, 22, 23;

3, 4, 5, 6, 15, 16, 17, 22, 24;	2, 4, 5, 7, 14, 16, 18, 20, 25;
1, 4, 5, 8, 10, 11, 19, 22, 25;	5, 6, 9, 10, 13, 14, 17, 18, 19;
1, 4, 9, 12, 14, 15, 19, 20, 24;	5, 7, 9, 11, 13, 15, 20, 21, 22;
1, 4, 6, 7, 13, 16, 19, 21, 23;	5, 8, 9, 12, 13, 16, 23, 24, 25;
2, 3, 6, 7, 9, 12, 19, 22, 25;	7, 8, 11, 12, 15, 16, 17, 18, 19;
2, 3, 10, 11, 13, 16, 19, 21, 24;	6, 8, 10, 12, 14, 16, 20, 21, 22;
2, 3, 5, 8, 14, 15, 19, 21, 23;	6, 7, 10, 11, 14, 15, 23, 24, 25.
17, 18, 19, 20, 21, 22, 23, 24, 25;	

From 9.20 we obtain by the process of residuation deleting all the varieties in the last block the design $v = 16$, $b = 24$, $r = 9$, $k = 6$, $\lambda = 3$ as follows:

(9.21)

1, 2, 5, 6, 11, 12;	1, 3, 5, 7, 10, 12;
1, 2, 9, 10, 15, 16;	1, 3, 9, 11, 14, 16;
1, 2, 7, 8, 13, 14;	1, 3, 6, 8, 13, 15;
3, 4, 7, 8, 9, 10;	2, 4, 6, 8, 9, 11;
3, 4, 11, 12, 13, 14;	2, 4, 10, 12, 13, 15;
3, 4, 5, 6, 15, 16;	2, 4, 5, 7, 14, 16;
1, 4, 5, 8, 10, 11;	5, 6, 9, 10, 13, 14;
1, 4, 9, 12, 14, 15;	5, 7, 9, 11, 13, 15;
1, 4, 6, 7, 13, 16;	5, 8, 9, 12, 13, 16;
2, 3, 6, 7, 9, 12;	7, 8, 11, 12, 15, 16;
2, 3, 10, 11, 13, 16;	6, 8, 10, 12, 14, 16;
2, 3, 5, 8, 14, 15;	6, 7, 10, 11, 14, 15.

The derived design is a triple system with $v = 9$, $b = 24$, $r = 8$, $k = 3$, $\lambda = 2$.

We shall now prove that in a symmetrical design every block different from the first block has exactly λ varieties in common with the first block. Let a_i be the number of varieties common to the first block and the ith block $i = 2, \cdots, b$. Then

$$\sum_i a_i = k(r - 1) \tag{9.22}$$

since each of the k varieties of the first block occurs $r - 1$ times in the remaining blocks. Also

$$\sum_i \frac{a_i(a_i - 1)}{2} = (\lambda - 1)\frac{k(k - 1)}{2} \tag{9.23}$$

since each of the $[k(k - 1)]/2$ pairs of varieties of the first block occurs $(\lambda - 1)$ times in the remaining blocks.

From 9.22 and 9.23 we get

$$\sum_i a_i^2 - 2\lambda \sum_i a_i + (b - 1)\lambda^2$$

$$= (\lambda - 1)k(k - 1) - (2\lambda - 1)k(r - 1) + (b - 1)\lambda^2,$$

but $b = v$, $k = r$, $k(r - 1) = \lambda(v - 1)$ by 7.13 and therefore

$$\sum_i (a_i - \lambda)^2 = -\lambda k(k - 1) + \lambda \cdot \lambda(v - 1) = 0.$$

Hence

$$a_i = \lambda.$$

We finally observe that from every incomplete balanced block design $B_1, \cdots, B_b$ another incomplete balanced block design $B_1', \cdots, B_b'$ can be obtained by putting into B_i' all varieties not in B_i. The parameters of this complementary design are: v, b, $b - r$, $v - k$, $b - 2r + \lambda$.

R. C. Bose's two theorems yield the following series of designs. Those derivable from them by derivation and residuation are not separately listed.

Designation	v	b	r	k	λ
T_1	$6t + 3$	$(2t + 1)(3t + 1)$	$3t + 1$	3	1
T_2	$6t + 1$	$t(6t + 1)$	$3t$	3	1
	(If v is the power of a prime or t odd.)				
D	$1 + r$	$\frac{r(1 + r)}{3}$	r	3	2
	$[r(1 + r) \equiv 0(3)]$				
F_1	$12t + 1$	$t(12t + 1)$	$4t$	4	1
	($12t + 1$ is the power of a prime and in G.F.$(12t + 1)$ there exists a primitive root x for which $x^{4t} + 1 = x^q$, $q \equiv 1(2)$.)				
F_2	$12t + 4$	$(4t + 1)(3t + 1)$	$4t + 1$	4	1
	($4t + 1$ is the power of a prime.)				
G_1	$20t + 1$	$t(20t + 1)$	$5t$	5	1
	($20t + 1$ is the power of a prime and in G.F.$(20t + 1)$ there exists a primitive root x for which $x^{4t+1} + 1 = x^q$, $q \equiv 1(2)$				
G_2	$20t + 5$	$(5t + 1)(4t + 1)$	$5t + 1$	5	1
	($4t + 1$ is the power of a prime.)				
S_1	$4\lambda + 3$	$4\lambda + 3$	$2\lambda + 1$	$2\lambda + 1$	λ
	($4\lambda + 3$ is the power of a prime.)				

Designation	v	b	r	k	λ
S_1'	$(2\lambda+1)(2\lambda+2)$	$(2\lambda+1)(2\lambda+2)+1$	$2\lambda + 2$	$2\lambda + 2$	λ
	($\lambda = 1$ or $\lambda = 2$.)				
S_n	$2n(2n\lambda + 1)$	$2n(2n\lambda + 1)$	$2n\lambda + 1$	$2n\lambda + 1$	λ
	(v is the power of a prime p, $x^{2n_i} - 1 = x^{q_i}$ where q_i is a full residue system mod n, and the differences arising from $n_1, \cdots, n_n$ mod p are symmetrically repeated each occurring once.)				
B_1	$2\lambda + 2$	$4\lambda + 2$	$2\lambda + 1$	$\lambda + 1$	λ.

A few designs in some of these series can also be constructed by means of finite geometries. For the details of the construction the reader is referred to R. C. Bose's original paper.

The series T_1 and T_2 do not, because of the restrictions on T_1 and T_2, contain all possible triple systems satisfying 7.12 and 7.13 although it is known that all can be constructed. However they contain all triple systems within that range of r that has so far been found useful in the design of experiments. The series D contains all possible triple systems with $\lambda = 2$. R. C. Bose made their construction dependent on the solution of two auxiliary problems, which were later solved by Bhattacharya. (Sankhya V.6 pp. 313-314). The series S_1, S_1', S_n and some of the other designs yield further designs by residuation and derivation. Although many of the designs constructed by R. C. Bose had been previously obtained by other methods, some of them were constructed by him for the first time. All the designs with $r \leq 10$ known up to 1943 are tabulated in Fisher and Yates' Statistical Tables. In these tables 12 blanks were still left, namely the following:

*Number**	v	b	r	k	λ
8	15	21	7	5	2
10	22	22	7	7	2
12	21	28	8	6	2
14	29	29	8	8	2
17	16	24	9	6	3
20	25	25	9	9	3
24	46	69	9	6	1
26	21	30	10	7	3
27	31	31	10	10	3
28	36	45	10	8	2
30	46	46	10	10	2
31	51	85	10	6	2

The impossibility of designs 8, 10, 14 has since been demonstrated by R. K. Nandi and Q. M. Husain in several papers which appeared in the 1946 issues of Sankhya.* The designs 17, 20, 26, 27 were constructed by Bhattacharya. (Sankhya V.7 pp. 423-424). The last two as follows:

---

*Reference Number in Fisher and Yates Tables.

*In a forthcoming paper to appear in the Canad. J. of Math. Chowla and Ryser prove that a symmetrical design with even v is impossible unless $k - \lambda$ is a square. This shows that also the design 30 is impossible.

The design (31, 31, 10, 10, 3) can be obtained from the blocks:

$$B_0 = (1_1\,, 2_1\,, 4_1\,, 1_2\,, 2_2\,, 4_2\,, 1_3\,, 2_3\,, 4_3\,, 0_4),$$

$$B_1 = (1_1\,, 6_1\,, 2_2\,, 5_2\,, 3_3\,, 4_3\,, 3_4\,, 5_4\,, 6_4\,, \infty_1),$$

$$B_2 = (2_1\,, 5_1\,, 3_2\,, 4_2\,, 1_3\,, 6_3\,, 3_4\,, 5_4\,, 6_4\,, \infty_2),$$

$$B_3 = (3_1\,, 4_1\,, 1_2\,, 6_2\,, 2_3\,, 5_3\,, 3_4\,, 5_4\,, 6_4\,, \infty_3).$$

by forming the blocks $B_{i\theta}$ mod 7 and then adjoining the blocks

$$B_1' = (0_1\,, 1_1\,, 2_1\,, 3_1\,, 4_1\,, 5_1\,, 6_1\,, \infty_1\,, \infty_2\,, \infty_3),$$

$$B_2' = (0_2\,, 1_2\,, 2_2\,, 3_2\,, 4_2\,, 5_2\,, 6_2\,, \infty_1\,, \infty_2\,, \infty_3),$$

$$B_3' = (0_3\,, 1_3\,, 2_3\,, 3_3\,, 4_3\,, 5_3\,, 6_3\,, \infty_1\,, \infty_2\,, \infty_3).$$

From this design the design (21, 30, 10, 7, 3) can be obtained by residuation.

Although a great many designs are now available, necessary and sufficient conditions for the existence of an incomplete balanced block design with given parameters v, b, r, k, λ are not known. Equations 7.12 and 7.13 are necessary conditions. The inequality 7.14 must also hold if $v > k$. We shall prove it now. The inequality $b \geq v$ is, because of 7.12, equivalent to $r \geq k$. We number the blocks and consider the number a_i of elements common to the first and the ith block.

From 9.22 and 9.23 it follows that

$$\sum_i a_i^2 = k([\lambda - 1]k + r - \lambda).$$

From 9.22 it also follows that $k(r - 1)/(b - 1)$ is the mean of the variable a_i and therefore

$$(9.24)\quad \sum_i a_i^2 \geq \frac{k^2(r-1)^2}{b-1}, \; (\lambda - 1)k + (r - \lambda) \geq \frac{k(r-1)^2}{b-1}.$$

From 7.13 we have $(r - \lambda) = rk - \lambda v$ and this substituted in 9.24 yields

$$(9.25) \qquad k(r-1) - \frac{k(r-1)^2}{b-1} \geq \lambda(v-k)$$

and

$$(9.26) \qquad k(r-1)\frac{(b-r)}{b-1} \geq \lambda(v-k).$$

From 7.12 we have

$$(9.27) \qquad \frac{b-r}{v-k} = \frac{r}{k}.$$

Since $v - k > 0$ we may divide 9.26 by $v - k$ and obtain on account of 9.27

$$(9.30) \qquad r(r-1) \geq \lambda(b-1).$$

Subtracting from this 7.13 yields

$$(9.31) \qquad r(r-k) \geq \lambda(b-v),$$

but $(b - v)/v = (r - k)/k$ by 7.12 and therefore

$$(9.32) \qquad r(r-k) \geq \frac{\lambda v}{k}(r-k),$$

$$(9.33) \qquad (r-k)(kr-\lambda v) \geq 0.$$

Since $kr - \lambda v = r - \lambda > 0$ it follows that $r \geq k$.

CHAPTER X

Non-orthogonal Data

THE r-WAY CLASSIFICATION design wtih an equal number of replications in every subclass is the best available design for investigating the effect of classifications. However, it is not always possible to keep the numbers in the subclasses equal. Suppose for instance that we wish to measure the variation in the weights of pigs at birth according to sex and litter. It is of course not possible to prescribe the litter size and the number of males in a litter. Thus we obtain a two way classification design with unequal numbers in the subclasses. Such incomplete data may also result from the fact that originally a complete layout, say a Latin square was planned, but one or more experiments miscarried so that some observations are missing. Such data can also be analyzed with the help of the likelihood ratio principle but the computations are much more laborious than those described in the preceding chapters.

The solution of all problems of this kind requires, as shown in Chapter IV, the finding of Q_a and $Q_r - Q_a$. That is to say we have to minimize a quadratic form

$$Q = \sum_{\alpha=1}^{N} \left(y_\alpha - \sum_{i=1}^{k} \beta_i x_{i\alpha} \right)^2. \tag{10.1}$$

under the restrictions

$$\sum_{j=1}^{k} c_{uj}\beta_j = 0 \qquad u = 1, \cdots, r < k \qquad \text{rank}\,(c_{uj}) = r. \tag{10.2}$$

The minimum of Q with respect to the β_i is denoted by Q_a if 10.2 denotes the restrictions imposed by the assumptions and Q_r if 10.2 denotes the restrictions imposed by assumption and hypothesis.

We shall prove the following theorem.

THEOREM 10.1: *Let S be the minimum of Q with respect to the β_p under the restrictions* 10.2. *Let*

$$a_{pq} = \sum_{\alpha=1}^{N} x_{p\alpha}x_{q\alpha} \qquad \text{for } k \geq p > 0,\ k \geq q > 0.$$

(10.3)
$$a_{q0} = a_{0q} = \sum_{\alpha=1}^{N} y_\alpha x_{q\alpha}\ ,$$

$$a_{00} = \sum_{\alpha=1}^{N} y_\alpha^2\ .$$

Then

(10.4)
$$S = \frac{\Delta}{\Delta_{00}}\ .$$

where

(10.5)
$$\Delta = \begin{vmatrix} a_{00} & a_{01} & \cdots & a_{0k} & 0 & \cdots & 0 \\ a_{10} & a_{11} & \cdots & a_{1k} & c_{11} & \cdots & c_{r1} \\ \cdot & \cdot & & \cdot & \cdot & & \\ \cdot & \cdot & & \cdot & \cdot & & \\ \cdot & \cdot & & \cdot & \cdot & & \\ a_{k0} & a_{k1} & \cdots & a_{kk} & c_{1k} & \cdots & c_{rk} \\ 0 & c_{11} & \cdots & c_{1k} & 0 & \cdots & 0 \\ \cdot & \cdot & & \cdot & \cdot & & \cdot \\ \cdot & \cdot & & \cdot & \cdot & & \cdot \\ \cdot & \cdot & & \cdot & \cdot & & \cdot \\ 0 & c_{r1} & \cdots & c_{rk} & 0 & \cdots & 0 \end{vmatrix}$$

and Δ_{00} is the minor of a_{00} in (Δ)

Applying the method of Lagrange operators we have

(10.6)
$$\left(\frac{\partial Q}{\partial \beta_p}\right)_{\beta_q=\hat{\beta}_q} + \sum_{u=1}^{r} \lambda_u c_{up}$$
$$= 2\left(-a_{0p} + \sum_{q=1}^{k} a_{pq}\hat{\beta}_q\right) + \sum_{u=1}^{r} \lambda_u c_{up}$$
$$= 0, \qquad p = 1, \cdots, k,$$

where as usual the caret denotes maximum likelihood estimates.

We multiply the pth equation by $\hat{\beta}_p$ and sum over p. Since $\sum_p c_{up}\,\hat{\beta}_p = 0$ this yields

$$-\sum_p a_{0p}\hat{\beta}_p + \sum_p \sum_q a_{pq}\hat{\beta}_p\hat{\beta}_q = 0. \tag{10.7}$$

We now expand S and obtain

$$\begin{aligned} S &= a_{00} - 2\sum_{p=1}^{k} a_{0p}\hat{\beta}_p + \sum_p \sum_q a_{pq}\hat{\beta}_p\hat{\beta}_q \\ &= a_{00} - \sum_p a_{0p}\hat{\beta}_p\,. \end{aligned} \tag{10.8}$$

Hence we obtain the following system of $k + r + 1$ equations for the $k + r + 1$ quantities $\hat{\beta}_0 = 1, \hat{\beta}_1, \cdots, \hat{\beta}_k, \lambda_1/2, \cdots \lambda_r/2$

$$\begin{aligned} (S - a_{00})\hat{\beta}_0 + \sum_p a_{0p}\hat{\beta}_p &= 0, \\ -a_{0p}\hat{\beta}_0 + \sum_q a_{pq}\hat{\beta}_q + \sum_u \frac{\lambda_u}{2} c_{up} &= 0, \quad p = 1, \cdots, k, \\ \sum_q c_{uq}\hat{\beta}_q &= 0, \quad u = 1, \cdots, r. \end{aligned} \tag{10.9}$$

Since $\hat{\beta}_0 = 1$ this system has a non-trivial solution and it follows that

$$\begin{vmatrix} S - a_{00} & a_{01} & \cdots & a_{0k} & 0 & \cdots & 0 \\ -a_{10} & a_{11} & \cdots & a_{1k} & c_{11} & \cdots & c_{r1} \\ \cdot & \cdot & & \cdot & \cdot & & \cdot \\ \cdot & \cdot & & \cdot & \cdot & & \cdot \\ \cdot & \cdot & & \cdot & \cdot & & \cdot \\ -a_{k0} & a_{k1} & \cdots & a_{kk} & c_{1k} & \cdots & c_{rk} \\ 0 & c_{11} & \cdots & c_{1k} & 0 & \cdots & 0 \\ \cdot & \cdot & & \cdot & \cdot & & \cdot \\ \cdot & \cdot & & \cdot & \cdot & & \cdot \\ \cdot & \cdot & & \cdot & \cdot & & \cdot \\ 0 & c_{r1} & \cdots & c_{rk} & 0 & \cdots & 0 \end{vmatrix} = 0.$$

It follows that

$$S\Delta_{00} - \Delta = 0, \qquad S = \frac{\Delta}{\Delta_{00}}.$$

In applying this result to an r-way classification one may use to advantage the following notation. Let

$$(10.10) \qquad (\alpha)^x = 1,\ (\alpha)^{x(i_1, \cdots, i_s; a_{i_1}, \cdots, a_{i_s})} = \begin{cases} 1 & \text{if } y_\alpha \text{ is in the } a_{i_1}, \cdots, a_{i_s} \text{ class of the } i_1, \cdots, i_s \text{ classification} \\ 0 & \text{otherwise,} \end{cases}$$

where $y_1, \cdots, y_N$ are the observations. Then with $\mu(i_1, \cdots, i_\alpha; a_{i_1}, \ldots, a_{i\alpha})$ defined as in Chapter V we have

$$(10.11) \qquad Q = \sum_\alpha \Big(Y_\alpha - \sum_{\beta=0}^{r} \sum_{1, \cdots, r} \sum_{a_{i_1}} \cdots \sum_{a_{i\beta}} \cdot (\alpha)^{x(i_1, \cdots, i_\beta; a_{i_1}, \cdots, a_{i\beta})} \mu(i_1, \cdots, i_\beta; a_{i_1}, \cdots, a_{i\beta}) \Big)^2.$$

In addition to the restrictions in 5.3 there may be other restrictions imposed by the hypothesis. If Δ, Δ_{00}, Δ', Δ'_{00} are the determinants of Theorem 10.1 under the restrictions imposed on the $\mu(i_1, \cdots i_k; a_{i_1}, \cdots, a_{i_k})$ under the assumption and the hypothesis respectively and if a and h respectively are the number of independent linear restrictions, then

$$(10.12) \qquad F = \frac{a}{h} \frac{\Delta'/\Delta'_{00} - \Delta/\Delta_{00}}{\Delta/\Delta_{00}}$$

has by Theorem 4.1 the F distribution and the test based on F is the likelihood ratio test.

Although Theorem 10.1 yields very neat mathematical formulae the numerical evaluation of Δ and Δ_{00}, although feasible with modern computational techniques, is rather laborious. There are several cases in which the solution can better be obtained by operating directly on the least square equations.

A special case in which the least square equations can easily be solved directly is the case of an r-way design with proportional class frequencies in the subclasses. We shall indicate the treatment in the case of a two-way design. If the class frequencies are proportional we may write the number of observations in the ith row and jth column ($i = 1, \cdots, r; j = 1, \cdots, k$) as $n_{i}.n._{j}$.

It will be convenient to use the following definitions.

$$
(10.13) \quad
\begin{aligned}
\bar{\mu}_{ij} &= \mu_{ij} - \frac{\sum_e n_{e}.\mu_{ej}}{\sum_e n_{e}.} - \frac{\sum_m n._{m}\mu_{im}}{\sum_m n._{m}} + \frac{\sum_e \sum_m n_{e}.n._{m}\mu_{em}}{\sum_e n_{e}. \sum_m n._{m}}, \\
\bar{\mu}_{i}. &= \mu_{i}. - \frac{\sum_e n_{e}.\mu_{e}.}{\sum_e n_{e}.} + \frac{\sum_m n._{m}\mu_{im}}{\sum_m n._{m}} - \frac{\sum_e \sum_m n_{e}.n._{m}\mu_{em}}{\sum_e n_{e}. \sum_m n._{m}}, \\
\bar{\mu}._{j} &= \mu._{j} + \frac{\sum_e n_{e}.\mu_{ej}}{\sum_e n_{e}.} - \frac{\sum_m n._{m}\mu._{m}}{\sum_m n._{m}} - \frac{\sum_e \sum_m n_{e}.n._{m}\mu_{em}}{\sum_e n_{e}. \sum_m n._{m}}, \\
\bar{\mu} &= \mu + \frac{\sum_e n_{e}.\mu_{e}.}{\sum_e n_{e}.} + \frac{\sum_m n._{m}\mu._{m}}{\sum_m n._{m}} + \frac{\sum_e \sum_m n_{e}.n._{m}\mu_{em}}{\sum_e n_{e}. \sum_m n._{m}},
\end{aligned}
$$

where $\mu(1, 2; i, j) = \mu_{ij}$, $\mu(1; i) = \mu_{i}$, $\mu(2; j) = \mu._{j}$ in 5.3. It is easily verified that with these definitions

$$
(10.14) \quad
\begin{aligned}
&\sum_i n_{i}.\bar{\mu}_{ij} = \sum_j n._{j}\bar{\mu}_{ij} = \sum_i n_{i}.\bar{\mu}_{i}. = \sum_j n._{j}\bar{\mu}._{j} = 0, \\
&\mu_{ij} + \mu_{i}. + \mu._{j} + \mu = \bar{\mu}_{ij} + \bar{\mu}_{i}. + \bar{\mu}._{j} + \bar{\mu}.
\end{aligned}
$$

Let y_{ijl} denote the lth observation in the ith row and jth column and put

$$
Y_{ij}. = \frac{1}{n_{i}.n._{j}} \sum_l Y_{ijl}, \qquad Y_{i}.. = \frac{1}{n_{i}. \sum_j n._{j}} \sum_k \sum_l Y_{ikl}
$$

$$
Y._{j}. = \frac{1}{n._{j} \sum_i n_{i}.} \sum_k \sum_l Y_{kjl},
$$

$$
Y = \frac{1}{\sum_i n_{i}. \sum_j n._{j}} \sum_p \sum_q \sum_l Y_{pql}
$$

then the assumption may be written as $E(Y_{ijl}) = \mu_{ij} + \mu_{i\cdot} + \mu_{\cdot j} + \mu = \bar{\mu}_{ij} + \bar{\mu}_{i\cdot} + \bar{\mu}_{1j} + \mu$ and the least square equations easily lead to

$$
(10.15)\qquad
\begin{aligned}
\hat{\bar{\mu}}_{ij} &= Y_{ij\cdot} - Y_{i\cdot\cdot} - Y_{\cdot j\cdot} + Y,\\
\hat{\bar{\mu}}_{i\cdot} &= Y_{i\cdot\cdot} - Y,\\
\hat{\bar{\mu}}_{\cdot j} &= Y_{\cdot j\cdot} - Y,\\
\hat{\bar{\mu}} &= Y.
\end{aligned}
$$

Thus $Q_a = \sum_i \sum_j \sum_l (Y_{ijl} - Y_{ij\cdot})^2$. The μ_{ij} , $\mu_{i\cdot}$, $\mu_{\cdot j}$, μ can be found from 10.13 utilizing the restrictions in 5.3.

$$
(10.16)\qquad
\begin{aligned}
\mu_{ij} &= \bar{\mu}_{ij} - \frac{\sum_e \bar{\mu}_{ej}}{r} - \frac{\sum_m \bar{\mu}_{im}}{k} + \frac{\sum_e \sum_m \bar{\mu}_{em}}{rk},\\
\mu_{i\cdot} &= \bar{\mu}_{i\cdot} - \frac{\sum_e \bar{\mu}_{e\cdot}}{r} + \frac{\sum_m \bar{\mu}_{im}}{k} - \frac{\sum_e \sum_m \bar{\mu}_{em}}{rk},\\
\mu_{\cdot j} &= \bar{\mu}_{\cdot j} + \frac{\sum_e \bar{\mu}_{ej}}{r} - \frac{\sum_m \bar{\mu}_{\cdot m}}{k} - \frac{\sum_e \sum_m \bar{\mu}_{em}}{rk},\\
\mu &= \bar{\mu} + \frac{\sum_e \bar{\mu}_{e\cdot}}{r} + \frac{\sum_m \bar{\mu}_{\cdot m}}{k} + \frac{\sum_e \sum_m \bar{\mu}_{em}}{rk}.
\end{aligned}
$$

The details of the derivations and the discussions of the tests of various hypotheses are left to the reader as an exercise.

Sometimes one or more experiments of a complete layout miscarry. It is then often still possible without excessive labor to solve the resulting least square equations. As an example we shall consider the case of an m sided Latin square in which only one observation is missing. We shall assume that this is the observation in the 1st row, 1st column and on the 1st variety.

We denote by $Y_{i..}$, $Y_{.i.}$, $Y_{..i}$ the sum of all observations in the ith row, ith column, ith variety respectively, and by Y the sum of all observations. Let r_i, c_i, v_i, denote the least square estimates of the effects of the ith row, ith column, and ith variety respectively and v the least square estimate of the general mean. The least square equations resulting from 7.1 are, on account of Theorem 4.5,

$$Y + r_1 + c_1 + v_1 - (m^2 - 1)v = 0,$$

$$Y_{1..} - mr_1 + r_1 + c_1 + v_1 - (m - 1)v = 0,$$

$$Y_{.1.} - mc_1 + r_1 + c_1 + v_1 - (m - 1)v = 0,$$

$$Y_{..1} - mv_1 + r_1 + c_1 + v_1 - (m - 1)v = 0,$$

$$Y_{j..} - mr_j - mv = 0, \qquad j = 2 \cdots m.$$

$$Y_{.j.} - mc_j - mv = 0,$$

$$Y_{..j} - mv_j - mv = 0.$$

From the first equation we obtain $r_1 + v_1 + c_1 = (m^2 - 1)v - Y$. Substituting this in the following 3 equations we find:

$$mr_1 = Y_{1..} + m(m - 1)v - Y,$$

$$mc_1 = Y_{.1.} + m(m - 1)v - Y,$$

$$mv_1 = Y_{..1} + m(m - 1)v - Y,$$

Thus $m(m^2 - 1)v - mY = Y_{1..} + Y_{.1.} + Y_{..1} + 3m(m - 1)v - 3Y$. Hence

$$v = \frac{Y_{1..} + Y_{.1.} + Y_{..1} + (m - 3)Y}{m(m - 1)(m - 2)}.$$

Thus finally

$$r_1 = \frac{(m-1)Y_{1..} + Y_{.1.} + Y_{..1} - Y}{m(m-2)},$$

$$c_1 = \frac{Y_{1..} + (m-1)Y_{.1.} + Y_{..1} - Y}{m(m-2)},$$

$$v_1 = \frac{Y_{1..} + Y_{.1.} + (m-1)Y_{..1} - Y}{m(m-2)}$$

and for $j \geq 2$

$$r_j = \frac{Y_{j..}}{m} - \frac{Y_{1..} + Y_{.1.} + Y_{..1} + (m-3)Y}{m(m-1)(m-2)},$$

$$c_j = \frac{Y_{.j.}}{m} - \frac{Y_{1..} + Y_{.1.} + Y_{..1} + (m-3)Y}{m(m-1)(m-2)},$$

$$v_j = \frac{Y_{..j}}{m} - \frac{Y_{1..} + Y_{.1.} + Y_{..1} + (m-3)Y}{m(m-1)(m-2)}.$$

In testing the hypothesis $v_j = 0$ $(j = 1, \cdots, m)$ one obtains an analogous result for r_j and c_j. The test of the hypothesis $v_j = v_k$ is best carried out by utilizing Theorem 4.3 and its corollary. The details of the analysis are left to the reader. A detailed discussion of the analysis of Latin squares when some observations are missing is given by D. B. DeLury (Journal of the American Statistical Association, Vol. 41, pp. 370-389). A general method for the treatment of missing observations was given by F. Yates (Empire Jour. Experimental Agric., Vol. I, 1933).

Yates proceeds as follows: Suppose we have a regression equation

$$(10.17) \qquad E(y_\alpha) = \sum_{i=1}^{s} g_{i\alpha}\beta_i \qquad \alpha = 1, \cdots, n$$

and suppose further that the observations $y_1, \cdots, y_k$ are missing. Differentiation of $Q = \sum_\alpha (y_\alpha - \sum_i g_{i\alpha}\beta_i)^2$ with respect to the β_i yields the least square equations

$$\text{(10.18)} \qquad \sum_\alpha g_{i\alpha} y_\alpha = \sum_j \sum_\alpha g_{i\alpha} g_{j\alpha} \hat{\beta}_j \qquad (i = 1, \cdots, s).$$

Differentiation of Q with respect to $y_1, \cdots, y_k$ which we also regard as unknown parameters yields the additional equations

$$\text{(10.19)} \qquad y_\alpha = \sum_1^s g_{i\alpha}\hat{\beta}_i, \qquad \alpha = 1, \cdots, k.$$

We may first solve 10.18 for the $\hat{\beta}_i$ and then substitute the values of $\hat{\beta}_i$ so obtained into 10.19. Thus we obtain k equations for the k unknown quantities $y_1, \cdots, y_k$ and the solutions to these equations are the least square estimates of $y_1, \cdots, y_k$.

This method is particularly advantageous in the case of designs where the expressions for the $\hat{\beta}_i$ are already known.

We shall exemplify Yates method in a Latin square with one observation missing. We obtain from 7.2 and 10.19 for the least square estimate $\hat{Y}_{111}$ of Y_{111}

$$\hat{Y}_{111} = \frac{3\hat{Y}_{111}}{m} + \frac{Y_{1..} + Y_{.1.} + Y_{..1}}{m} - \frac{2\hat{Y}_{111}}{m^2} - \frac{2Y}{m^2},$$

$$\hat{Y}_{111} = \frac{m^2}{(m-1)(m-2)} \frac{Y_{1..} + Y_{.1.} + Y_{..1}}{m} - \frac{2Y}{m^2}.$$

Substituting $\hat{Y}_{111}$ for Y_{111} in 7.2 one then obtains equations for v_i, c_i, r_i. The reader may verify that these equations are the same that were previously derived by a direct application of the maximum likelihood principle.

CHAPTER XI

Factorial Experiments

IT WILL BE CONVENIENT in this as in the previous chapters to use the picture of an agricultural field experiment. This is done to give the reader a concrete picture but should not be taken to imply that the use of the designs presented is restricted to agricultural experimentation.

Suppose that the influence of m factors, say m different fertilizers, on the yield of wheat is to be tested. Each of these factors may be applied on different levels. Let the ith factor be applied on t_i levels, so that all in all $t_1 t_2 \cdots t_m$ treatment combinations are possible.

If we consider the ith level of the αth factor as the ith class of the αth classification in an m way classification design, we can use the methods of analysis of Chapter V. The estimates of the main effects and interactions $A(1, \cdots, \alpha; a_1, \cdots, a_\alpha)$ appearing in 5.5 are linear forms of the observations of the form

$$(11.1) \qquad \sum_{b_1} \cdots \sum_{b_\alpha} l_{b_1, \cdots, b_\alpha} x(1, \cdots, \alpha; b_1, \cdots, b_\alpha),$$

where $x(1, \cdots, \alpha; b_1, \cdots, b_\alpha)$ is defined as in Chapter 5. We proceed to compute the coefficient of $x(1, \cdots, s, s+1, \cdots, \alpha; a_1, \cdots, a_s, b_{s+1}, \cdots, b_\alpha)(b_i \neq a_i)$ in $A(1, \cdots, \alpha; a_1, \cdots, a_\alpha)$. This term occurs as a summand in all $x(k_1, \cdots, k_\beta; a_{k_1}, \cdots, a_{k_\beta})$ where $k_1 \cdots, k_\beta$ is a combination out of $1, \cdots, s$ and it occurs there with the coefficient $(t_{k_1} \cdots t_{k_\beta})/(t_1 \cdots t_\alpha)$. Hence using the notation of Chapter 5, the coefficient of $x(1, \cdots, s, s+1, \cdots, \alpha; a_1, \cdots, a_s, b_{s+1}, \cdots, b_\alpha)$ in $A(1, \cdots, \alpha; a_1, \cdots, a_\alpha)$ may be written as

$$\sum_{1, \cdots, s} \sum_{\beta=0}^{s} (-1)^{\alpha-\beta} \frac{t_{k_1} \cdots t_{k_\beta}}{t_1 \cdots t_\alpha}.$$

Thus

$$\sum_{c_{s+1}} l_{a_1, \cdots, a_s c_{s+1} b_{s+2}, \cdots, b_\alpha}$$

$$(11.2) \qquad = \left(\sum_{1, \cdots, s} \sum_{\beta=0}^{s} (-1)^{\alpha-\beta} \frac{t_{k_1} \cdots t_{k\beta}}{t_1 \cdots t_\alpha} \right) (t_{s+1} - 1)$$

$$+ \sum_{1, \cdots, s+1} \sum_{\beta=0}^{s+1} (-1)^{\alpha-\beta} \frac{t_{k_1} \cdots t_{k\beta}}{t_1 \cdots t_\alpha}.$$

By splitting the second term on the right side of 11.2 into terms for which $k_\beta = s + 1$ and terms for which $k_\beta < s + 1$ one obtains $\sum_{c_{s+1}} l_{a_1 \cdots a_s c_{s+1} b_{s+2} \cdots b_\alpha} = 0$. Similarly one proves that the coefficients $l_{b_1 \cdots b_\alpha}$ appearing in 11.1 satisfy the equation

$$(11.3) \qquad \sum_{b_i} l_{b_1, \cdots, b_\alpha} = 0 \qquad i = 1, \cdots, \alpha.$$

We generalize the concept of interaction and define: *Any linear form*

$$(11.4) \qquad L = \sum_{a_1} \cdots \sum_{a_\alpha} l_{a_1, \cdots, a_\alpha} x(i_1, \cdots, i_\alpha; a_1, \cdots, a_\alpha)$$

which is not identically 0 *will be termed a component of the interaction between the factors* $i_1, \cdots, i_\alpha$ *if*

$$(11.5) \qquad \sum_{a_i} l_{a_1, \cdots, a_\alpha} = 0 \qquad i = 1, \cdots, \alpha$$

for all choices $a_1 \cdots a_{i-1} a_{i+1} \cdots a_\alpha$.

Two linear forms

$$\sum_{k=1}^{n} a_k x_k \qquad \text{and} \qquad \sum_{j=1}^{n} b_j x_j$$

are called orthogonal if

$$(11.6) \qquad \sum_{k=1}^{n} a_k b_k = 0.$$

THEOREM 11.1: *Two interaction components G and H belonging to two different sets of factors are orthogonal.*

We may always arrange the notation so that G is a component of the interaction of the factors 1, 2, $\cdots$, u and H of the factors $p, p + 1, \cdots, v$ where $p > 1$. Let

$$G = \sum_{\alpha} l_\alpha x_\alpha = \sum_{a_1} \cdots \sum_{a_u} l_{a_1, \cdots, a_u} x(1, \cdots, u; a_1, \cdots, a_u),$$

$$H = \sum_{\alpha} l_\alpha^* x_\alpha = \sum_{a_p} \cdots \sum_{a_v} l_{a_p, \cdots, a_v} x(p, \cdots, v; a_p, \cdots, a_v).$$

If $x_\alpha = x_{a_1 \cdots a_m}$ then $l_\alpha = l_{a_1 \cdots a_u}/t_{u+1} \cdots t_m$. Thus writing $w = \max(u, v)$

$$(11.7) \qquad \sum_{\alpha} l_\alpha l_\alpha^* = \frac{(t_1 \cdots t_u)(t_p \cdots t_v)(t_{w+1} \cdots t_m)}{(t_1 \cdots t_m)^2}$$

$$\cdot \sum_{a_2} \cdots \sum_{a_w} \sum_{a_1} l_{a_1, \cdots, a_u} l_{a_p, \cdots, a_v} = 0$$

by 11.5.

Lemma 11.1: *If $L_1, \cdots, L_s$ are orthogonal to L then $\sum_i \lambda_i L_i$ is orthogonal to L for all values $\lambda_1, \cdots, \lambda_s$.*

The proof of Lemma 11.1 is left to the reader.

Solving the equations 11.5 we may choose arbitrarily the quantities $l_{a_1 \cdots a_\alpha}$ for $a_i \leq t_i - 1$. The equations 11.5 can then be satisfied by putting successively

$$l_{t_1 a_2, \cdots, a_\alpha} = - \sum_{a_1 = 1}^{t_1 - 1} l_{a_1 a_2, \cdots, a_\alpha}, \qquad a_2 < t_2, \cdots, a_\alpha < t_\alpha,$$

$$l_{a_1 t_2, \cdots, a_\alpha} = - \sum_{a_2 = 1}^{t_1 - 1} l_{a_1 a_2, \cdots, a_\alpha}, \qquad a_3 < t_3, \cdots, a_\alpha < t_\alpha,$$

$$\vdots$$

$$l_{a_1, \cdots, a_{\alpha - 1} t_\alpha} = - \sum_{a_\alpha = 1}^{t_\alpha - 1} l_{a_1 a_2, \cdots, a_\alpha}.$$

Thus the equations 11.5 have exactly $(t_1 - 1) \cdots (t_\alpha - 1)$ independent solutions. That means that every solution of 11.5

can be expressed as a linear combination of any $(t_1 - 1) \cdots (t_\alpha - 1)$ linearly independent solutions. By the method used in the proof of lemma 4.1 we can therefore find a system S of $(t_1 - 1) \cdots (t_\alpha - 1)$ normalized orthogonal linear forms such that every form in S is a component of the interaction between the factors $i_1, \cdots, i_\alpha$ and such that every component of such an interaction is a linear combination of forms in the system S.

The interaction components of different factors are orthogonal to each other and hence linearly independent. Thus together with the mean we obtain

$$1 + \sum_{k=1}^{m} \sum_{1,\cdots,m} (t_{i_1} - 1) \cdots (t_{i_k} - 1) = t_1 t_2, \cdots, t_m$$

independent linear forms and therefore any linear function of the observations may be expressed as a linear combination of the mean and any set of $(t_1 \cdots t_m) - 1$ linearly independent interactions.

In considering the analysis of factorial designs we may therefore consider the following general problem. Given n normally distributed random variables $x_1, \cdots, x_n$ all with the same variance but different means. We know that certain linear forms in $x_1 \cdots x_n$

$$L_i = \sum_{j=1}^{n} a_{ij} x_j \qquad i = 1, \cdots, s \tag{11.8}$$

have the mean value 0. We wish to test, whether certain other forms

$$L_i = \sum_{j=1}^{n} a_{ij} x_j \qquad i = s + 1, \cdots, r \tag{11.9}$$

also have mean value 0.

In the first place we may eliminate, from the assumption and hypothesis successively, forms such that $L_1, \cdots, L_s, L_{s+1}, \cdots, L_r$ may be assumed to be independent. Next we may orthogonalize and normalize the assumption and hypothesis by the method used in the proof of lemma 4.1. We may then add $n - $ r linear forms

$$L_i = \sum_{j=1}^{n} a_{ij}x_j \qquad i = r + 1, \cdots, n.$$

such that the matrix

$$\begin{pmatrix} a_{11} & \cdots & a_{1n} \\ \cdot & & \cdot \\ \cdot & & \cdot \\ \cdot & & \cdot \\ a_{n1} & \cdots & a_{nn} \end{pmatrix}$$

is orthogonal. Then

$$Q = \sum_{i=1}^{n} (x_i - E(x_i))^2 = \sum_{i=1}^{n} (L_i - E(L_i))^2$$

Thus

$$Q_a = \sum_{i=1}^{s} L_i^2, \; Q_r - Q_a = \sum_{i=s+1}^{r} L_i^2 \text{ and } F = \frac{s}{r-s}\frac{Q_r - Q_a}{Q_a}$$

is the likelihood ratio statistic for testing the hypothesis $E(L_i) = 0 (i = s + 1, \cdots, r)$ under the assumption $E(L_i) = 0$, $(i = 1, \cdots, s)$.

In the analysis of factorial experiments we shall always put

$$L_1 = \frac{x_1 + \cdots + x_n}{n^{1/2}}$$

so that the sum of the coefficients of $L_2, \cdots, L_n$ is 0 because of the orthogonality.

We then consider the mean yield $E(x_i)$ as composed of the treatment effect T_i and the block effect b_α due to the soil fertility of the αth block. The experiment is replicated in h different blocks each containing a complete replication of all treatments. We shall denote by x_i^α the value observed under the ith treatment in the αth block and put $L_i^\alpha = L_i(x_1^\alpha, \cdots, x_n^\alpha)$. Then since $L_1^\alpha = (x_1^\alpha + \cdots + x_n^\alpha)/n^{1/2}$ we see that $E(L_i^\alpha) = L_i(T_1, \cdots, T_n) \equiv S_i$ for $i = 2, \cdots, n$

and $E(L_1^\alpha) = L_1(T_1, \cdots, T_n) + n^{1/2} b_\alpha \equiv S_1 + n^{1/2} b_\alpha$. Let $\bar{L}_i$ be the mean of all L_i^α then

$$Q = \sum_{\alpha=1}^{h} \sum_{i=1}^{n} (x_i^\alpha - T_i - b_\alpha)^2$$

$$= \sum_{\alpha=1}^{h} \sum_{i=2}^{n} (L_i^\alpha - \bar{L}_i)^2 + h \sum_{i=2}^{n} (\bar{L}_i - S_i)^2$$

$$+ \sum_{\alpha=1}^{h} (L_1^\alpha - S_1 - n^{1/2} b_\alpha)^2.$$

If we now test the hypothesis $S_{k+1} = \cdots = S_{k+u} = 0$ under the assumption $S_2 = \cdots = S_k = 0$ then

$$Q_a = \sum_{\alpha=1}^{h} \sum_{i=2}^{n} (L_i^\alpha - \bar{L}_i)^2 + h \sum_{i=2}^{k} \bar{L}_i^2,$$

$$Q_r - Q_a = h \sum_{i=k+1}^{k+u} \bar{L}_i^2 .$$

Thus Q_a has $(k - 1) + (h - 1)(n - 1)$ degrees of freedom and $Q_r - Q_a$ has u degrees of freedom. Note that more than one replication is needed unless certain of the S_i are known to be 0.

We recall that one of the necessary assumptions of the analysis was the uniformity of the soil. If the number of treatment combinations is large then the blocks become too large to make this assumption. In this case one conducts the experiment in several blocks containing among themselves a complete replication and resorts to the technique of confounding linear forms of the treatment effects in which one is not interested.

A linear form

$$S = \sum_{i=1}^{n} a_i T_i$$

will be called confounded in the block B_α *if* $a_i = c_\alpha$ *whenever* T_i *is the effect of a treatment applied in the* αth *block* B_α. A *linear form S will be called orthogonal to* B_α *if* $\sum_{T_i \subset B_\alpha} a_i = 0$. *A linear form* $S = \sum_i a_i T_i$ *is called normalized if* $\sum_i a_i^2 = 1$.

Lemma 11.2: *If* $S_1, \cdots, S_v$ *are confounded in the block B then any linear function* $S = \lambda_1 S_1 + \cdots + \lambda_v S_v$ *is also confounded in B.*

The proof of Lemma 11.2 is left to the reader.

Lemma 11.3: *If* $L_1, \cdots, L_n$ *are n orthogonal functions of the variables* $x_1, \cdots, x_n$ *and L is orthogonal to* L_1 *then*

11.10 $$L = a_2 L_2 + \cdots + a_n L_n .$$

Proof: Since $L_1, \cdots, L_n$ are independent we certainly have $L = a_1 L_1 + \cdots + a_n L_n$. Let $L = \sum_i \lambda_i x_i$, $L_k = \sum_i \lambda_{ki} x_i$ then $\sum_i \lambda_i \lambda_{ui} = \sum_k a_k \sum_i \lambda_{ki} \lambda_{ui} = a_u \sum_i \lambda_{ui}^2$. Thus

(11.11) $$a_u = \frac{\sum_i \lambda_i \lambda_{ui}}{\sum_i \lambda_{ui}^2} .$$

Since L is orthogonal to L_1 we must have $a_1 = 0$.

Theorem 11.2: *If* $S_1, S_2, \cdots, S_n$ *is a system of orthogonal linear forms in the treatment effects* $T_1, \cdots, T_n$ *and* $S_1, S_2, \cdots, S_v$ *are confounded in the blocks* $B_1, \cdots, B_v$ *consisting of a complete replication of the treatments, then* $S_{v+1}, \cdots, S_n$ *are orthogonal to these blocks.*

Proof: Let S_i' $(i = 1 \cdots v)$ be the sum of the treatment effects of all the treatments in the ith block then $S_1, \cdots, S_v$ are linear functions of $S_1', \cdots, S_v'$. However since $S_1, \cdots, S_v$ are independent we may express $S_1', \cdots, S_v'$ also by $S_1, \cdots, S_v$. Therefore by Lemma 11.1 $S_1', \cdots, S_v'$ are orthogonal to $S_{v+1}, \cdots, S_n$.

Suppose now that we are interested in certain linear functions $S_{v+1}, \cdots, S_{v+k}$ of the treatment effects $T_1, \cdots, T_n$, $n = u \cdot v$, and wish to arrange our experiment in v blocks of u treatments each. We may assume that $S_{v+1}, \cdots, S_{v+k}$ are normalized and orthogonal to each other. We first add forms $S_1, \cdots, S_v$, $S_{v+k+1}, \cdots, S_n$ in order to obtain a set of n normalized orthogonal forms. Suppose that we can find an arrangement of the treatments in v blocks such that $S_1, \cdots, S_v$ are confounded in all the blocks. Then $S_{v+1}, \cdots, S_n$ will be orthogonal to all the blocks by Theorem 11.2.

Let y_α denote the yield of the αth plot and consider

$$Q = \sum_{\alpha=1}^{n} (y_\alpha - T_\alpha - b_{i_\alpha})^2, \tag{11.12}$$

where T_α is the effect of the treatment applied to the αth plot and b_{i_α} is the effect of the block in which the αth plot lies. Let $S_\alpha = \sum_\beta t_{\alpha\beta} T_\beta$ and put $L_\alpha = \sum_\beta t_{\alpha\beta} y_\beta$. Then

$$Q = \sum_\alpha (L_\alpha - S_\alpha - \sum_\beta t_{\alpha\beta} b_{i_\beta})^2. \tag{11.13}$$

If L_α is orthogonal to all the blocks then $\sum_\beta t_{\alpha\beta} b_{i_\beta} = \sum_j b_j \sum_{v_\beta \subset B_j} t_{\alpha\beta} = 0$. If L_α is confounded in all the blocks then $t_{\alpha\beta} = c_{\alpha j}$ whenever $i_\beta = j$. Hence

$$\sum_\beta t_{\alpha\beta} b_{i_\beta} = u \sum_j c_{\alpha j} b_j . \tag{11.14}$$

But the linear forms $L_1, \cdots, L_v$ are orthogonal and therefore the matrix $(c_{\alpha j})$ is an orthogonal matrix and hence non-singular. We can therefore always solve the system of equations

$$L_\alpha - S_\alpha = u \sum_j c_{\alpha j} b_j \qquad \alpha = 1, \cdots, v$$

whatever the value of S_α. Thus in minimizing Q under certain assumptions on $S_{v+1}, \cdots, S_{v+k}$ with respect to the S_α and b_i we may always choose the b_i so that the first v terms of 11.13 vanish. We therefore need only minimize

$$Q' = \sum_{\alpha=v+1}^{n} (L_\alpha - S_\alpha)^2. \tag{11.15}$$

The same argument also applies if the experiment is replicated several times. We shall formulate this result as

THEOREM 11.3: *Let $x_1, \cdots, x_{uv}$ be uv observations from v different blocks $B_1, \cdots, B_v$ of u observations each obtained in applying the treatments $T_1, \cdots, T_{uv}$ respectively. Let $S_1, \cdots,$*

S_{uv} be uv normalized orthogonal forms $S_\alpha = \sum_\beta t_{\alpha\beta}T_\beta$ in the treatment effects $T_1, \cdots, T_{uv}$ and assume that $S_1, \cdots, S_v$ are confounded in all blocks.

If the hypothesis $S_\alpha = 0, \alpha = v + k + 1, \cdots, v + k + s$ is tested under the assumption $S_\alpha = 0, \alpha = v + 1, \cdots, v + k$, $E(x_\alpha) = T_\alpha + b_{i\alpha}$, then

$$Q_a = \sum_{v+1}^{v+k} L_\alpha^2, \qquad Q_r - Q_a = \sum_{v+k+1}^{v+k+s} L_\alpha^2,$$

where

$$L_\alpha = \sum_\beta t_{\alpha\beta}x_\beta .$$

If the experiment is replicated r times and $L_{\alpha i}$ is the value of L_α in the ith replication then

$$(11.16) \qquad \begin{aligned} Q_a &= r \sum_{\alpha=v+1}^{v+k} \bar{L}_\alpha^2 + \sum_{\alpha=v+1}^{uv} \sum_{i=1}^{r} (L_{\alpha i} - \bar{L}_\alpha)^2, \\ Q_r - Q_a &= r \sum_{v+k+1}^{v+k+s} \bar{L}_\alpha^2, \end{aligned}$$

where

$$\bar{L}_\alpha = \frac{1}{r} \sum_{i=1}^{r} L_{\alpha i} .$$

Thus if we are interested in the linear forms $S_{v+1}, \cdots, S_{v+k}$ and wish to arrange the treatments $T_1, \cdots, T_{uv}$ into v blocks we have to find v linear forms $S_1, \cdots, S_v$ orthogonal to $S_{v+1}, \cdots, S_{v+k}$ and a design with v blocks where $S_1, \cdots, S_v$ are confounded in all the blocks. Since the mean is always confounded this can only be possible if $S_{v+1}, \cdots, S_{v+k}$ are orthogonal to the mean, that is to say if the sum of the coefficients of $S_{v+1}, \cdots, S_{v+k}$ vanishes.

In the case of a factorial experiment the method of attack is as follows. If $S_\alpha = \sum_\beta t_{\alpha\beta}T_\beta$ then we first form the linear forms $L_\alpha = \sum_\beta t_{\alpha\beta}x_\beta$. Let $I_1, \cdots, I_{uv}$ be a complete normalized system of interaction components as constructed at the beginning of this chapter. Then

$$(11.17)\quad L_\alpha = \sum_\beta u_{\alpha\beta} I_\beta \qquad \alpha = v + 1, \cdots, v + k$$

with certain values of the $u_{\alpha\beta}$. If it is possible to confound v interaction components which have the coefficient 0 in all equations of the system 11.17, then L_α and thus also S_α ($\alpha = v + 1, \cdots, v + k$) will be orthogonal to all the blocks by Theorem 11.2. The L_α are by Theorem 11.1 and Lemma 11.1 orthogonal to all the components say $I_1, \cdots, I_r$ of Interactions which do not enter in 11.17. The L_α may then be orthogonalized and normalized so that Theorem 11.3 applies. If the experiment is replicated we may have to add some functions of the interaction components $I_{r+1}, \cdots, I_{uv}$ to obtain a complete normalized orthogonal system.

The linear forms of interest to the experimenter are usually the main effects and 1st order interactions themselves or linear combinations of them. Thus it is important to construct designs where only interactions of order 2 or higher are confounded. The problem of constructing such designs when all factors are at two or three levels respectively was solved by F. Yates (The Design and Analysis of Factorial Experiments, Technical Communication No. 35, Imperial Bureau of Soil Science). Yates' publication contains also many examples and presents in detail efficient methods of computation applicable to factorial designs. The more general problem of confounding only interactions of order 2 or higher in designs where each factor is at s levels and s is the power of a prime p was first solved by R. A. Fisher (Ann. of Eugenics (1945) 12, pp. 376-381). An alternative method has been given by Radhakrishna Rao (Sankhya 11 pp. 67-78). In the following we shall present Rao's method.

Let $\alpha_0 = 0$, $\alpha_1 = 1$, $\alpha_2, \cdots, \alpha_{s-1}$ be the elements of G.F.(s). Denote the levels of the factors by $\alpha_0, \cdots, \alpha_{s-1}$ and let $y(\alpha_{i_1} \cdots \alpha_{i_m})$ be the observations with the first factor at the α_{i_1} st level, the 2nd factor at the α_{i_2} nd level and so on. Consider then for every α_i the set of observations $y_{x_1 \cdots x_m}$ where $x_{i_1}, \cdots, x_{i_k}$ satisfy the equation

$$(11.18) \qquad b_1 x_{i_1} + \cdots + b_k x_{i_k} = \alpha_j ,$$

$$j = 0, \cdots, s - 1, b_1 \neq 0, \cdots, b_k \neq 0.$$

Corresponding to the s different values of α_j we obtain s sets of observations $M_1, \cdots, M_s$ and each observation is contained in exactly one of the M_i. Consider now any orthogonal matrix $\lambda_{ij}(i, j = 1, \cdots, s)$ whose first row is $(s^{-1/2}, \cdots, s^{-1/2})$. Let $T_1, \cdots, T_s$ stand for the sum of all observations $y_{x_1 \cdots x_m}$ whose indices satisfy the equation 11.18 with $j = 0, \cdots, s - 1$ respectively and consider the expressions

$$(11.19) \qquad L_i = \sum_{j=1}^{s} \lambda_{ij} T_j \qquad i = 1, \cdots, s.$$

We shall prove that $L_2, \cdots, L_s$ are all components of the interaction between the factors $i_1, \cdots, i_k$. All observations with any fixed values $x_{i_1}, \cdots, x_{i_k}$ must lie in T_j if one of them does. Hence $L_i = \sum \lambda_{ij} T_j$ are linear forms in the means $y(i_1, \cdots, i_k; x_{i_1}, \cdots, x_{i_k})$. Keeping now $x_{i_2}, \cdots, x_{i_k}$ fixed and summing over the coefficients of $y(i_1, \cdots, i_k; x_{i_1}, \cdots, x_{i_k})$ with respect to x_{i_1} we obtain $\sum_j \lambda_{ij}$ because if x_{i_1} takes all values $\alpha_0, \cdots, \alpha_{s-1}$ then α_j in 11.18 takes all values in G.F.(s). Since $\sum_j \lambda_{ij} = 0$ for $i = 2, \cdots, s$, 11.5 is fulfilled and the L_i $i > 1$ in 11.19 are therefore components of the interaction between the $i_1, \cdots, i_k$th factors. There are $(s - 1)^{k-1}$ systems of coefficients $b_1, \cdots, b_k$ leading to different functions $L_2, \cdots, L_s$ since $\sigma b_1, \cdots, \sigma b_k$ leads to the same functions as $b_1, \cdots, b_k$. Thus there are $(s - 1)^k$ different interaction components obtained by taking all possible values for $b_1, \cdots, b_k$. That they are independent of each other and hence give a complete system of components of the interaction between the factors $i_1, \cdots, i_k$ will be proved by showing that two interaction components belonging to two different coefficient systems are orthogonal to each other. Consider then

$$(11.20) \qquad b_1 x_{i_1} + \cdots + b_k x_{i_k} = \alpha_i ,$$

$$(11.21) \qquad c_1 x_{i_1} + \cdots + c_k x_{i_k} = \alpha_j .$$

Since the matrix

$$\begin{pmatrix} b_1, & \cdots, & b_k \\ c_1, & \cdots, & c_k \end{pmatrix}$$

is of rank 2 there is at least one 2 by 2 submatrix of rank 2. Suppose therefore that

$$\begin{vmatrix} b_1 & b_2 \\ c_1 & c_2 \end{vmatrix} \neq 0.$$

Then we may fix $x_{i_3}, \cdots, x_{i_k}$ arbitrarily and this completely determines x_1, x_2. Hence we obtain exactly s^{k-2} points $(x_1, \cdots, x_k)$ which satisfy 11.20 and 11.21 simultaneously. Thus if $T_1, \cdots, T_s$ are the sums of all observations satisfying 11.20 for $i = 0, \cdots, s-1$ resp. and $U_1, \cdots, U_s$ is similarly defined for 11.21 and if $L_i = \sum_j \lambda_{ij} T_j = \sum_\alpha \lambda_\alpha y_\alpha$, $L'_t = \sum_j \lambda_{tj} U_j = \sum_\alpha \mu_\alpha y_\alpha$. Then since $\sum_j \lambda_{ij} = 0$ we must have

$$\sum_\alpha \lambda_\alpha \mu_\alpha = s^{k-2} \sum_j \sum_l \lambda_{tl} \lambda_{ij} = 0. \tag{11.22}$$

Thus L_i is orthogonal to L'_t. We shall state this result as a theorem.

THEOREM 11.4: *Let $(b_1, \cdots, b_m)$ be any set of m elements of* G.F.(s), *not all* 0, *and consider the sets M_k of points $(x_1, \cdots, x_m)$ in* E.G.(m, s) *satisfying the equation*

$$b_1 x_1 + \cdots + b_m x_m = \alpha_k$$

resp. where $\alpha_0, \cdots, \alpha_{s-1}$ are the marks of G.F.(s). *Let $(x_1, \cdots, x_m)$ stand for the treatment combination having the αth factor at the level x_α and let (λ_{ij}) be an orthogonal $s \times s$ matrix whose first row is $(1/s^{1/2}, \cdots, 1/s^{1/2})$ and let T_k be the sum of all observations $y_{x_1 \cdots x_m}$ where $(x_1, \cdots, x_m)$ is in M_k. Then the functions $L_i = \sum_j \lambda_{ij} T_j$ are components of the interaction between the factors $i_1, \cdots, i_k$ if $b_{i_\alpha} \neq 0$ $(\alpha = 1, \cdots, k)$ and $b_j = 0$ for $j \neq i_\alpha$, $(\alpha = 1, \cdots, k)$.*

The interaction component L_i will be said to correspond to the point $(b_1, \cdots, b_m)$ of P.G.(m, s). *Two interaction components corresponding to different points are orthogonal.*

We consider the solutions of the system

$$b_{i1}x_1 + \cdots + b_{im}x_m = \alpha_{k_i},$$

(11.23) $$i = 1 \cdots u < m, \qquad \text{rank } (b_{ij}) = u.$$

$$x_i, b_{ij} \subset \text{G.F.}(s).$$

There are s^{m-u} solutions for $x_1, \cdots, x_m$. If we solve 11.23 for all combinations $(\alpha_{k_1}, \cdots, \alpha_{k_u})$ we obtain s^u sets of s^{m-u} treatment combinations each. If these are taken as the contents of s^u blocks then the set of interaction components corresponding to any linear combination $\sum_i \lambda_i(b_{i_1}, \cdots, b_{im})$ will be confounded in all the blocks. Thus $(s^u - 1)/(s - 1)$ sets of interaction components will be confounded giving $(s - 1)(s^u - 1)/(s - 1) = s^u - 1$ or with the mean s^u independent orthogonal functions confounded. The remaining ones are orthogonal to all the blocks by Theorem 11.2.

We wish to confound only interactions between at least 3 factors. We put $u = m - t$ and assume that $m \leq (s^t - 1)/(s - 1)$. There are $(s^t - 1)/(s - 1)$ linear forms in the variables $x_1, \cdots, x_t$ with coefficients in G.F.(s) independent in pairs. From these we choose m and each of these forms will now be identified with a factor. We then consider all points $(x_1, \cdots, x_t)$ where $x_1, \cdots, x_t$ are elements of G.F.(s). Let

(11.24) $$L_i = \sum_{k=1}^{t} \alpha_{ik}x_k \qquad i = 1, \cdots, m$$

be the m linear forms chosen. In substituting the points $(x_1, \cdots, x_t)$ we obtain

(11.25) $$\sum_{k=1}^{t} \alpha_{ik}x_k = y_i.$$

Thus we obtain a set S of s^t points of E.G.(m, s). We shall show that

1.) *S is a subspace of* E.G.(m, s).

2.) *To every pair y_i, y_j $i, j \leq m$ there are exactly s^{t-2} points in S which contain both y_i as* ith *coordinate and y_j as* jth *coordinate.*

Proof of 1. Let $y_1, \cdots, y_m$; $z_1, \cdots, z_m$ be two points in S. Then there are two points $(x_1^{(1)}, \cdots, x_t^{(1)})$ and $(x_1^{(2)}, \cdots, x_t^{(2)})$ in E.G.(t, s) such that

$$\sum_k \alpha_{ik} x_k^{(1)} = \lambda y_i \; ; \; \sum_k \alpha_{ik} x_k^{(2)} = \mu z_i$$

hence

$$\sum_k \alpha_{ik}(x_k^{(1)} + x_k^{(2)}) = \lambda y_i + \mu z_i \, .$$

Thus $\{\lambda y_i + \mu z_i\}$ is a point of S which proves 1.

The number of points in S containing y_i as ith coordinate and y_j as jth coordinate is the number of solutions of the equations

$$L_i = \sum_{k=1}^{t} \alpha_{ik} x_k = y_i \, ,$$

(11.26)

$$L_j = \sum_{k=1}^{t} \alpha_{ik} x_k = y_j \, .$$

Since L_i and L_j are independent there are exactly s^{t-2} solutions. Thus 2 is proved.

The point $(0, 0, \cdots, 0)$ is in S. Let the point $(y_1, \cdots, y_m)$ correspond to the experiment where the ith factor is on the y_ith level, where the elements of G.F.(s) are numbered in some arbitrary way. Let the blocks be constructed as follows. Take S as the initial block. To obtain the second block take any point P not in S and add it to all the points in S. We shall denote the second block by $(S + P)$. If there is a point Q left which is neither in S nor in $(S + P)$ form $(S + Q)$ and continue the process until all points of E.G.(m, s) are exhausted. Since S is a subspace it follows easily that any two sets $(S + P)$, $(S + Q)$ are either identical or have no point in common. Thus the sets obtained by our construction have no point in common.

If the interaction components belonging to $b_1, \cdots, b_m$ are confounded in S then for all points $(y_1, \cdots, y_m)$ in S we must have, since S contains the point $(0, 0, \cdots, 0)$,

$$b_1y_1 + \cdots + b_my_m = 0.$$

Let the element $z_1, \cdots, z_m$ be an element of $(S + P)$ then $b_1(y_1 + z_1) + \cdots + b_m(y_m + z_m) = b_1z_1 + \cdots + b_mz_m =$ const. The confounded interactions form the space orthogonal to S whose dimension is $m - t$. Thus s^{m-t} interactions are confounded. We shall show that only interactions between at least three factors are confounded. Otherwise we should have a b_i and b_j not both equal to 0 such that

$$b_iy_i + b_jy_j = 0 \tag{11.27}$$

for all points in S. But S contains a point with ith coordinate 1 and jth coordinate 0. Hence $b_i = 0$ and similarly $b_j = 0$. Thus only interactions between more than 2 factors are confounded.

As an example we shall arrange the 27 treatment combinations of a three way experiment with every factor at three levels into 3 blocks of 9 each so that only interactions between 3 factors are confounded. We first have to find three independent linear functions of two variables, for instance

$$x,\ y,\ x + y.$$

Next we substitute the points of E.G.(2, 3) into these lines giving us the subset S of E.G.(3, 3) or the initial block of our design

$$S = \{000, 011, 022, 101, 112, 120, 202, 210, 221\}$$

The other two blocks are obtained by adding, mod 3, the points 111 and 222 to S

$$S + 111 = \{111, 122, 100, 212, 220, 201, 010, 021, 002\}$$

$$S + 222 = \{222, 200, 211, 020, 001, 012, 121, 102, 110\}$$

To find the confounded interactions we choose two independent points in S, for instance, 011 and 101, and solve the equation

$$a \cdot 0 + b \cdot 1 + c \cdot 1 = 0$$

$$a \cdot 1 + b \cdot 0 + c \cdot 1 = 0$$

We obtain the solutions $(a, b, c) = (112), (221)$. Thus only the two interaction components corresponding to (112) and the mean are confounded giving 3 orthogonal functions confounded.

Rao gives in his paper a more general method by which it is often possible to confound only interactions between more than d factors where d may be larger than 2.

If all treatment combinations are replicated in several sets of blocks each containing a complete replication, it is also possible to confound some functions in some of the replications and to leave them unconfounded in others. This technique is known as partial confounding. The analysis of partially confounded designs is given by formulae analogous to 11.16, where however, $\bar{L}_\alpha$ is the mean value of L_α over those blocks where T_α is unconfounded and the sum

$$\sum_{i=1}^{r} (L_{\alpha i} - \bar{L}_\alpha)^2$$

extends only over the same blocks.

F. Yates has in his previously mentioned publication given various designs where not all factors are at the same number of levels and some of the main effects and interactions between 2 factors are only partially, but never totally, confounded.

CHAPTER XII

Randomized Designs, Randomized Blocks, and Quasifactorial Designs

THE USE OF ORTHOGONAL LATIN SQUARES and balanced incomplete block designs is only possible if the number of varieties, replications, and the block size fit into one of these designs. In cases where no suitable design of these two types can be found it is necessary to use other designs, some of which will be discussed in this book. This usually entails a loss in efficiency and sometimes also of mathematical precision.

A design which can be accommodated to any number of varieties, any block size, and any number of replications can be obtained by arranging the varieties randomly over a field. The assumption of the underlying linear hypothesis is then given by

$$E(y_{ij}) = v_i + \eta_j + \mu + \epsilon_{ij}\,, \qquad \sum_i v_i = \sum_j \eta_j = 0,$$

where y_{ij} is the yield of the ith variety in the jth block, v_i is the effect of the ith variety, η_j the effect of the jth block, μ the general mean and the ϵ_{ij} are normally and independently distributed variables with mean 0 and the same but unknown variance. Since the varieties are assigned at random to the blocks, the block effect η_j becomes a random variable. However, η_j takes if the blocks are of equal size any of b values, $b_1 \cdots b_b$, with equal probability and therefore we cannot assume that $y'_{ij} = y_{ij} - v_i - \mu$ is normally distributed. Also $\sigma_{(\eta i + \epsilon ij)(\eta l + \epsilon ij)} = \sigma_{\eta i \eta l}$. If the blocks are of equal size each containing k varieties then

$$P(\eta_i = b_e\,, \eta_j = b_m) = \frac{k - \delta_{em}}{b(bk - 1)}, \qquad \delta_{em} = \begin{cases} 1 & \text{if } e = m \\ 0 & \text{if } e \neq m. \end{cases}$$

Hence

$$\sigma_{\eta_i \eta_j} = \sum_{e,m} \left(\frac{k - \delta_{em}}{b(bk - 1)} \right) b_e b_m = \frac{-\sum_e b_e^2}{b(bk - 1)} .$$

Hence the y'_{ij} are not independent. Thus it is not quite correct to treat such a design as a one way classification design, the classes being the varieties, as is usually done. The objections raised against this treatment are not serious if the sample is large, but may affect the size of the critical region for small samples. It must be admitted that one intuitively feels that a minor deviation from the assumptions will not greatly influence the distribution of F. A rigorous study of the deviation of F as computed from such randomized designs from the distribution computed in Chapter I has not been made. The theoretical statistician should not overlook the fact that it is immaterial to the practical research worker whether the size of his critical region is exactly 5% or 1 or even 2% more or less. At any rate he cannot veto the use of slightly inaccurate methods as long as he has not succeeded in replacing them by accurate ones.

A rigorous treatment of the randomized design is possible if we consider not block but plot effects and regard these as chosen at random from a normal population of plot effects. Under these assumptions we may treat the design with complete rigor as a one way classification design. We are then ignoring the fact that neighboring plots have similar plot effects. Thus we are intentionally using a mathematical model which we know to be slightly different from the true situation. In this procedure we do, however, not differ from the physicist who computes the laws of a freely falling body and intentionally disregards air friction. One should also be aware of the fact, that our customary assumption of normality is at best an approximation to the truth.

An improvement over complete randomization is the arrangement of the varieties in randomized blocks. In this arrangement all varieties are replicated in each block and the design is then treated as a two way classification design by blocks and varieties. We then have to assume that the soil fertility within the blocks is uniform. The position within the block is chosen at random for each variety.

In all designs which are based on randomization only, the block effects increase the error very considerably and in most cases a systematic arrangement, if available, is preferable.

In recent years the quasifactorial designs, particularly lattices and lattice squares, have become very popular. In these designs the techniques of partial confounding are utilized. As an example suppose that we have $q_1 q_2$ varieties. These are arranged into a rectangle of q_1 rows and q_2 columns for instance for $q_1 = 3$, $q_2 = 4$.

$$\begin{array}{ccc} V_{11} & \cdots & V_{14} \\ \cdot & & \cdot \\ \cdot & & \cdot \\ \cdot & & \cdot \\ V_{31} & \cdots & V_{34} . \end{array} \tag{12.1}$$

Two sets of blocks are formed. The first set contains q_1 blocks of q_2 varieties each. The varieties in these blocks are those occurring in the 1st, 2nd, $\cdots$, q_1st rows of the rectangle. The second set of blocks contains q_2 blocks with q_1 varieties each and the blocks contain the varieties in the 1st, 2nd, $\cdots$, q_2nd column of the rectangle. Thus from 12.1 one obtains the following blocks:

$$(V_{11}, V_{12}, V_{13}, V_{14}), (V_{21}, V_{22}, V_{23}, V_{24}),$$
$$(V_{31}, V_{32}, V_{33}, V_{34}),$$
$$(V_{11}, V_{21}, V_{31}), (V_{12}, V_{22}, V_{32}),$$
$$(V_{13}, V_{23}, V_{33}), (V_{14}, V_{24}, V_{34}).$$

The whole design may be replicated any number of times. We may formally consider the varietal effects as if they were the result of the action of two factors at q_1 and q_2 levels respectively. Thus if V_{ij} is the effect of the variety v_{ij} we may write

$$\begin{gathered} V_{ij} = v_{ij} + v_{i\cdot} + v_{\cdot j} , \\ \sum_j v_{ij} = \sum_i v_{ij} = \sum_i v_{i\cdot} = \sum_j v_{\cdot j} = 0. \end{gathered} \tag{12.2}$$

We may therefore regard the row set and the column set of blocks as two complete replications of a factorial design. The main effects of the first factor are confounded in the row set, the main effects of the second factor in the column set, the interaction remains unconfounded in both sets. Thus applying Theorem 11.3 with the modification appropriate to partially confounded arrangements discussed at the end of Chapter XI, we see that, because of 5.9, we have to minimize

$$Q = \sum_{l=1}^{2} \sum_{a_1} \sum_{a_2} [(l)A(1, 2; a_1, a_2) - v_{a_1a_2}]^2$$
$$+ q_2 \sum_{a_1} [(2)A(1; a_1) - v_{a_1\cdot}]^2 \qquad (12.3)$$
$$+ q_1 \sum_{a_2} [(1)A(2; a_2) - v_{\cdot a_2}]^2,$$

where the quantities $(l)A(1, 2; a_1, a_2)$, $(l)A(1; a_1)$, $(l)A(2; a_2)$ are computed by formula 5.5 from the lth set of blocks. Thus the least square estimates $\hat{v}_{a_1a_2}$, $\hat{v}_{a_1\cdot}$, $\hat{v}_{\cdot a_2}$ become

$$\hat{v}_{a_1a_2} = \frac{1}{2} \sum_{l=1}^{2} (l)A(1, 2; a_1, a_2), \qquad (12.4)$$
$$\hat{v}_{a_1\cdot} = (2)A(1; a_1), \hat{v}_{\cdot a_2} = (1)A(2; a_2).$$

Hence

$$Q_a = \sum_{l=1}^{2} \sum_{a_1} \sum_{a_2} [(l)A(1, 2; a_1, a_2) \qquad (12.5)$$
$$- \tfrac{1}{2}(1)A(1, 2; a_1, a_2) + (2)A(1, 2; a_1, a_2)]^2$$

and if we test the hypothesis $V_{a_1a_2} = 0$, $a_1 = 1, \cdots, q_1$, $a_2 = 1, \cdots, q_2$,

$$(12.6) \quad Q_r - Q_a = \sum_{a_1} \sum_{a_2} \hat{v}^2_{a_1a_2} + q_2 \sum_{a_1} \hat{v}^2_{a_1\cdot} + q_1 \sum_{a_2} \hat{v}^2_{\cdot a_2} .$$

The idea of a lattice may be generalized. Suppose we wish to test $q_1 \cdots q_r$ varieties. We may then consider the varietal effects as treatment combinations in a factorial experiment. Thus we denote the varietal effects by $V_{a_1 \cdots a_r}$ $1 \leq a_i \leq q_i$ and write

(12.7)
$$V_{a_1, \cdots, a_r} = \sum_{\alpha=1}^{r} \sum_{1 \cdots r} v(i_1, \cdots, i_\alpha; a_{i_1}, \cdots, a_{i_\alpha}),$$
$$\sum_{a_j} v(i_1, \cdots, i_k; a_1, \cdots, a_k) = 0.$$

We then form r sets of blocks. The blocks of the first set are formed by keeping the indices $a_2, \cdots, a_r$ fixed and allowing a_1 to vary from 1 to q_1. Thus $q_2 \cdots q_r$ blocks are obtained. The blocks in the ith set are formed similarly by keeping $a_1, \cdots, a_{i-1}, a_{i+1}, \cdots, a_r$ fixed and allowing a_i to vary from 1 to q_i. In the ith set all interactions which do not contain the ith factor are confounded giving $q_1 \cdots q_{i-1}q_{i+1} \cdots q_r$ interaction components confounded. The remaining interaction components are by Theorem 11.2 orthogonal to the blocks. Thus to obtain Q_a we have to minimize the sum of the unconfounded parts of the right side of 5.9 over all the r sets of blocks. That is to say we have to minimize

(12.8)
$$Q = \sum_{\alpha=1}^{r} \sum_{1, \cdots, r} \frac{q_1 \cdots q_r}{q_{i_1} \cdots q_{i_\alpha}} \sum_{a_{i_1}} \cdots \sum_{a_{i_\alpha}} \sum_{l=1}^{\alpha}$$
$$\cdot [(i_l) A(i_1, \cdots, i_\alpha; a_{i_1}, \cdots, a_{i_\alpha})$$
$$- v(i_1, \cdots, i_\alpha; a_{i_1}, \cdots, a_{i_\alpha})]^2,$$

where $(l)A(i_1, \cdots, i_\alpha; a_{i_1}, \cdots, a_{i_\alpha})$ is obtained by 5.5 from the lth set of blocks. Thus

(12.9)
$$\hat{v}(i_1, \cdots, i_\alpha; a_{i_1}, \cdots, a_{i_\alpha})$$
$$= \frac{1}{\alpha} \sum_{l=1}^{\alpha} (i_l) A(i_1, \cdots, i_\alpha; a_{i_1}, \cdots, a_{i_\alpha}).$$

Hence

$$Q_a = \sum_{\alpha=1}^{r} \sum_{1,\cdots,r} \frac{q_1 \cdots q_r}{q_{i_1} \cdots q_{i_\alpha}} \sum_{a_{i_1}} \cdots \sum_{a_{i_\alpha}}$$

$$(12.10) \qquad \cdot \left[\sum_{l=1}^{\alpha} \{(i_l)A(i_1, \cdots, i_\alpha; a_{i_1}, \cdots, a_{i_\alpha})\}^2 - \alpha\{\hat{v}(i_1, \cdots, i_\alpha; a_{i_1}, \cdots, a_{i_\alpha})\}^2 \right].$$

If the hypothesis $V_{a_1 \cdots a_r} = 0$, $1 \leq a_i \leq q_i$, is tested we obtain

$$(12.11) \qquad Q_r - Q_a = \sum_{\alpha=1}^{r} \sum_{1,\cdots,r} \frac{q_1 \cdots q_r}{q_{i_1} \cdots q_{i_\alpha}} \sum_{a_{i_1}} \cdots \sum_{a_{i_\alpha}} \alpha \cdot [\hat{v}(i_1, \cdots, i_\alpha; a_{i_1}, \cdots, a_{i_\alpha})]^2.$$

The degrees of freedom for Q_a are

$$\sum_{\alpha=1}^{r} \sum_{1,\cdots,r} (\alpha - 1)(q_{i_1} - 1) \cdots (q_{i_\alpha} - 1)$$

because each of the $(q_{i_1} - 1) \cdots (q_{i_\alpha} - 1)$ independent components of the interaction between the factors $i_1, \cdots, i_\alpha$ contributes $(\alpha - 1)$ squares of independent linear functions to Q_a. The degrees of freedom for $Q_r - Q_a$ are $(q_1 \cdots q_r) - 1$.

We proceed to compute the variances of the varietal effects and of differences between them. In doing this we may, without loss of generality, assume that $V_{a_1 \cdots a_r} = 0$, $1 \leq a_i \leq q_i$.

Applying Cochran's Theorem 2.1 to 5.7 we see that

$$\sum_{a_{i_1}} \cdots \sum_{a_{i_\alpha}} \frac{q_1 \cdots q_r}{q_{i_1} \cdots q_{i_\alpha}} (A(i_1, \cdots, i_\alpha; a_{i_1}, \cdots, a_{i_\alpha}))^2$$

has the χ^2 distribution with $(q_{i_1} - 1) \cdots (q_{i_\alpha} - 1)$ degrees of freedom. The quantities $A(i_1, \cdots, i_\alpha; a_{i_1}, \cdots, a_{i_\alpha})$ $1 \leq a_{i_j} \leq q_{i_j}$ are composed from independent observations in exactly the same fashion and hence must have the same variance $\sigma^2_{A(i_1, \cdots, i_\alpha)}$. Hence

$$\frac{q_1 \cdots q_r}{q_{i_1} \cdots q_{i_\alpha}} q_{i_1} \cdots q_{i_\alpha} \sigma^2_{A(i_1, \cdots, i_\alpha)} = (q_{i_1} - 1) \cdots (q_{i_\alpha} - 1)\sigma^2.$$

Thus

$$(12.12) \qquad \sigma^2_{A(i_1, \cdots, i_\alpha)} = \frac{(q_{i_1} - 1) \cdots (q_{i_\alpha} - 1)}{q_1 \cdots q_r} \sigma^2.$$

Let $\hat{V}_{a_1 \cdots a_r}$ be the least square estimate of $V_{a_1 \cdots a_r}$ then

$$(12.13) \qquad \hat{V}_{a_1, \cdots, a_r} = \sum_{\alpha=1}^{r} \sum_{1, \cdots, r} \hat{v}(i_1, \cdots, i_\alpha; a_{i_1}, \cdots, a_{i_\alpha}).$$

But by 12.9 the $\hat{v}(i_1, \cdots, i_\alpha; a_{i_1}, \cdots, a_{i_\alpha})$ are sums of components of the interaction between the factors $i_1, \cdots, i_\alpha$ and hence by Theorem 11.1 orthogonal to each other, moreover by 12.9 and 12.12 $\hat{v}(i_1, \cdots, i_\alpha; a_{i_1}, \cdots, a_{i_\alpha})$ has the variance

$$\frac{1}{\alpha} \frac{(q_{i_1} - 1) \cdots (q_{i_\alpha} - 1)}{q_1 \cdots q_r} \sigma^2.$$

Thus

$$(12.14) \qquad \sigma^2_{\hat{V}a_1, \cdots, a_r} = \sigma^2 \sum_{\alpha=1}^{r} \frac{1}{\alpha} \sum_{1, \cdots, r} \frac{(q_{i_1} - 1) \cdots (q_{i_\alpha} - 1)}{q_1 \cdots q_r}.$$

To obtain the variance of the difference between two factors we first compute the covariance between $A(i_1, \cdots, i_\alpha; a_{i_1}, \cdots, a_{i_\alpha})$ and $A(i_1, \cdots, i_s, i_{s+1}, \cdots, i_\alpha; a_{i_1}, \cdots, a_{i_s}, b_{i_{s+1}}, \cdots, b_{i_\alpha})$ where $a_{i_k} \neq b_{i_k}$. We first compute the coefficient of $x_{c_1 \cdots c_r}$ in $A(i_1, \cdots, i_\alpha; a_{i_1}, \cdots, a_{i_\alpha})$. Suppose that $c_{i_1} = a_{i_1}, \cdots, c_{i_j} = a_{i_j}, c_{i_{j+1}} \neq a_{i_{j+1}}, \cdots, c_{i_\alpha} \neq a_{i_\alpha}$. Then $x_{c_1 \cdots c_r}$ occurs in 5.5 only in terms for which $k_1 \cdots k_\beta$ are chosen from $i_1, \cdots, i_j$. The coefficient of $x_{c_1 \cdots c_r}$ in $x(k_1, \cdots, k_\beta; c_{k_1}, \cdots, c_{k_\beta})$ is $(q_{k_1}, \cdots, q_{k_\beta})/(q_1, \cdots, q_r)$. Hence the coefficient of $x_{c_1 \cdots c_r}$ in $A(i_1, \cdots, i_\alpha; a_{i_1}, \cdots, a_{i_\alpha})$ becomes

$$\sum_{\beta=0}^{j}(-1)^{\alpha-\beta}\sum_{i_1,\cdots,i_j}\frac{q_{k_1}\cdots q_{k\beta}}{q_1\cdots q_r}$$

$$(12.15)\qquad =\frac{(-1)^{\alpha-j}}{q_1\cdots q_r}\sum_{\beta=0}^{j}\sum_{i_1,\cdots,i_j}(-1)^{j-\beta}q_{k_1},\cdots,q_{k\beta}$$

$$=\frac{(-1)^{\alpha-j}}{q_1\cdots q_r}(q_{i_1}-1)\cdots(q_{i_j}-1).$$

From 5.4 we then have

$$(12.16)\qquad x_{c_1,\cdots,c_r}=\sum_{\beta=0}^{r}\sum_{1,\cdots,r}A(k_1,\cdots,k_\beta;c_{k_1},\cdots,c_{k\beta}).$$

We multiply 12.16 by $A(i_1,\cdots,i_\alpha;a_{i_1},\cdots,a_{i\alpha})$ and take expectations on both sides. The left side then becomes

$$\frac{(-1)^{\alpha-j}}{q_1\cdots q_r}(q_{i_1}-1)\cdots(q_{i_j}-1)\sigma^2$$

On the right side we obtain the covariance $\sigma[A(i_1,\cdots,i_\alpha;a_{i_1},\cdots,a_{i\alpha})A(i_1,\cdots,i_\alpha;c_{i_1},\cdots,c_{i\alpha})]$ of $A(i_1,\cdots,i_\alpha;a_{i_1},\cdots,a_{i\alpha})$ and $A(i_1,\cdots,i_\alpha;c_{i_1},\cdots,c_{i\alpha})$ since interactions between different factors are by Theorem 11.1 orthogonal and therefore independent. Thus

$$\sigma[A(i_1,\cdots,i_si_{s+1},\cdots,i_\alpha;a_{i_1},\cdots,a_{i_s}a_{i_{s+1}},\cdots,a_{i\alpha})$$
$$\cdot A(i_1,\cdots,i_si_{s+1},\cdots,i_\alpha;a_{i_1},\cdots,a_{i_s}b_{i_{s+1}},\cdots,b_{i\alpha})]$$

$$(12.17)\qquad =\frac{(-1)^{\alpha-s}}{q_1\cdots q_r}(q_{i_1}-1)\cdots(q_{i_s}-1)\sigma^2\qquad\text{for } b_{i_k}\neq a_{i_k}.$$

We therefore have

$$\sigma^2[A(i_1,\cdots,i_\alpha;a_{i_1},\cdots,a_{i\alpha})-A(i_1,\cdots,i_s,i_{s+1},$$
$$\cdots,i_\alpha;a_{i_1},\cdots,a_{i_s},b_{i_{s+1}},\cdots,b_{i\alpha})]$$

$$(12.18)\qquad =\frac{2}{q_1\cdots q_r}[(q_{i_1}-1)\cdots(q_{i\alpha}-1)+(-1)^{\alpha-s+1}$$
$$\cdot(q_{i_1}-1)\cdots(q_{i_s}-1)]\sigma^2$$

Thus

$$\sigma^2(V_{a_1,\cdots,a_r} - V_{a_1,\cdots,a_s,b_{s+1},\cdots,b_r})$$

$$= \frac{2\sigma^2}{q_1 \cdots q_r} \sum_{\alpha=0}^{s} \sum_{1,\cdots,s} (q_{i_1} - 1) \cdots (q_{i_\alpha} - 1)$$

(12.19)

$$\cdot \sum_{\beta=0}^{r-s} \sum_{s+1,\cdots,r} \frac{1}{\alpha + \beta} [(q_{k_1} - 1) \cdots (q_{k_\beta} - 1) + (-1)^{\beta+1}].$$

In the case of a two dimensional lattice 12.19 reduces to

$$\sigma^2_{V_{ij}-V_{kl}} = \begin{cases} \sigma^2 \dfrac{q_1q_2 + q_1 + q_2}{q_1q_2}, & i \neq k, j \neq l, \\ \\ \sigma^2 \dfrac{q_1q_2 + q_2}{q_1q_2}, & i = k, j \neq l. \end{cases}$$

In a three dimensional lattice

$$\sigma^2_{V_{ijk}-V_{lmn}} =$$

$$\begin{cases} \sigma^2 \dfrac{2q_1q_2q_3 + q_1q_2 + q_2q_3 + q_1q_3 + 2(q_1 + q_2 + q_3)}{3q_1q_2q_3}, \\ \qquad\qquad i \neq l, j \neq m, k \neq n, \\ \\ \sigma^2 \dfrac{2q_1q_2q_3 + q_1q_2 + q_1q_3 + q_2q_3 + 2(q_2 + q_3)}{3q_1q_2q_3}, \\ \qquad\qquad i = l, j \neq m, k \neq n, \\ \\ \sigma^2 \dfrac{2q_1q_2q_3 + q_1q_3 + q_2q_3 + 2q_3}{3q_1q_2q_3}, \\ \qquad\qquad i = l, j = m, k \neq n. \end{cases}$$

The calculation of the efficiency factors with respect to the varietal estimates and differences between them is left to the reader.

If the number of varieties is the square of a power of a

prime, then the experiment may be laid out to advantage in a so called lattice square, which like a Latin square permits us to break the soil fertility into two rectangular components. In a lattice square m^2 varieties are replicated in r square arrays each with m^2 plots in such a way that every pair of varieties occurs together in the same row or the same column the same number λ of times. To construct a lattice square one needs $(m - 1)$ orthogonal squares. The individual boxes of these squares may be denoted by $v_1, \cdots, v_{m^2}$. Together with the row and column number of the Latin square each box corresponds to $(m + 1)$ numbers $i_1, \cdots, i_{m+1}$ $0 \leq i_k \leq m - 1$ and the m^2 vectors $v_\alpha = (i_1^{(\alpha)}, \cdots, i_{m+1}^{(\alpha)})$, $\alpha = 1, \cdots, m^2$ have the property that for every $0 \leq \rho, \tau \leq m - 1$ and each pair t, s there is exactly one vector v_α for which $i_t^{(\alpha)} = \rho$, $i_s^{(\alpha)} = \tau$.

We now form the first square by ordering the varieties into a square according to the first pair of coordinates. That is to say if $v_\alpha = (i_1^{(\alpha)}, i_2^{(\alpha)}, \cdots)$ then v_α is placed into the i_1st row and the i_2nd column. The second square is similarly arranged according to i_3, i_4 and so forth. If m is odd we obtain in this manner $(m + 1)/2$ replications. Since the rows and the columns of the squares are the lines of a finite Euclidean plane whose points are the varieties, it follows that every pair of varieties occurs just once together either in a row or in a column. If m is even we arrange according to the indices (i_1, i_2), (i_3, i_4), $\cdots, (i_{m-1}, i_m)$, (i_{m+1}, i_1), $\cdots, (i_m, i_{m+1})$. Thus every line of the corresponding Euclidean Geometry occurs twice, once as a row and once as a column, and therefore every pair of varieties will appear together twice, once in the same row and once in the same column. We shall exemplify the procedure by constructing a lattice square for 9 and for 4 varieties. We start from 2 orthogonal 3 sided Latin squares

$$\begin{array}{ccc} 1,_{v_1}1 & 2,_{v_2}2 & 3,_{v_3}3 \\ 2,_{v_4}3 & 3,_{v_5}1 & 1,_{v_6}2 \\ 3,_{v_7}2 & 1,_{v_8}3 & 2,_{v_9}1 \,. \end{array}$$

The two squares of the lattice square then are

$$L_1 = \begin{matrix} v_1 & v_2 & v_3 \\ v_4 & v_5 & v_6 \\ v_7 & v_8 & v_9 \end{matrix} \qquad L_2 = \begin{matrix} v_1 & v_6 & v_8 \\ v_9 & v_2 & v_4 \\ v_5 & v_7 & v_3 \end{matrix} .$$

Similarly from

$$\begin{matrix} 1 & v_1 & 2 & v_2 \\ 2 & v_3 & 1 & v_4 . \end{matrix}$$

We obtain 3 squares of a lattice square with 4 varieties

$$L_1 = \begin{matrix} v_1 & v_2 \\ v_3 & v_4 \end{matrix} \qquad L_2 = \begin{matrix} v_1 & v_4 \\ v_2 & v_3 \end{matrix} \qquad L_3 = \begin{matrix} v_1 & v_3 \\ v_4 & v_2 \end{matrix}$$

The assumptions underlying the lattice square are

$$\begin{aligned} &y_{ij}^{(\alpha)} = r_i^{(\alpha)} + c_j^{(\alpha)} + v_{k^{\alpha}{}_{ij}} + \mu^{(\alpha)} + \mu + \epsilon_{ij}^{(\alpha)} , \\ (12.20) \qquad &\sum_i r_i^{(\alpha)} = \sum_j c_j^{(\alpha)} = \sum_\alpha \mu^{(\alpha)} = \sum_k v_k = 0, \end{aligned}$$

where

$y_{ij}^{(\alpha)}$ is the observed yield in the ith row and jth column of the αth replication.
$r_i^{(\alpha)}$ is the effect of the ith row in the αth replication.
$c_j^{(\alpha)}$ is the effect of the jth column in the αth replication.
$v_{k^{\alpha}{}_{ij}}$ is the effect of the variety in the ith row and jth column of the αth replication.
$\mu^{(\alpha)}$ is the effect of the αth replication.
μ is the general mean.

The $\epsilon_{ij}^{(\alpha)}$ are normally and independently distributed random variables with mean 0 and the same but unknown variance σ^2.

The equations resulting from minimizing

$$Q = \sum_\alpha \sum_i \sum_j (y_{ij}^{(\alpha)} - r_i^{(\alpha)} - c_j^{(\alpha)} - v_{k^{\alpha}{}_{ij}} - \mu^{\alpha} - \mu)^2$$

become, if the Lagrange operator is ignored,

$$\hat{\mu} = \frac{1}{rm^2} \sum_{\alpha} \sum_{i} \sum_{j} y_{ij}^{(\alpha)} = y,$$

$$\hat{\mu}^{(\alpha)} = \frac{1}{m^2} \sum_{i} \sum_{j} y_{ij}^{(\alpha)} - y = y^{(\alpha)} - y,$$

$$\text{(12.21)} \quad \sum_{vk} y_{ij}^{(\alpha)} = \sum_{vk} \hat{r}_i^{(\alpha)} + \sum_{vk} c_j^{(\alpha)} + r\hat{v}_k + r\hat{\mu},$$

$$my_{i\cdot}^{(\alpha)} = m\hat{r}_i^{(\alpha)} + \sum_{r_i(\alpha)} \hat{v}_j + m\hat{\mu}^{(\alpha)} + m\hat{\mu},$$

$$my_{ij}^{(\alpha)} = m\hat{c}_j^{(\alpha)} + \sum_{c_j(\alpha)} \hat{v}_i + m\hat{\mu}^{(\alpha)} + m\hat{\mu},$$

where $\sum_{vk}$ denotes summation over all plots containing the kth variety, $\sum_{r_i(\alpha)}$ ($\sum_{c_j(\alpha)}$) denotes summation over all plots contained in the ith row, (or column), of the αth replication.

Summing the fourth and fifth equations over all rows and columns respectively which contain the kth variety we obtain

$$\text{(12.22)} \quad \begin{aligned} &m\Big[\sum_{vk} (y_{i\cdot}^{(\alpha)} - y) + \sum_{vk} (y_{\cdot j}^{(\alpha)} - y)\Big] \\ &\qquad = m \sum_{vk} \hat{r}_i^{(\alpha)} + m \sum_{vk} \hat{c}_j^{(\alpha)} + (2r - \lambda)v_k \,. \end{aligned}$$

Dividing 12.22 by m and subtracting from 12.21 yields on account of $r = (m + 1)/2\,\lambda$

$$\text{(12.23)} \quad \hat{v}_k = \frac{2}{\lambda(m - 1)} \sum_{vk} (y_{ij}^{(\alpha)} - y_{i\cdot}^{(\alpha)} - y_{\cdot j}^{(\alpha)} + y).$$

Hence

$$\text{(12.24)} \quad \begin{cases} \hat{r}_i^{(\alpha)} = y_{i\cdot}^{(\alpha)} - y^{(\alpha)} - \dfrac{1}{m} \displaystyle\sum_{r_i(\alpha)} \hat{v}_j \,, \\[2ex] \hat{c}_j^{(\alpha)} = y_{\cdot j}^{(\alpha)} - y^{(\alpha)} - \dfrac{1}{m} \displaystyle\sum_{c_j(\alpha)} \hat{v}_i \,. \end{cases}$$

If $\hat{r}_i^{*(\alpha)}$, $\hat{c}_j^{*(\alpha)}$ are the least square estimates of $r_i^{(\alpha)}$, $c_j^{(\alpha)}$ under the hypothesis $v_j = 0$, $j = (1, \cdots, m^2)$ then

$$\hat{r}_i^{*(\alpha)} = y_{i\cdot}^{(\alpha)} - y^{(\alpha)},$$

(12.25)

$$\hat{c}_j^{*(\alpha)} = y_{\cdot j}^{(\alpha)} - y^{(\alpha)}.$$

It is easily verified that these solutions satisfy the restrictions in 12.20. Hence by Theorem 4.2

(12.26)

$$\begin{aligned} Q_a = &\sum_\alpha \sum_i \sum_j (y_{ij}^{(\alpha)})^2 \\ &- m \sum_\alpha [\sum_i (y_{i\cdot}^{(\alpha)})^2 + \sum_j (y_{\cdot j}^{(\alpha)})^2] \\ &- \sum_\alpha \sum_i \sum_j \left[\hat{v}_{k\alpha_{ij}} - \frac{1}{m} \sum_{\substack{(\alpha)\\ ri}} \hat{v}_s - \frac{1}{m} \sum_{\substack{(\alpha)\\ cj}} \hat{v}_t\right]^2 \\ &+ m^2 \sum_\alpha (y^{(\alpha)})^2, \end{aligned}$$

$$\begin{aligned} Q_r - Q_a = &\sum_\alpha \sum_i \sum_j \left(\hat{v}_{k\alpha_{ij}} - \frac{1}{m} \sum_{\substack{(\alpha)\\ ri}} \hat{v}_s \right. \\ &\left. - \frac{1}{m} \sum_{\substack{(\alpha)\\ cj}} \hat{v}_t\right)^2. \end{aligned}$$

We shall now compute the variance of $\hat{v}_k$. We shall simply compute the coefficients of the observations entering into $\hat{v}_k$. There are r observations on the kth variety which enter into $\hat{v}_k$ with the coefficient $[2(m - 1)]/(\lambda m^2)$. Further $2r(m - 1)$ varieties different from v_k each of which occurs either in a row or in a column together with v_k which enter into $\hat{v}_k$ with the coefficient $- 2/(\lambda m^2)$ and $r(m - 1)^2$ observations not together with the kth variety in a row or column and therefore entering with the coefficient $2/[\lambda m^2(m - 1)]$. Thus

$$\frac{\sigma_{\hat{v}_k}^2}{\sigma^2} = \frac{4r(m-1)^2}{\lambda^2 m^4} + \frac{2r(m-1)\cdot 4}{\lambda^2 m^4} + \frac{4r}{\lambda^2 m^4}$$

$$= \frac{4rm^2}{\lambda^2 m^4} = \frac{4r}{\lambda^2 m^2} = \frac{2(m+1)}{\lambda m^2}.$$

Since every pair of varieties occurs exactly λ times $Q_r - Q_a$ must be symmetric in the $\hat{v}_k$. Therefore applying Theorem 4.5, 12.26 simplifies to

$$Q_a = \sum_\alpha \sum_i \sum_j (y_{ij}^{(\alpha)})^2 - m \sum_\alpha [\sum_i (y_{i\cdot}^{(\alpha)})^2$$

$$+ \sum_j (y_{\cdot j}^{(\alpha)})^2] - (r - \lambda) \sum_k \hat{v}_k^2 + m^2 \sum_\alpha (y^{(\alpha)})^2 \tag{12.27}$$

$$Q_r - Q_a = (r - \lambda) \sum_k \hat{v}_k^2 .$$

The degrees of freedom of Q_a are $m^2 r - (m^2 - 1) - 2r(m - 1) - (r - 1) - 1$ and of $Q_r - Q_a$, $m^2 - 1$.

The variance of $\hat{v}_i - \hat{v}_j$ can also be obtained by simple enumeration of the observations entering into $\hat{v}_i - \hat{v}_j$ and turns out to be

$$\frac{\sigma^2_{(\hat{v}_i - \hat{v}_j)}}{\sigma^2} = \frac{2}{r - \lambda} .$$

The details of this enumeration are left to the reader.

The efficiency factors with respect to $\hat{v}_i$ and with respect to $\hat{v}_i - \hat{v}_j$ both turn out to be $(m - 1)/(m + 1)$.

Several more complicated designs are in use which all evaluate the idea of treating the varietal effects as treatment combinations of several factors. It is for instance always possible to superimpose a Latin square on a square lattice and then to introduce a third set of blocks by grouping the varieties according to the letters of a Latin square. Such arrangements are called triple lattices. Similarly with a set of r orthogonal squares it is possible to obtain an $(r + 2)$ fold lattice. If $r = (p - 1)$ where p is the length of the side then the resulting design is termed a balanced lattice. The designs discussed in this chapter were invented by F. Yates and proposed by him in several important publications. (Journal of Agr. Science 26, pp. 424-455, Ann. Eugenics, pp. 319-332, Journal of Agricultural Science 30, pp. 672-728.)

CHAPTER XIII

Analysis of Covariance

We shall consider in this chapter the following linear hypothesis. Suppose we have N observations $y_1, y_2, \cdots, y_N$ and constants $x_{1\alpha}, \cdots, x_{p\alpha}(\alpha = 1, \cdots, N)$. We assume

$$(13.1)\quad \begin{aligned} &E(y_\alpha) = \mu_\alpha + \beta_1 x_{1\alpha} + \cdots + \beta_p x_{p\alpha} \quad \alpha = 1, \cdots, N, \\ &\sum_\gamma \lambda_{i\gamma}\mu_\gamma = 0 \quad i = 1, \cdots, s \leq N \quad \text{rank } (\lambda_{i\gamma}) = s > p. \end{aligned}$$

The hypotheses to be tested may concern either the μ_α or the β_i. Accordingly we shall consider two kinds of hypotheses

$$(13.2)\quad \begin{aligned} &H_1 : \quad \sum_\gamma \lambda_{i\gamma}\mu_\gamma = 0, \quad i = s + 1, \cdots, r \leq N, \\ &\qquad\qquad \text{rank } (\lambda_{i\gamma}) = r, \\ &H_2 : \quad \sum_i v_{ij}\beta_i = 0, \quad i = 1, \cdots, p. \end{aligned}$$

Both hypotheses are linear hypotheses and Theorem 4.1 applies. The degrees of freedom for Q_a are obtained as follows: The expectations $E(y_\alpha)$, $\alpha = 1, \cdots, N$, are first expressed by the $N + p$ parameters μ_α, $\alpha = 1, \cdots, N$; β_i, $i = 1, \cdots, p$. The linear restrictions in 13.1 enable us to eliminate s of the μ_α. If we arrange it so that $\mu_1, \cdots, \mu_s$ are eliminated this will lead to

$$(13.3)\quad E(y_\alpha) = \sum_{j=s+1}^{N} a_{j\alpha}\mu_j + \beta_1 x_{1\alpha} + \cdots + \beta_p x_{p\alpha} .$$

If the matrix

$$(13.4)\quad \begin{pmatrix} a_{(s+1)1} & \cdots & a_{N1} & x_{11} & \cdots & x_{p1} \\ \cdot & & \cdot & \cdot & & \cdot \\ \cdot & & \cdot & \cdot & & \cdot \\ \cdot & & \cdot & \cdot & & \cdot \\ a_{(s+1)N} & \cdots & a_{NN} & x_{1N} & \cdots & x_{pN} \end{pmatrix}.$$

has the rank $N + p - s$ then we have expressed the N expectations $E(y_\alpha)$ by $N + p - s$ parameters and this is equivalent to $s - p$ linear restrictions on $E(y_\alpha)$. Thus Q_a will have $s - p$ degrees of freedom if the matrix 13.4 has the rank $N + p - s$. The degrees of freedom for $Q_r - Q_a$ are obtained by a straight forward application of Theorem 4.1.

The analysis of covariance is frequently applied to r way classification designs. Thus we might have taken observations on the weight gains of animals from r different races at k different diets and might have recorded the initial weight of each animal. Assuming that the interaction is 0 and that weight gains of animals depend linearly on the initial weight we can write our assumptions as

$$E(y_{ij}) = \mu_{i\cdot} + \mu_{\cdot j} + \mu + \beta x_{ij} \qquad i = 1, \cdots, r; j = 1, \cdots, k,$$

where y_{ij} is the weight gain of the animal from the ith race receiving the jth diet and x_{ij} is the initial weight of this animal. The hypotheses to be tested may be

$$H_1 : \ \mu_{i\cdot} = 0, i = 1, \cdots, r,; \ H_2 : \ \mu_{\cdot j} = 0, j = 1, \cdots, k;$$

$$H_3 : \ \beta = 0.$$

The tests for these hypotheses are obtained by a straight forward application of Theorem 4.1.

CHAPTER XIV

Interblock Estimates and Interblock Variance

THE BLOCK WHICH WILL CONTAIN a certain set of treatment combinations or varieties is actually always chosen at random so that the block effect may also be regarded as a random variable. This point of view makes it possible to obtain unbiased and consistent estimates also of confounded interactions in a factorial experiment. Thus from formula 11.13 we see that if L_α presents the linear form $\sum_\beta t_{\alpha\beta} x_\beta$ corresponding to the linear form $S_\alpha = \sum_\beta t_{\alpha\beta} T_\beta$ in the treatment combinations T_β then

$$(14.1) \qquad L_\alpha = S_\alpha + \sum_\beta t_{\alpha\beta} b_{i_\beta} + \sum_\beta t_{\alpha\beta} \epsilon_\beta ,$$

where the ϵ_β are normally and independently distributed with mean 0 and variance σ^2. If the block effects are considered as normally distributed random variables independent of each other and of the random error ϵ_α with variance σ'^2 and mean γ, then L_α is an unbiased estimate of S_α if S_α is not the mean and thus comparisons between confounded linear functions are still possible. The variance of a confounded form L_α becomes by 11.14 $u^2\sigma'^2 \sum_i c_{\alpha i}^2 + \sigma^2 \sum_\beta t_{\alpha\beta}^2$. Now $u \sum_i c_{\alpha i}^2 = 1$, $\sum_\beta t_{\alpha\beta}^2 = 1$ because of the orthogonality of the substitution. Hence

$$(14.2) \qquad \sigma_{L_\alpha}^2 = u\sigma'^2 + \sigma^2.$$

If L_β is another confounded linear form then $\sigma_{L_\alpha L_\beta} = u^2\sigma'^2 \sum_i c_{\alpha i} c_{\beta i} + \sigma^2 \sum_\gamma t_{\alpha\gamma} t_{\beta\gamma} = 0$ because of the orthogonality of the matrix $(t_{\alpha\beta})$ and the assumption of independence of the block effects. Similarly $\sigma_{L_\alpha L_\beta} = 0$ if L_α is confounded and L_β unconfounded. Thus comparisons involving confounded linear functions become possible. The estimates of L_α obtained in this way are called interblock estimates and the comparisons between interblock estimates are termed interblock comparisons. The variance $u\sigma'^2 + \sigma^2$ can be estimated if several complete replications are available. The confounded forms are then treated as a separate set of observations all with the same variance and with means S_α. As long as no partial confounding takes place confounded linear forms may be compared with each other applying the F test, with Q_a being obtained from the sum of the squares of deviations of these forms from their mean values. The degrees of freedom of Q_a are $(r - 1)f$ where r is the number of replications and f the number of linear forms confounded. For comparisons of confounded with unconfounded forms no exact test is available at present.

If the linear form S_α in the treatment combinations is confounded in some replications and orthogonal to the blocks in other replications, we shall obtain two independent estimates of S_α : intrablock estimates from those replications where S_α is orthogonal to the blocks and interblock estimates from replications in which S_α is confounded with all the blocks. If we would know the interblock and the intrablock variance then these two estimates could be combined so as to yield minimum variance. Let L_α and L'_α be the intrablock and the interblock estimate respectively of S_α and let σ_α^2 and $\sigma_\alpha'^2$ be the variances of L_α and L'_α respectively. L_α and L'_α are independent being derived from different observations and both are also independent of Q_a as may be seen from Theorem 11.3. An easy calculation shows that

$$L_\alpha^* = \frac{\sigma_\alpha'^2 L_\alpha + \sigma_\alpha^2 L'_\alpha}{\sigma_\alpha'^2 + \sigma_\alpha^2}$$

has the smallest variance among all linear combinations of the form $(aL_\alpha + bL'_\alpha)/(a + b)$. Moreover L_α^* is normally distributed with variance $(\sigma_\alpha'^2 \sigma_\alpha^2)/(\sigma_\alpha'^2 + \sigma_\alpha^2)$ so that

$$F = \frac{f}{1} \frac{\sigma_\alpha'^2 + \sigma_\alpha^2}{\sigma_\alpha'^2 \sigma_\alpha^2} \frac{L_\alpha^{*2}}{Q_a/\sigma^2}. \tag{14.3}$$

has the F distribution with 1 and f degrees of freedom where f is the number of degrees of freedom for Q_a as given by Theorem 11.3 and σ_α^2 is some known multiple of σ^2. However σ^2 and

σ'^2 are not accurately known. As an estimate of σ^2 we may use Q_a/f and an estimate of $u\sigma'^2 + \sigma^2$ may be obtained from those linear forms which are confounded in more than one replication and also by comparing the observations on the same linear form in replications where it is confounded with those in replications where it is unconfounded. However, if we replace σ^2 and σ'^2 by these estimates then F as given by 14.3 does not have the F distribution. If the estimates σ^2 and σ'^2 are both based on a large number of degrees of freedom then F in 14.3 will at least be approximately distributed as F since σ^2 and σ'^2 converge stochastically to their true values. Thus although we might gain somewhat in efficiency by utilizing the interblock estimates we do so at the expense of mathematical rigor. It may also be remembered that a decrease in variance is not necessarily equivalent to an increase in power. Formula 14.2 shows moreover that the variance of the interblock estimates is large compared to the variance of the intrablock estimates, whenever there is any appreciable variation from block to block. Thus a sizeable advantage is derived from the use of the interblock estimates only if the blocks are nearly uniform in fertility.

In quasifactorial designs the procedure described in the preceding paragraph applies without change. In other designs for varietal trials, for instance incomplete balanced blocks, the application is not immediate. We note however that the sums of the yields of whole blocks involve differences in the varietal content of the blocks. Thus estimates of the varietal effects may be obtained by considering the regression of the block totals on the varietal effects. The estimates of the varietal effects obtained in this manner will be linear functions of the block totals. We shall show that the block totals are independent of the intrablock estimates and independent of Q_a. We refer to the assumptions 7.8 of a general arrangement of varieties in blocks where however no variety occurs more than once in any block. The estimate $\hat{v}_i$ is consistent by 4.49. Hence if $\hat{v}_i = \sum \lambda_\alpha x_\alpha$ where $x_1, \cdots, x_N$ are the observations then $E(\hat{v}_i) = v_i + \sum \lambda_\alpha b_{i\alpha} + \mu \sum \lambda_\alpha$, where x_α lies in the ith block. Since $\hat{v}_i$ is an unbiased estimate of v_i we must have $\sum_{x_\alpha \subset b_i} \lambda_\alpha = \sum_{x_\alpha \subset b_j} \lambda_\alpha$ for all i and j and $\sum_\alpha \lambda_\alpha = 0$. Hence $\sum_{x_\alpha \subset b_i} \lambda_\alpha = 0$ which means that $\hat{v}_i$ is orthogonal to, and therefore independent of the block sums.

If in the set up 7.8 we test the hypothesis $v_i = 0$ then the estimates of the block effects will be given by the block averages. Applying Theorem 4.2 and 4.1 we then see that the block sums are also independent of Q_a obtained by minimizing 7.9. Since the interblock estimates are linear functions of the block sums it follows that they are independent of the intrablock estimates and of Q_a computed from the intrablock estimates. Interblock and intrablock estimates may be combined as in factorial experiments so as to give minimum variance. For this process it is necessary to estimate the interblock variance. To obtain such an estimate it will be convenient to write the assumptions 7.8 in the form

$$(14.4) \qquad E(y_{ij}) = v_i + b_j \qquad \sum_i v_i = 0.$$

We shall also assume that no variety occurs twice in the same block.

If we test the hypothesis $b_j = \mu; j = 1, \cdots, b$ then the regression value of y_{ij} becomes V_i/r_i and hence by Theorem 4.2

$$(14.5) \quad Q_r - Q_a = \sum y_{ij}^2 - \sum (y_{ij} - \hat{v}_i - \hat{b}_j)^2 - \sum \frac{V_i^2}{r_i}.$$

Since 14.5 is the proper statistic for testing the hypothesis $b_j = \mu$ it must have $(b - 1)$ degrees of freedom where b is the number of blocks. Moreover it can not depend on the v_i. Thus

$$Q_r - Q_a = \sum_i \sum_j a_{ij} b_i b_j + \sum_i a_i b_i + W.$$

Where W is independent of the b_j and v_i. The a_{ij} are, moreover, constants and the a_i independent of b_j.

If the b_i are all equal to μ then $\sum_i \sum_j a_{ij} b_i b_j + \sum_i a_i b_i = \mu^2 \sum_i \sum_j a_{ij} + \mu \sum_i a_i$ must be independent of μ and therefore $\sum_i \sum_j a_{ij} = \sum_i a_i = 0$ and $E(W) = (b - 1)\sigma^2$. Then if the b_j are considered as random variables with the expectation μ

$$E(\sum_i \sum_j a_{ij} b_i b_j + \sum_i a_i b_i)$$

$$= \sigma'^2 \sum_i a_{ii} + \mu^2 \sum_i \sum_j a_{ij} + \mu \sum_i a_i$$

$$= \sigma'^2 \sum_i a_{ii} .$$

Thus the expectation of $Q_r - Q_a$ when the b_j are considered as independent random variables must be of the form $a\sigma'^2 + (b - 1)\sigma^2$. To find a we have to find the sum of the coefficients of the b_j^2 appearing in 14.5.

The middle term in 14.5 is an estimate of a multiple of σ^2 and therefore independent of b_j . In the first term b_j^2 occurs with the coefficient k_j , in the last term with the coefficient $\sum^{(i)} 1/r_i$ where $\sum^{(i)} f(i)$ denotes the summation of $f(i)$ over all i such that the ith variety occurs in the jth block. Hence

$$\begin{aligned} E(Q_r - Q_a) &= \left(N - \sum_j \sum^{(i)} \frac{1}{r_i}\right)\sigma'^2 + (b - 1)\sigma^2 \\ &= (N - v)\sigma'^2 + (b - 1)\sigma^2, \end{aligned} \tag{14.6}$$

where N is the number of experiments and v the number of varieties. Since Q_a has $N - v - b + 1$ degrees of freedom

$$Q_r - Q_a - \frac{b - 1}{N - v - b + 1} Q_a = Q_r - \frac{N - v}{N - v - b + 1} Q_a$$

may be used as an estimate of $(N - v)\sigma'^2$.

We shall apply these results to incomplete balanced block designs. The interblock variance σ_B^2 of the block totals becomes

$$\sigma_B^2 = k^2\sigma'^2 + k\sigma^2.$$

To estimate σ_B^2 we use

$$M = \sum y_{ij}^2 - \sum (y_{ij} - \hat{v}_i - \hat{b}_j + \hat{\mu})^2 - \frac{1}{r} \sum V_i^2 ,$$

where $\hat{v}_i$, $\hat{b}_j$, $\hat{\mu}$ are given by 7.19. From 14.6 we have

$$E(M) = v(r-1)\sigma'^2 + (b-1)\sigma^2. \tag{14.7}$$

Thus putting

$$\frac{Q_a}{bk - v - b + 1} = S^2$$

$$E\left(\frac{kM - (v-k)S^2}{v(r-1)}\right) = k\sigma'^2 + \sigma^2 = \frac{\sigma_B^2}{k}. \tag{14.8}$$

Thus $k\ [kM - (v-k)s^2]/[v(r-1)]$ may be used as an estimate of σ_B^2. The intrablock estimate of v_i is $\hat{v}_i = (kV_i - T_i)/(\lambda v)$. The interblock estimate is found by minimizing

$$Q' = \sum_j (B_j - \sum^{(j)} v_i - k\mu)^2 \tag{14.9}$$

under the restriction $\sum_i v_i = 0$. Differentiation with respect to v_i and μ yields

$$\begin{aligned} kr\hat{\mu}' + (r-\lambda)\hat{v}'_i &= T_i + \tau, \qquad i = 1, \cdots, v, \\ \hat{\mu}' &= \frac{\sum y_{ij}}{bk} = y = \hat{\mu}. \end{aligned} \tag{14.10}$$

where τ is the Lagrange operator and $\hat{v}'_i$, $\hat{\mu}'$ the interblock estimates of v_i, μ. Adding the first of the equations 14.10 over the varieties yields $\tau = 0$ and hence

$$\hat{v}'_i = \frac{T_i - kr\hat{\mu}}{r - \lambda}. \tag{14.11}$$

We shall usually want maximum precision with respect to the estimates of varietal differences. Now

$$\begin{aligned} \sigma^2_{\hat{v}_i - \hat{v}_j} &= \frac{2k}{\lambda v}\sigma^2, \\ \sigma^2_{\hat{v}'_i - \hat{v}'_j} &= \frac{2\sigma_B^2}{(r-\lambda)^2}(r-\lambda) = \frac{2}{(r-\lambda)}\sigma_B^2. \end{aligned} \tag{14.12}$$

Thus maximum precision for the varietal differences is obtained if we use as their estimates the differences of the quantities

$$
\begin{aligned}
v_i^* &= \frac{\sigma_B^2/(r-\lambda)\hat{v}_i + (k\sigma^2)/(\lambda v)\hat{v}'_i}{\sigma_B^2/(r-\lambda) + (k\sigma^2)/(\lambda v)} \\
&= \frac{\lambda v \sigma_B^2 \hat{v}_i + k(r-\lambda)\sigma^2 \hat{v}'_i}{\lambda v \sigma_B^2 + k(r-\lambda)\sigma^2} .
\end{aligned} \tag{14.13}
$$

The variance of the difference $v_i^* - v_j^*$ is given by

$$\sigma^2_{v^*_i - v^*_j} = \frac{2k\sigma^2\sigma_B^2}{\sigma^2 k(r-\lambda) + \lambda v \sigma_B^2} .$$

Thus

$$F = \frac{bk - v - b + 1}{1} \frac{\sigma^2 k(r-\lambda) + \lambda v \sigma_B^2}{2k\sigma_B^2} \frac{(v_i^* - v_j^*)^2}{Q_a}$$

has the F distribution with 1 and $bk - v - b + 1$ degrees of freedom respectively. Actually however σ^2 and σ_B^2 are not accurately known and must be replaced by $Q_a/(bk - v - b + 1)$ and

$$k \frac{kM - (v-k)S^2}{v(r-1)} = S_B^2 .$$

This will not lead to a very serious inaccuracy if the number of blocks is sufficiently large. However an advantage is only gained if the soil fertility differences between the blocks is actually very small. Sometimes it may happen that the estimate for σ_B^2 becomes smaller than S^2. In this case it is recommended to replace it by S^2 in formula 14.13 since $\sigma_B^2 \geq \sigma^2$ under all circumstances and since S^2 is a better estimate of σ^2 than S_B^2 even if there are no block differences.

The procedure for utilizing interblock estimates in the analysis of incomplete balanced block designs which we derived above is arranged for easy calculation in the 1943 edition of the statistical Tables of Fisher and Yates.

Index

Tables

TABLES OF THE 5% AND 1% POINTS FOR THE DISTRIBUTION OF F
From Snedecor, George W., *Statistical Methods Applied to Experiments in Agriculture and Biology.* The Iowa State College Press, Ames, Iowa. 4th. Ed., 1946.

Permission to include these tables has been obtained.

TABLE OF $E^2_{0.01}$ AND THE CORRESPONDING VALUES OF P_{II} and TABLE OF $E^2_{0.05}$ AND THE CORRESPONDING VALUES OF P_{II} . From Tang, P. C., "The Power Function of the Analysis of Variance Tests with Tables and Illustrations of Their Use." *Statistical Research Memoirs,* Department of Statistics, University of London, Vol. II, pp. 126-57.

Permission to include these tables has been obtained.

TABLE 10.7—5% (Roman Type) and 1% (Bold

n_2	1	2	3	4	5	6	7	8	9	10	11	12
	n_1 degrees of freedom for numerator											
1	161	200	216	225	230	234	237	239	241	242	243	244
	4,052	**4,999**	**5,403**	**5,625**	**5,764**	**5,859**	**5,928**	**5,981**	**6,022**	**6,056**	**6,082**	**6,106**
2	18.51	19.00	19.16	19.25	19.30	19.33	19.36	19.37	19.38	19.39	19.40	19.41
	98.49	**99.00**	**99.17**	**99.25**	**99.30**	**99.33**	**99.34**	**99.36**	**99.38**	**99.40**	**99.41**	**99.42**
3	10.13	9.55	9.28	9.12	9.01	8.94	8.88	8.84	8.81	8.78	8.76	8.74
	34.12	**30.82**	**29.46**	**28.71**	**28.24**	**27.91**	**27.67**	**27.49**	**27.34**	**27.23**	**27.13**	**27.05**
4	7.71	6.94	6.59	6.39	6.26	6.16	6.09	6.04	6.00	5.96	5.93	5.91
	21.20	**18.00**	**16.69**	**15.98**	**15.52**	**15.21**	**14.98**	**14.80**	**14.66**	**14.54**	**14.45**	**14.37**
5	6.61	5.79	5.41	5.19	5.05	4.95	4.88	4.82	4.78	4.74	4.70	4.68
	16.26	**13.27**	**12.06**	**11.39**	**10.97**	**10.67**	**10.45**	**10.27**	**10.15**	**10.05**	**9.96**	**9.89**
6	5.99	5.14	4.76	4.53	4.39	4.28	4.21	4.15	4.10	4.06	4.03	4.00
	13.74	**10.92**	**9.78**	**9.15**	**8.75**	**8.47**	**8.26**	**8.10**	**7.98**	**7.87**	**7.79**	**7.72**
7	5.59	4.74	4.35	4.12	3.97	3.87	3.79	3.73	3.68	3.63	3.60	3.57
	12.25	**9.55**	**8.45**	**7.85**	**7.46**	**7.19**	**7.00**	**6.84**	**6.71**	**6.62**	**6.54**	**6.47**
8	5.32	4.46	4.07	3.84	3.69	3.58	3.50	3.44	3.39	3.34	3.31	3.28
	11.26	**8.65**	**7.59**	**7.01**	**6.63**	**6.37**	**6.19**	**6.03**	**5.91**	**5.82**	**5.74**	**5.67**
9	5.12	4.26	3.86	3.63	3.48	3.37	3.29	3.23	3.18	3.13	3.10	3.07
	10.56	**8.02**	**6.99**	**6.42**	**6.06**	**5.80**	**5.62**	**5.47**	**5.35**	**5.26**	**5.18**	**5.11**
10	4.96	4.10	3.71	3.48	3.33	3.22	3.14	3.07	3.02	2.97	2.94	2.91
	10.04	**7.56**	**6.55**	**5.99**	**5.64**	**5.39**	**5.21**	**5.06**	**4.95**	**4.85**	**4.78**	**4.71**
11	4.84	3.98	3.59	3.36	3.20	3.09	3.01	2.95	2.90	2.86	2.82	2.79
	9.65	**7.20**	**6.22**	**5.67**	**5.32**	**5.07**	**4.88**	**4.74**	**4.63**	**4.54**	**4.46**	**4.40**
12	4.75	3.88	3.49	3.26	3.11	3.00	2.92	2.85	2.80	2.76	2.72	2.69
	9.33	**6.93**	**5.95**	**5.41**	**5.06**	**4.82**	**4.65**	**4.50**	**4.39**	**4.30**	**4.22**	**4.16**
13	4.67	3.80	3.41	3.18	3.02	2.92	2.84	2.77	2.72	2.67	2.63	2.60
	9.07	**6.70**	**5.74**	**5.20**	**4.86**	**4.62**	**4.44**	**4.30**	**4.19**	**4.10**	**4.02**	**3.96**
14	4.60	3.74	3.34	3.11	2.96	2.85	2.77	2.70	2.65	2.60	2.56	2.53
	8.86	**6.51**	**5.56**	**5.03**	**4.69**	**4.46**	**4.28**	**4.14**	**4.03**	**3.94**	**3.86**	**3.80**
15	4.54	3.68	3.29	3.06	2.90	2.79	2.70	2.64	2.59	2.55	2.51	2.48
	8.68	**6.36**	**5.42**	**4.89**	**4.56**	**4.32**	**4.14**	**4.00**	**3.89**	**3.80**	**3.73**	**3.67**
16	4.49	3.63	3.24	3.01	2.85	2.74	2.66	2.59	2.54	2.49	2.45	2.42
	8.53	**6.23**	**5.29**	**4.77**	**4.44**	**4.20**	**4.03**	**3.89**	**3.78**	**3.69**	**3.61**	**3.55**
17	4.45	3.59	3.20	2.96	2.81	2.70	2.62	2.55	2.50	2.45	2.41	2.38
	8.40	**6.11**	**5.18**	**4.67**	**4.34**	**4.10**	**3.93**	**3.79**	**3.68**	**3.59**	**3.52**	**3.45**
18	4.41	3.55	3.16	2.93	2.77	2.66	2.58	2.51	2.46	2.41	2.37	2.34
	8.28	**6.01**	**5.09**	**4.58**	**4.25**	**4.01**	**3.85**	**3.71**	**3.60**	**3.51**	**3.44**	**3.37**
19	4.38	3.52	3.13	2.90	2.74	2.63	2.55	2.48	2.43	2.38	2.34	2.31
	8.18	**5.93**	**5.01**	**4.50**	**4.17**	**3.94**	**3.77**	**3.63**	**3.52**	**3.43**	**3.36**	**3.30**
20	4.35	3.49	3.10	2.87	2.71	2.60	2.52	2.45	2.40	2.35	2.31	2.28
	8.10	**5.85**	**4.94**	**4.43**	**4.10**	**3.87**	**3.71**	**3.56**	**3.45**	**3.37**	**3.30**	**3.23**
21	4.32	3.47	3.07	2.84	2.68	2.57	2.49	2.42	2.37	2.32	2.28	2.25
	8.02	**5.78**	**4.87**	**4.37**	**4.04**	**3.81**	**3.65**	**3.51**	**3.40**	**3.31**	**3.24**	**3.17**
22	4.30	3.44	3.05	2.82	2.66	2.55	2.47	2.40	2.35	2.30	2.26	2.23
	7.94	**5.72**	**4.82**	**4.31**	**3.99**	**3.76**	**3.59**	**3.45**	**3.35**	**3.26**	**3.18**	**3.12**

The function, $F = e$ with exponent $2z$, is computed in part from Fisher's table

FACE TYPE) POINTS FOR THE DISTRIBUTION OF F

n_1 degrees of freedom for numerator												
14	16	20	24	30	40	50	75	100	200	500	∞	n_2
245	246	248	249	250	251	252	253	253	254	254	254	1
6,142	**6,169**	**6,208**	**6,234**	**6,258**	**6,286**	**6,302**	**6,323**	**6,334**	**6,352**	**6,361**	**6,366**	
19.42	19.43	19.44	19.45	19.46	19.47	19.47	19.48	19.49	19.49	19.50	19.50	2
99.43	**99.44**	**99.45**	**99.46**	**99.47**	**99.48**	**99.48**	**99.49**	**99.49**	**99.49**	**99.50**	**99.50**	
8.71	8.69	8.66	8.64	8.62	8.60	8.58	8.57	8.56	8.54	8.54	8.53	3
26.92	**26.83**	**26.69**	**26.60**	**26.50**	**26.41**	**26.35**	**26.27**	**26.23**	**26.18**	**26.14**	**26.12**	
5.87	5.84	5.80	5.77	5.74	5.71	5.70	5.68	5.66	5.65	5.64	5.63	4
14.24	**14.15**	**14.02**	**13.93**	**13.83**	**13.74**	**13.69**	**13.61**	**13.57**	**13.52**	**13.48**	**13.46**	
4.64	4.60	4.56	4.53	4.50	4.46	4.44	4.42	4.40	4.38	4.37	4.36	5
9.77	**9.68**	**9.55**	**9.47**	**9.38**	**9.29**	**9.24**	**9.17**	**9.13**	**9.07**	**9.04**	**9.02**	
3.96	3.92	3.87	3.84	3.81	3.77	3.75	3.72	3.71	3.69	3.68	3.67	6
7.60	**7.52**	**7.39**	**7.31**	**7.23**	**7.14**	**7.09**	**7.02**	**6.99**	**6.94**	**6.90**	**6.88**	
3.52	3.49	3.44	3.41	3.38	3.34	3.32	3.29	3.28	3.25	3.24	3.23	7
6.35	**6.27**	**6.15**	**6.07**	**5.98**	**5.90**	**5.85**	**5.78**	**5.75**	**5.70**	**5.67**	**5.65**	
3.23	3.20	3.15	3.12	3.08	3.05	3.03	3.00	2.98	2.96	2.94	2.93	8
5.56	**5.48**	**5.36**	**5.28**	**5.20**	**5.11**	**5.06**	**5.00**	**4.96**	**4.91**	**4.88**	**4.86**	
3.02	2.98	2.93	2.90	2.86	2.82	2.80	2.77	2.76	2.73	2.72	2.71	9
5.00	**4.92**	**4.80**	**4.73**	**4.64**	**4.56**	**4.51**	**4.45**	**4.41**	**4.36**	**4.33**	**4.31**	
2.86	2.82	2.77	2.74	2.70	2.67	2.64	2.61	2.59	2.56	2.55	2.54	10
4.60	**4.52**	**4.41**	**4.33**	**4.25**	**4.17**	**4.12**	**4.05**	**4.01**	**3.96**	**3.93**	**3.91**	
2.74	2.70	2.65	2.61	2.57	2.53	2.50	2.47	2.45	2.42	2.41	2.40	11
4.29	**4.21**	**4.10**	**4.02**	**3.94**	**3.86**	**3.80**	**3.74**	**3.70**	**3.66**	**3.62**	**3.60**	
2.64	2.60	2.54	2.50	2.46	2.42	2.40	2.36	2.35	2.32	2.31	2.30	12
4.05	**3.98**	**3.86**	**3.78**	**3.70**	**3.61**	**3.56**	**3.49**	**3.46**	**3.41**	**3.38**	**3.36**	
2.55	2.51	2.46	2.42	2.38	2.34	2.32	2.28	2.26	2.24	2.22	2.21	13
3.85	**3.78**	**3.67**	**3.59**	**3.51**	**3.42**	**3.37**	**3.30**	**3.27**	**3.21**	**3.18**	**3.16**	
2.48	2.44	2.39	2.35	2.31	2.27	2.24	2.21	2.19	2.16	2.14	2.13	14
3.70	**3.62**	**3.51**	**3.43**	**3.34**	**3.26**	**3.21**	**3.14**	**3.11**	**3.06**	**3.02**	**3.00**	
2.43	2.39	2.33	2.29	2.25	2.21	2.18	2.15	2.12	2.10	2.08	2.07	15
3.56	**3.48**	**3.36**	**3.29**	**3.20**	**3.12**	**3.07**	**3.00**	**2.97**	**2.92**	**2.89**	**2.87**	
2.37	2.33	2.28	2.24	2.20	2.16	2.13	2.09	2.07	2.04	2.02	2.01	16
3.45	**3.37**	**3.25**	**3.18**	**3.10**	**3.01**	**2.96**	**2.89**	**2.86**	**2.80**	**2.77**	**2.75**	
2.33	2.29	2.23	2.19	2.15	2.11	2.08	2.04	2.02	1.99	1.97	1.96	17
3.35	**3.27**	**3.16**	**3.08**	**3.00**	**2.92**	**2.86**	**2.79**	**2.76**	**2.70**	**2.67**	**2.65**	
2.29	2.25	2.19	2.15	2.11	2.07	2.04	2.00	1.98	1.95	1.93	1.92	18
3.27	**3.19**	**3.07**	**3.00**	**2.91**	**2.83**	**2.78**	**2.71**	**2.68**	**2.62**	**2.59**	**2.57**	
2.26	2.21	2.15	2.11	2.07	2.02	2.00	1.96	1.94	1.91	1.90	1.88	19
3.19	**3.12**	**3.00**	**2.92**	**2.84**	**2.76**	**2.70**	**2.63**	**2.60**	**2.54**	**2.51**	**2.49**	
2.23	2.18	2.12	2.08	2.04	1.99	1.96	1.92	1.90	1.87	1.85	1.84	20
3.13	**3.05**	**2.94**	**2.86**	**2.77**	**2.69**	**2.63**	**2.56**	**2.53**	**2.47**	**2.44**	**2.42**	
2.20	2.15	2.09	2.05	2.00	1.96	1.93	1.89	1.87	1.84	1.82	1.81	21
3.07	**2.99**	**2.88**	**2.80**	**2.72**	**2.63**	**2.58**	**2.51**	**2.47**	**2.42**	**2.38**	**2.36**	
2.18	2.13	2.07	2.03	1.98	1.93	1.91	1.87	1.84	1.81	1.80	1.78	22
3.02	**2.94**	**2.83**	**2.75**	**2.67**	**2.58**	**2.53**	**2.46**	**2.42**	**2.37**	**2.33**	**2.31**	

VI(7). Additional entries are by interpolation, mostly graphical.

TABLE 10.7—5% (ROMAN TYPE) AND 1% (BOLD

n_2	n_1 degrees of freedom for numerator											
	1	2	3	4	5	6	7	8	9	10	11	12
23	4.28	3.42	3.03	2.80	2.64	2.53	2.45	2.38	2.32	2.28	2.24	2.20
	7.88	**5.66**	**4.76**	**4.26**	**3.94**	**3.71**	**3.54**	**3.41**	**3.30**	**3.21**	**3.14**	**3.07**
24	4.26	3.40	3.01	2.78	2.62	2.51	2.43	2.36	2.30	2.26	2.22	2.18
	7.82	**5.61**	**4.72**	**4.22**	**3.90**	**3.67**	**3.50**	**3.36**	**3.25**	**3.17**	**3.09**	**3.03**
25	4.24	3.38	2.99	2.76	2.60	2.49	2.41	2.34	2.28	2.24	2.20	2.16
	7.77	**5.57**	**4.68**	**4.18**	**3.86**	**3.63**	**3.46**	**3.32**	**3.21**	**3.13**	**3.05**	**2.99**
26	4.22	3.37	2.98	2.74	2.59	2.47	2.39	2.32	2.27	2.22	2.18	2.15
	7.72	**5.53**	**4.64**	**4.14**	**3.82**	**3.59**	**3.42**	**3.29**	**3.17**	**3.09**	**3.02**	**2.96**
27	4.21	3.35	2.96	2.73	2.57	2.46	2.37	2.30	2.25	2.20	2.16	2.13
	7.68	**5.49**	**4.60**	**4.11**	**3.79**	**3.56**	**3.39**	**3.26**	**3.14**	**3.06**	**2.98**	**2.93**
28	4.20	3.34	2.95	2.71	2.56	2.44	2.36	2.29	2.24	2.19	2.15	2.12
	7.64	**5.45**	**4.57**	**4.07**	**3.76**	**3.53**	**3.36**	**3.23**	**3.11**	**3.03**	**2.95**	**2.90**
29	4.18	3.33	2.93	2.70	2.54	2.43	2.35	2.28	2.22	2.18	2.14	2.10
	7.60	**5.42**	**4.54**	**4.04**	**3.73**	**3.50**	**3.33**	**3.20**	**3.08**	**3.00**	**2.92**	**2.87**
30	4.17	3.32	2.92	2.69	2.53	2.42	2.34	2.27	2.21	2.16	2.12	2.09
	7.56	**5.39**	**4.51**	**4.02**	**3.70**	**3.47**	**3.30**	**3.17**	**3.06**	**2.98**	**2.90**	**2.84**
32	4.15	3.30	2.90	2.67	2.51	2.40	2.32	2.25	2.19	2.14	2.10	2.07
	7.50	**5.34**	**4.46**	**3.97**	**3.66**	**3.42**	**3.25**	**3.12**	**3.01**	**2.94**	**2.86**	**2.80**
34	4.13	3.28	2.88	2.65	2.49	2.38	2.30	2.23	2.17	2.12	2.08	2.05
	7.44	**5.29**	**4.42**	**3.93**	**3.61**	**3.38**	**3.21**	**3.08**	**2.97**	**2.89**	**2.82**	**2.76**
36	4.11	3.26	2.86	2.63	2.48	2.36	2.28	2.21	2.15	2.10	2.06	2.03
	7.39	**5.25**	**4.38**	**3.89**	**3.58**	**3.35**	**3.18**	**3.04**	**2.94**	**2.86**	**2.78**	**2.72**
38	4.10	3.25	2.85	2.62	2.46	2.35	2.26	2.19	2.14	2.09	2.05	2.02
	7.35	**5.21**	**4.34**	**3.86**	**3.54**	**3.32**	**3.15**	**3.02**	**2.91**	**2.82**	**2.75**	**2.69**
40	4.08	3.23	2.84	2.61	2.45	2.34	2.25	2.18	2.12	2.07	2.04	2.00
	7.31	**5.18**	**4.31**	**3.83**	**3.51**	**3.29**	**3.12**	**2.99**	**2.88**	**2.80**	**2.73**	**2.66**
42	4.07	3.22	2.83	2.59	2.44	2.32	2.24	2.17	2.11	2.06	2.02	1.99
	7.27	**5.15**	**4.29**	**3.80**	**3.49**	**3.26**	**3.10**	**2.96**	**2.86**	**2.77**	**2.70**	**2.64**
44	4.06	3.21	2.82	2.58	2.43	2.31	2.23	2.16	2.10	2.05	2.01	1.98
	7.24	**5.12**	**4.26**	**3.78**	**3.46**	**3.24**	**3.07**	**2.94**	**2.84**	**2.75**	**2.68**	**2.62**
46	4.05	3.20	2.81	2.57	2.42	2.30	2.22	2.14	2.09	2.04	2.00	1.97
	7.21	**5.10**	**4.24**	**3.76**	**3.44**	**3.22**	**3.05**	**2.92**	**2.82**	**2.73**	**2.66**	**2.60**
48	4.04	3.19	2.80	2.56	2.41	2.30	2.21	2.14	2.08	2.03	1.99	1.96
	7.19	**5.08**	**4.22**	**3.74**	**3.42**	**3.20**	**3.04**	**2.90**	**2.80**	**2.71**	**2.64**	**2.58**
50	4.03	3.18	2.79	2.56	2.40	2.29	2.20	2.13	2.07	2.02	1.98	1.95
	7.17	**5.06**	**4.20**	**3.72**	**3.41**	**3.18**	**3.02**	**2.88**	**2.78**	**2.70**	**2.62**	**2.56**
55	4.02	3.17	2.78	2.54	2.38	2.27	2.18	2.11	2.05	2.00	1.97	1.93
	7.12	**5.01**	**4.16**	**3.68**	**3.37**	**3.15**	**2.98**	**2.85**	**2.75**	**2.66**	**2.59**	**2.53**
60	4.00	3.15	2.76	2.52	2.37	2.25	2.17	2.10	2.04	1.99	1.95	1.92
	7.08	**4.98**	**4.13**	**3.65**	**3.34**	**3.12**	**2.95**	**2.82**	**2.72**	**2.63**	**2.56**	**2.50**
65	3.99	3.14	2.75	2.51	2.36	2.24	2.15	2.08	2.02	1.98	1.94	1.90
	7.04	**4.95**	**4.10**	**3.62**	**3.31**	**3.09**	**2.93**	**2.79**	**2.70**	**2.61**	**2.54**	**2.47**
70	3.98	3.13	2.74	2.50	2.35	2.23	2.14	2.07	2.01	1.97	1.93	1.89
	7.01	**4.92**	**4.08**	**3.60**	**3.29**	**3.07**	**2.91**	**2.77**	**2.67**	**2.59**	**2.51**	**2.45**

The function, $F = e$ with exponent $2z$, is computed in part from Fisher's Table

n_1 degrees of freedom for numerator												n_2
14	16	20	24	30	40	50	75	100	200	500	∞	
2.14	2.10	2.04	2.00	1.96	1.91	1.88	1.84	1.82	1.79	1.77	1.76	23
2.97	**2.89**	**2.78**	**2.70**	**2.62**	**2.53**	**2.48**	**2.41**	**2.37**	**2.32**	**2.28**	**2.26**	
2.13	2.09	2.02	1.98	1.94	1.89	1.86	1.82	1.80	1.76	1.74	1.73	24
2.93	**2.85**	**2.74**	**2.66**	**2.58**	**2.49**	**2.44**	**2.36**	**2.33**	**2.27**	**2.23**	**2.21**	
2.11	2.06	2.00	1.96	1.92	1.87	1.84	1.80	1.77	1.74	1.72	1.71	25
2.89	**2.81**	**2.70**	**2.62**	**2.54**	**2.45**	**2.40**	**2.32**	**2.29**	**2.23**	**2.19**	**2.17**	
2.10	2.05	1.99	1.95	1.90	1.85	1.82	1.78	1.76	1.72	1.70	1.69	26
2.86	**2.77**	**2.66**	**2.58**	**2.50**	**2.41**	**2.36**	**2.28**	**2.25**	**2.19**	**2.15**	**2.13**	
2.08	2.03	1.97	1.93	1.88	1.84	1.80	1.76	1.74	1.71	1.68	1.67	27
2.83	**2.74**	**2.63**	**2.55**	**2.47**	**2.38**	**2.33**	**2.25**	**2.21**	**2.16**	**2.12**	**2.10**	
2.06	2.02	1.96	1.91	1.87	1.81	1.78	1.75	1.72	1.69	1.67	1.65	28
2.80	**2.71**	**2.60**	**2.52**	**2.44**	**2.35**	**2.30**	**2.22**	**2.18**	**2.13**	**2.09**	**2.06**	
2.05	2.00	1.94	1.90	1.85	1.80	1.77	1.73	1.71	1.68	1.65	1.64	29
2.77	**2.68**	**2.57**	**2.49**	**2.41**	**2.32**	**2.27**	**2.19**	**2.15**	**2.10**	**2.06**	**2.03**	
2.04	1.99	1.93	1.89	1.84	1.79	1.76	1.72	1.69	1.66	1.64	1.62	30
2.74	**2.66**	**2.55**	**2.47**	**2.38**	**2.29**	**2.24**	**2.16**	**2.13**	**2.07**	**2.03**	**2.01**	
2.02	1.97	1.91	1.86	1.82	1.76	1.74	1.69	1.67	1.64	1.61	1.59	32
2.70	**2.62**	**2.51**	**2.42**	**2.34**	**2.25**	**2.20**	**2.12**	**2.08**	**2.02**	**1.98**	**1.96**	
2.00	1.95	1.89	1.84	1.80	1.74	1.71	1.67	1.64	1.61	1.59	1.57	34
2.66	**2.58**	**2.47**	**2.38**	**2.30**	**2.21**	**2.15**	**2.08**	**2.04**	**1.98**	**1.94**	**1.91**	
1.98	1.93	1.87	1.82	1.78	1.72	1.69	1.65	1.62	1.59	1.56	1.55	36
2.62	**2.54**	**2.43**	**2.35**	**2.26**	**2.17**	**2.12**	**2.04**	**2.00**	**1.94**	**1.90**	**1.87**	
1.96	1.92	1.85	1.80	1.76	1.71	1.67	1.63	1.60	1.57	1.54	1.53	38
2.59	**2.51**	**2.40**	**2.32**	**2.22**	**2.14**	**2.08**	**2.00**	**1.97**	**1.90**	**1.86**	**1.84**	
1.95	1.90	1.84	1.79	1.74	1.69	1.66	1.61	1.59	1.55	1.53	1.51	40
2.56	**2.49**	**2.37**	**2.29**	**2.20**	**2.11**	**2.05**	**1.97**	**1.94**	**1.88**	**1.84**	**1.81**	
1.94	1.89	1.82	1.78	1.73	1.68	1.64	1.60	1.57	1.54	1.51	1.49	42
2.54	**2.46**	**2.35**	**2.26**	**2.17**	**2.08**	**2.02**	**1.94**	**1.91**	**1.85**	**1.80**	**1.78**	
1.92	1.88	1.81	1.76	1.72	1.66	1.63	1.58	1.56	1.52	1.50	1.48	44
2.52	**2.44**	**2.32**	**2.24**	**2.15**	**2.06**	**2.00**	**1.92**	**1.88**	**1.82**	**1.78**	**1.75**	
1.91	1.87	1.80	1.75	1.71	1.65	1.62	1.57	1.54	1.51	1.48	1.46	46
2.50	**2.42**	**2.30**	**2.22**	**2.13**	**2.04**	**1.98**	**1.90**	**1.86**	**1.80**	**1.76**	**1.72**	
1.90	1.86	1.79	1.74	1.70	1.64	1.61	1.56	1.53	1.50	1.47	1.45	48
2.48	**2.40**	**2.28**	**2.20**	**2.11**	**2.02**	**1.96**	**1.88**	**1.84**	**1.78**	**1.73**	**1.70**	
1.90	1.85	1.78	1.74	1.69	1.63	1.60	1.55	1.52	1.48	1.46	1.44	50
2.46	**2.39**	**2.26**	**2.18**	**2.10**	**2.00**	**1.94**	**1.86**	**1.82**	**1.76**	**1.71**	**1.68**	
1.88	1.83	1.76	1.72	1.67	1.61	1.58	1.52	1.50	1.46	1.43	1.41	55
2.43	**2.35**	**2.23**	**2.15**	**2.06**	**1.96**	**1.90**	**1.82**	**1.78**	**1.71**	**1.66**	**1.64**	
1.86	1.81	1.75	1.70	1.65	1.59	1.56	1.50	1.48	1.44	1.41	1.39	60
2.40	**2.32**	**2.20**	**2.12**	**2.03**	**1.93**	**1.87**	**1.79**	**1.74**	**1.68**	**1.63**	**1.60**	
1.85	1.80	1.73	1.68	1.63	1.57	1.54	1.49	1.46	1.42	1.39	1.37	65
2.37	**2.30**	**2.18**	**2.09**	**2.00**	**1.90**	**1.84**	**1.76**	**1.71**	**1.64**	**1.60**	**1.56**	
1.84	1.79	1.72	1.67	1.62	1.56	1.53	1.47	1.45	1.40	1.37	1.35	70
2.35	**2.28**	**2.15**	**2.07**	**1.98**	**1.88**	**1.82**	**1.74**	**1.69**	**1.62**	**1.56**	**1.53**	

VI(7). Additional entries are by interpolation, mostly graphical.

TABLE 10.7—5% (ROMAN TYPE) AND 1% (BOLD

n_2	n_1 degrees of freedom for numerator											
	1	2	3	4	5	6	7	8	9	10	11	12
80	3.96 **6.96**	3.11 **4.88**	2.72 **4.04**	2.48 **3.56**	2.33 **3.25**	2.21 **3.04**	2.12 **2.87**	2.05 **2.74**	1.99 **2.64**	1.95 **2.55**	1.91 **2.48**	1.88 **2.41**
100	3.94 **6.90**	3.09 **4.82**	2.70 **3.98**	2.46 **3.51**	2.30 **3.20**	2.19 **2.99**	2.10 **2.82**	2.03 **2.69**	1.97 **2.59**	1.92 **2.51**	1.88 **2.43**	1.85 **2.36**
125	3.92 **6.84**	3.07 **4.78**	2.68 **3.94**	2.44 **3.47**	2.29 **3.17**	2.17 **2.95**	2.08 **2.79**	2.01 **2.65**	1.95 **2.56**	1.90 **2.47**	1.86 **2.40**	1.83 **2.33**
150	3.91 **6.81**	3.06 **4.75**	2.67 **3.91**	2.43 **3.44**	2.27 **3.14**	2.16 **2.92**	2.07 **2.76**	2.00 **2.62**	1.94 **2.53**	1.89 **2.44**	1.85 **2.37**	1.82 **2.30**
200	3.89 **6.76**	3.04 **4.71**	2.65 **3.88**	2.41 **3.41**	2.26 **3.11**	2.14 **2.90**	2.05 **2.73**	1.98 **2.60**	1.92 **2.50**	1.87 **2.41**	1.83 **2.34**	1.80 **2.28**
400	3.86 **6.70**	3.02 **4.66**	2.62 **3.83**	2.39 **3.36**	2.23 **3.06**	2.12 **2.85**	2.03 **2.69**	1.96 **2.55**	1.90 **2.46**	1.85 **2.37**	1.81 **2.29**	1.78 **2.23**
1000	3.85 **6.66**	3.00 **4.62**	2.61 **3.80**	2.38 **3.34**	2.22 **3.04**	2.10 **2.82**	2.02 **2.66**	1.95 **2.53**	1.89 **2.43**	1.84 **2.34**	1.80 **2.26**	1.76 **2.20**
∞	3.84 **6.64**	2.99 **4.60**	2.60 **3.78**	2.37 **3.32**	2.21 **3.02**	2.09 **2.80**	2.01 **2.64**	1.94 **2.51**	1.88 **2.41**	1.83 **2.32**	1.79 **2.24**	1.75 **2.18**

The function, $F = e$ with exponent $2z$, is computed in part from Fisher's Table

n_1 degrees of freedom for numerator												
14	16	20	24	30	40	50	75	100	200	500	∞	n_2
1.82	1.77	1.70	1.65	1.60	1.54	1.51	1.45	1.42	1.38	1.35	1.32	80
2.32	**2.24**	**2.11**	**2.03**	**1.94**	**1.84**	**1.78**	**1.70**	**1.65**	**1.57**	**1.52**	**1.49**	
1.79	1.75	1.68	1.63	1.57	1.51	1.48	1.42	1.39	1.34	1.30	1.28	100
2.26	**2.19**	**2.06**	**1.98**	**1.89**	**1.79**	**1.73**	**1.64**	**1.59**	**1.51**	**1.46**	**1.43**	
1.77	1.72	1.65	1.60	1.55	1.49	1.45	1.39	1.36	1.31	1.27	1.25	125
2.23	**2.15**	**2.03**	**1.94**	**1.85**	**1.75**	**1.68**	**1.59**	**1.54**	**1.46**	**1.40**	**1.37**	
1.76	1.71	1.64	1.59	1.54	1.47	1.44	1.37	1.34	1.29	1.25	1.22	150
2.20	**2.12**	**2.00**	**1.91**	**1.83**	**1.72**	**1.66**	**1.56**	**1.51**	**1.43**	**1.37**	**1.33**	
1.74	1.69	1.62	1.57	1.52	1.45	1.42	1.35	1.32	1.26	1.22	1.19	200
2.17	**2.09**	**1.97**	**1.88**	**1.79**	**1.69**	**1.62**	**1.53**	**1.48**	**1.39**	**1.33**	**1.28**	
1.72	1.67	1.60	1.54	1.49	1.42	1.38	1.32	1.28	1.22	1.16	1.13	400
2.12	**2.04**	**1.92**	**1.84**	**1.74**	**1.64**	**1.57**	**1.47**	**1.42**	**1.32**	**1.24**	**1.19**	
1.70	1.65	1.58	1.53	1.47	1.41	1.36	1.30	1.26	1.19	1.13	1.08	1000
2.09	**2.01**	**1.89**	**1.81**	**1.71**	**1.61**	**1.54**	**1.44**	**1.38**	**1.28**	**1.19**	**1.11**	
1.69	1.64	1.57	1.52	1.46	1.40	1.35	1.28	1.24	1.17	1.11	1.00	∞
2.07	**1.99**	**1.87**	**1.79**	**1.69**	**1.59**	**1.52**	**1.41**	**1.36**	**1.25**	**1.15**	**1.00**	

VI(7). Additional entries are by interpolation, mostly graphical.

TABLE I. TABLE OF $E^2_{0.01}$ AND THE CORRESPONDING VALUES OF P_{II}

$f_1 = 1$

f_2	$E^2_{0.01}$	ϕ									
		1	1.5	2	2.5	3	4	5	6	7	8
2	.980	.970	.947	.914	.874	.828	.720	.602	.484	.373	.277
4	.841	.949	.885	.784	.651	.501	.233	.077	.018	.003	
6	.696	.934	.839	.687	.498	.312	.076	.010	.001		
7	.636	.928	.822	.652	.447	.258	.049	.006			
8	.585	.924	.808	.624	.409	.221	.034	.002			
9	.540	.920	.796	.601	.379	.193	.025	.001			
10	.501	.916	.786	.582	.355	.172	.019	.001			
11	.467	.913	.777	.567	.336	.156	.015				
12	.437	.911	.770	.553	.320	.144	.012				
13	.411	.909	.763	.542	.307	.133	.010				
14	.388	.907	.758	.532	.296	.125	.009				
15	.367	.905	.753	.523	.286	.118	.008				
16	.348	.904	.749	.516	.278	.112	.007				
17	.331	.902	.745	.509	.271	.107	.006				
18	.315	.901	.741	.503	.264	.103	.006				
19	.301	.900	.738	.498	.259	.099	.005				
20	.288	.899	.735	.493	.254	.096	.005				
22	.265	.897	.730	.484	.245	.090	.004				
24	.246	.896	.726	.477	.238	.086	.004				
26	.229	.894	.722	.471	.232	.082	.003				
28	.214	.893	.718	.466	.227	.079	.003				
30	.201	.892	.716	.462	.223	.077	.003				
60	.106	.885	.696	.430	.194	.061	.002				
∞		.877	.675	.400	.169	.048	.001				

$f_1 = 2$

f_2	$E^2_{0.01}$	ϕ									
		1	1.5	2	2.5	3	4	5	6	7	8
2	.990	.975	.957	.932	.901	.865	.779	.680	.577	.475	.379
4	.900	.957	.901	.810	.685	.540	.266	.095	.024	.004	.001
6	.785	.941	.850	.695	.498	.305	.068	.007			
7	.732	.934	.828	.649	.431	.235	.035	.004			
8	.684	.929	.809	.611	.379	.187	.021	.001			
9	.641	.924	.793	.579	.338	.152	.013				
10	.602	.920	.779	.552	.306	.127	.008				
11	.567	.916	.767	.528	.278	.108	.006				
12	.536	.912	.756	.508	.255	.093	.005				
13	.508	.909	.746	.491	.237	.082	.003				
14	.482	.907	.738	.476	.223	.074	.002				
15	.459	.904	.730	.463	.211	.066	.002				
16	.438	.902	.723	.452	.201	.060	.001				
17	.418	.900	.717	.442	.193	.055	.001				
18	.401	.898	.711	.433	.185	.051	.001				
19	.384	.896	.706	.424	.177	.048	.001				
20	.369	.895	.701	.417	.170	.045	.001				
22	.342	.893	.693	.404	.160	.040	.001				
24	.319	.890	.686	.394	.151	.036					
26	.298	.888	.680	.385	.144	.034					
28	.280	.886	.675	.377	.138	.031					
30	.264	.885	.670	.370	.134	.029					
60	.142	.873	.637	.324	.102	.019					
∞		.860	.601	.279	.076	.011					

TABLE I. TABLE $E^2_{0.01}$ AND THE CORRESPONDING VALUES OF P_{II} (*continued*)

$f_1 = 3$

f_2	$E^2_{0.01}$	ϕ									
		1	1.5	2	2.5	3	4	5	6	7	8
2	.993	.977	.961	.939	.911	.878	.800	.709	.612	.515	.421
4	.926	.959	.907	.818	.695	.552	.276	.100	.026	.005	.001
6	.830	.943	.850	.691	.486	.290	.059	.006			
7	.784	.936	.825	.636	.408	.210	.025	.002			
8	.740	.929	.803	.590	.347	.158	.014				
9	.700	.923	.783	.550	.299	.120	.008				
10	.663	.918	.765	.517	.261	.094	.004				
11	.629	.913	.749	.487	.231	.075	.002				
12	.598	.909	.735	.463	.206	.062	.001				
13	.570	.906	.723	.441	.186	.051	.001				
14	.544	.902	.711	.422	.170	.044	.001				
15	.520	.899	.701	.406	.156	.038	.001				
16	.498	.896	.692	.391	.145	.033					
17	.478	.893	.683	.378	.135	.029					
18	.459	.891	.676	.367	.126	.026					
19	.442	.889	.669	.356	.119	.023					
20	.426	.887	.662	.347	.112	.021					
22	.396	.883	.651	.331	.102	.017					
24	.371	.880	.641	.318	.094	.015					
26	.349	.877	.633	.307	.087	.013					
28	.329	.875	.625	.297	.081	.012					
30	.311	.872	.619	.289	.077	.011					
60	.171	.856	.571	.233	.050	.005					
∞		.836	.519	.182	.030	.002					

$f_1 = 4$

f_2	$E^2_{0.01}$	ϕ									
		1	1.5	2	2.5	3	4	5	6	7	8
2	.995	.978	.962	.942	.915	.884	.810	.724	.631	.536	.444
4	.941	.960	.909	.822	.700	.557	.280	.102	.027	.005	.001
6	.859	.943	.849	.685	.475	.277	.053	.005			
7	.818	.936	.821	.624	.389	.191	.018				
8	.778	.928	.796	.571	.322	.136	.010				
9	.741	.922	.773	.526	.269	.098	.003				
10	.706	.916	.752	.487	.227	.073	.002				
11	.673	.911	.733	.453	.195	.055	.001				
12	.643	.906	.716	.424	.169	.042	.001				
13	.616	.901	.700	.398	.148	.034					
14	.590	.897	.687	.376	.131	.028					
15	.566	.893	.674	.357	.117	.022					
16	.544	.890	.662	.340	.106	.018					
17	.523	.886	.652	.325	.096	.015					
18	.504	.883	.642	.312	.088	.013					
19	.486	.880	.633	.301	.081	.011					
20	.470	.878	.625	.290	.075	.010					
22	.440	.873	.611	.272	.066	.008					
24	.413	.869	.598	.257	.059	.006					
26	.389	.865	.588	.244	.053	.005					
28	.368	.862	.578	.234	.048	.005					
30	.349	.860	.570	.225	.044	.004					
60	.196	.837	.509	.165	.024	.001					
∞		.810	.443	.115	.011						

TABLE I. TABLE OF $E^2_{0.01}$ AND THE CORRESPONDING VALUES OF P_{II} (*continued*)

$f_1 = 5$

f_2	$E^2_{0.01}$	ϕ									
		1	1.5	2	2.5	3	4	5	6	7	8
2	.996	.978	.964	.944	.918	.888	.817	.733	.642	.549	.458
4	.951	.961	.910	.824	.702	.559	.282	.103	.027	.005	.001
6	.879	.943	.848	.679	.466	.266	.048	.004			
7	.842	.935	.818	.614	.394	.177	.014				
8	.806	.928	.790	.556	.301	.121	.007				
9	.771	.920	.764	.505	.245	.083	.003				
10	.738	.914	.740	.461	.201	.058	.001				
11	.707	.908	.718	.424	.168	.042					
12	.679	.902	.699	.391	.141	.031					
13	.652	.897	.681	.363	.120	.023					
14	.626	.892	.664	.339	.104	.018					
15	.603	.888	.649	.318	.090	.014					
16	.581	.883	.636	.299	.079	.011					
17	.561	.880	.624	.283	.071	.009					
18	.541	.876	.612	.269	.063	.007					
19	.523	.873	.602	.256	.057	.006					
20	.506	.870	.592	.245	.052	.005					
22	.475	.864	.575	.225	.044	.004					
24	.448	.859	.560	.210	.037	.003					
26	.423	.855	.547	.196	.033	.002					
28	.401	.851	.536	.185	.029	.002					
30	.381	.847	.526	.176	.026	.002					
60	.218	.819	.452	.116	.011						
∞		.784	.373	.070	.004						

$f_1 = 6$

f_2	$E^2_{0.01}$	ϕ									
		1	1.5	2	2.5	3	4	5	6	7	8
2	.997	.978	.964	.945	.920	.891	.821	.739	.650	.558	.468
4	.958	.962	.911	.825	.704	.560	.283	.104	.027	.005	.001
6	.894	.944	.847	.675	.459	.258	.044	.003			
7	.860	.935	.815	.605	.362	.166	.011				
8	.827	.927	.784	.543	.285	.109	.006				
9	.795	.919	.756	.488	.226	.071	.003				
10	.764	.912	.730	.441	.181	.048	.001				
11	.734	.905	.706	.400	.147	.033					
12	.707	.899	.683	.365	.120	.023					
13	.681	.893	.663	.334	.100	.017					
14	.656	.888	.645	.308	.084	.013					
15	.633	.882	.628	.286	.071	.009					
16	.612	.878	.612	.266	.061	.007					
17	.591	.873	.598	.249	.053	.005					
18	.572	.869	.585	.233	.046	.004					
19	.554	.865	.573	.220	.041	.003					
20	.537	.862	.562	.208	.036	.003					
22	.506	.855	.542	.188	.029	.002					
24	.478	.849	.524	.172	.024	.001					
26	.453	.844	.510	.159	.020	.001					
28	.430	.839	.497	.147	.017	.001					
30	.410	.835	.486	.138	.015	.001					
60	.238	.801	.401	.081	.006						
∞		.755	.311	.042	.001						

TABLE I. TABLE OF $E^2_{0.01}$ AND THE CORRESPONDING VALUES OF P_{II} (*continued*)

$f_1 = 7$

f_2	$E^2_{0.01}$	ϕ									
		1	1.5	2	2.5	3	4	5	6	7	8
2	.997	.979	.965	.946	.922	.893	.824	.743	.655	.564	.475
4	.963	.962	.912	.826	.705	.561	.283	.104	.027	.005	.001
6	.906	.944	.845	.671	.452	.251	.041	.003			
7	.875	.935	.812	.598	.351	.158	.009				
8	.844	.926	.779	.532	.272	.100	.005				
9	.814	.918	.749	.474	.211	.063	.002				
10	.785	.910	.720	.423	.166	.041	.001				
11	.757	.903	.694	.379	.131	.027					
12	.730	.896	.670	.342	.105	.018					
13	.705	.889	.648	.310	.085	.013					
14	.681	.883	.627	.283	.069	.009					
15	.659	.878	.608	.259	.057	.007					
16	.638	.872	.591	.238	.048	.004					
17	.618	.868	.575	.220	.041	.003					
18	.599	.863	.561	.205	.035	.002					
19	.581	.859	.548	.191	.030	.002					
20	.564	.854	.535	.179	.026	.002					
22	.533	.847	.513	.159	.020	.001					
24	.505	.840	.494	.143	.016	.001					
26	.479	.834	.477	.130	.013						
28	.456	.829	.463	.119	.011						
30	.435	.824	.450	.110	.009						
60	.256	.783	.355	.056	.003						
∞		.729	.256	.024							

$f_1 = 8$

f_2	$E^2_{0.01}$	ϕ									
		1	1.5	2	2.5	3	4	5	6	7	8
2	.997	.979	.965	.946	.923	.894	.826	.746	.659	.569	.481
4	.967	.962	.912	.826	.705	.562	.284	.104	.027	.005	.001
6	.915	.944	.844	.668	.447	.246	.039	.003			
7	.887	.934	.809	.592	.343	.151	.007				
8	.858	.925	.775	.522	.261	.093	.004				
9	.829	.917	.743	.461	.199	.056					
10	.802	.908	.712	.408	.153	.035					
11	.775	.901	.684	.363	.118	.022					
12	.750	.893	.658	.324	.092	.014					
13	.726	.886	.634	.290	.073	.009					
14	.703	.880	.612	.261	.058	.006					
15	.681	.874	.591	.237	.047	.004					
16	.660	.868	.573	.216	.039	.003					
17	.641	.862	.555	.197	.032	.002					
18	.622	.857	.539	.181	.027	.002					
19	.605	.852	.525	.168	.023	.001					
20	.588	.848	.511	.156	.019	.001					
22	.557	.839	.487	.135	.014						
24	.529	.832	.466	.119	.011						
26	.503	.825	.447	.107	.009						
28	.480	.819	.432	.096	.007						
30	.458	.813	.418	.088	.006						
60	.274	.766	.315	.039	.001						
∞		.702	.211	.014							

TABLE II. TABLE OF $E^2_{0.05}$ AND THE CORESPONDING VALUES OF P_{II}

$f_1 = 1$

f_2	$E^2_{0.05}$	ϕ = 1	1.5	2	2.5	3	4	5	6	7	8
2	.903	.862	.763	.643	.517	.395	.200	.083	.028	.008	.002
4	.658	.805	.631	.428	.247	.120	.016	.001			
6	.500	.777	.570	.343	.164	.061	.004				
7	.444	.768	.552	.319	.144	.050	.003				
8	.399	.761	.537	.302	.129	.041	.002				
9	.362	.756	.526	.288	.119	.036	.001				
10	.332	.751	.517	.278	.111	.032	.001				
11	.306	.747	.510	.269	.105	.029	.001				
12	.284	.744	.504	.262	.100	.027	.001				
13	.264	.741	.499	.256	.096	.025	.001				
14	.247	.739	.494	.251	.093	.024	.001				
15	.232	.737	.490	.247	.090	.023					
16	.219	.735	.487	.243	.087	.022					
17	.207	.734	.484	.240	.085	.021					
18	.197	.732	.481	.237	.084	.020					
19	.187	.731	.479	.235	.082	.020					
20	.179	.730	.477	.233	.081	.019					
22	.164	.728	.473	.229	.078	.018					
24	.151	.726	.470	.226	.076	.018					
26	.140	.725	.467	.223	.075	.017					
28	.130	.723	.465	.221	.073	.017					
30	.122	.722	.463	.219	.072	.016					
60	.063	.715	.450	.205	.065	.014					
∞		.707	.437	.193	.058	.011					

$f_1 = 2$

f_2	$E^2_{0.05}$	ϕ = 1	1.5	2	2.5	3	4	5	6	7	8
2	.950	.881	.803	.704	.595	.484	.286	.146	.064	.024	.008
4	.776	.824	.661	.460	.272	.135	.020	.001			
6	.632	.789	.579	.340	.153	.052	.002				
7	.575	.777	.551	.304	.124	.037	.001				
8	.527	.767	.530	.277	.104	.027	.001				
9	.486	.759	.513	.257	.090	.022					
10	.451	.752	.498	.241	.080	.017					
11	.420	.747	.486	.228	.072	.015					
12	.393	.742	.476	.217	.066	.013					
13	.369	.737	.468	.208	.061	.011					
14	.348	.734	.461	.201	.057	.010					
15	.329	.730	.454	.195	.054	.009					
16	.312	.727	.448	.189	.051	.008					
17	.297	.725	.443	.184	.048	.008					
18	.283	.722	.439	.180	.046	.007					
19	.270	.720	.435	.177	.044	.007					
20	.259	.718	.431	.173	.043	.006					
22	.238	.715	.425	.168	.040	.006					
24	.221	.712	.420	.163	.038	.005					
26	.206	.710	.415	.159	.037	.005					
28	.193	.708	.411	.155	.035	.005					
30	.181	.706	.408	.153	.034	.004					
60	.095	.692	.384	.134	.027	.003					
∞		.678	.362	.117	.021	.002					

TABLE II. Table of $E^2_{0.05}$ and the corresponding values of P_{II} (*continued*)

$f_1 = 3$

f_2	$E^2_{0.05}$	ϕ 1	1.5	2	2.5	3	4	5	6	7	8
2	.966	.888	.817	.726	.624	.519	.324	.177	.084	.035	.013
4	.832	.830	.670	.468	.278	.139	.020	.001			
6	.704	.791	.574	.326	.139	.044	.002				
7	.651	.776	.540	.283	.106	.028					
8	.604	.764	.513	.251	.084	.018					
9	.563	.754	.491	.226	.068	.013					
10	.527	.745	.472	.206	.057	.010					
11	.495	.738	.457	.190	.049	.008					
12	.466	.731	.444	.178	.043	.006					
13	.440	.726	.433	.167	.038	.005					
14	.418	.721	.422	.158	.035	.004					
15	.397	.716	.414	.151	.032	.004					
16	.378	.712	.406	.144	.029	.003					
17	.361	.709	.399	.139	.027	.003					
18	.345	.705	.393	.134	.025	.002					
19	.331	.702	.388	.130	.024	.002					
20	.317	.700	.383	.126	.022	.002					
22	.294	.695	.375	.119	.020	.002					
24	.273	.691	.367	.114	.019	.001					
26	.255	.687	.361	.110	.017	.001					
28	.240	.084	.356	.106	.016	.001					
30	.226	.682	.352	.103	.015	.001					
60	.121	.662	.320	.083	.010	.001					
∞		.642	.289	.067	.007						

$f_1 = 4$

f_2	$E^2_{0.05}$	ϕ 1	1.5	2	2.5	3	4	5	6	7	8
2	.975	.892	.824	.738	.640	.537	.345	.195	.097	.043	.017
4	.865	.833	.673	.471	.279	.139	.020	.001			
6	.751	.791	.567	.314	.128	.038	.001				
7	.702	.774	.529	.265	.092	.022					
8	.657	.760	.497	.229	.069	.013					
9	.618	.748	.471	.201	.054	.008					
10	.582	.738	.449	.179	.043	.006					
11	.550	.729	.430	.161	.035	.004					
12	.521	.721	.414	.148	.030	.003					
13	.494	.714	.401	.136	.025	.002					
14	.471	.708	.389	.127	.022	.002					
15	.449	.702	.378	.119	.019	.002					
16	.429	.697	.369	.112	.017	.001					
17	.411	.693	.361	.106	.016	.001					
18	.394	.689	.354	.101	.014	.001					
19	.379	.685	.347	.097	.013	.001					
20	.364	.681	.341	.093	.012	.001					
22	.339	.675	.331	.086	.010	.001					
24	.316	.670	.322	.080	.009						
26	.297	.665	.315	.076	.008						
28	.279	.661	.309	.072	.008						
30	.264	.658	.303	.069	.007						
60	.144	.632	.265	.049	.004						
∞		.604	.227	.036	.002						

TABLE II. TABLE OF $E^2_{0.05}$ AND THE CORRESPONDING VALUES OF P_{II} (*continued*)

$f_1 = 5$

f_2	$E^2_{0.05}$	ϕ									
		1	1.5	2	2.5	3	4	5	6	7	8
2	.980	.894	.828	.745	.649	.549	.359	.207	.106	.048	.019
4	.887	.835	.675	.473	.280	.138	.020	.001			
6	.785	.790	.561	.304	.119	.033	.001				
7	.739	.772	.519	.251	.082	.018					
8	.697	.756	.483	.211	.059	.010					
9	.659	.743	.454	.181	.044	.006					
10	.625	.731	.429	.158	.033	.004					
11	.593	.720	.408	.140	.026	.002					
12	.564	.711	.390	.125	.021	.002					
13	.538	.703	.374	.113	.017	.001					
14	.514	.695	.360	.103	.015	.001					
15	.492	.689	.348	.095	.012	.001					
16	.471	.683	.338	.088	.011	.001					
17	.452	.678	.328	.083	.009						
18	.435	.673	.320	.078	.008						
19	.419	.668	.312	.073	.007						
20	.404	.664	.305	.069	.007						
22	.377	.656	.294	.063	.006						
24	.353	.650	.284	.058	.005						
26	.332	.644	.275	.054	.004						
28	.314	.640	.268	.050	.004						
30	.297	.635	.262	.048	.003						
60	.165	.604	.219	.031	.001						
∞		.567	.177	.019	.001						

$_1 = 6$

f_2	$E^2_{0.05}$	ϕ									
		1	1.5	2	2.5	3	4	5	6	7	8
2	.983	.895	.831	.749	.656	.557	.368	.216	.112	.052	.022
4	.902	.836	.677	.473	.280	.138	.019	.001			
6	.811	.789	.556	.296	.113	.030	.001				
7	.768	.769	.510	.239	.074	.015					
8	.729	.753	.472	.198	.051	.008					
9	.692	.738	.440	.166	.037	.005					
10	.659	.725	.412	.142	.027	.003					
11	.628	.713	.389	.123	.020	.002					
12	.600	.702	.369	.108	.016	.001					
13	.574	.693	.351	.096	.012	.001					
14	.550	.685	.336	.086	.010	.001					
15	.527	.677	.323	.078	.008						
16	.507	.669	.311	.071	.007						
17	.488	.663	.301	.065	.006						
18	.470	.657	.291	.061	.005						
19	.454	.652	.283	.056	.004						
20	.438	.648	.276	.053	.004						
22	.410	.639	.262	.047	.003						
24	.385	.632	.252	.043	.003						
26	.363	.625	.242	.039	.002						
28	.344	.620	.234	.036	.002						
30	.326	.615	.228	.033	.002						
60	.184	.576	.181	.019	.001						
∞		.532	.138	.010							

TABLE II. TABLE OF $E^2_{0.05}$ AND THE CORRESPONDING VALUES OF P_{II} (*continued*)

$f_1 = 7$

f_2	$E^2_{0.05}$	ϕ									
		1	1.5	2	2.5	3	4	5	6	7	8
2	.986	.896	.833	.753	.660	.563	.374	.222	.117	.055	.023
4	.914	.837	.678	.474	.280	.138	.019	.001			
6	.831	.788	.552	.289	.108	.028	.001				
7	.791	.767	.503	.230	.068	.013					
8	.754	.749	.462	.187	.046	.007					
9	.719	.733	.427	.154	.031	.004					
10	.687	.719	.398	.129	.022	.002					
11	.657	.706	.373	.110	.016	.001					
12	.630	.695	.351	.094	.012	.001					
13	.604	.684	.332	.082	.009						
14	.580	.675	.316	.073	.007						
15	.558	.667	.301	.065	.006						
16	.538	.659	.289	.058	.005						
17	.518	.652	.277	.053	.004						
18	.501	.645	.267	.048	.003						
19	.484	.639	.258	.044	.003						
20	.468	.634	.250	.041	.002						
22	.439	.624	.236	.036	.002						
24	.414	.615	.224	.032	.001						
26	.391	.607	.215	.028	.001						
28	.371	.601	.206	.026	.001						
30	.353	.595	.199	.023	.001						
60	.202	.550	.150	.012							
∞		.498	.105	.005							

$f_1 = 8$

f_2	$E^2_{0.05}$	ϕ									
		1	1.5	2	2.5	3	4	5	6	7	8
2	.987	.897	.835	.755	.664	.567	.380	.227	.121	.057	.024
4	.924	.838	.678	.474	.279	.137	.019	.001			
6	.847	.787	.548	.284	.103	.026	.001				
7	.810	.765	.497	.222	.064	.012					
8	.775	.746	.454	.178	.041	.006					
9	.742	.729	.417	.144	.028	.003					
10	.711	.714	.386	.119	.019	.001					
11	.682	.700	.359	.099	.013	.001					
12	.655	.688	.336	.084	.009						
13	.630	.677	.316	.072	.007						
14	.607	.666	.298	.062	.005						
15	.585	.657	.283	.055	.004						
16	.564	.648	.269	.048	.003						
17	.545	.641	.257	.043	.003						
18	.527	.634	.247	.039	.002						
19	.510	.627	.237	.035	.002						
20	.495	.620	.228	.032	.001						
22	.466	.609	.213	.027	.001						
24	.440	.600	.201	.024	.001						
26	.417	.591	.191	.021	.001						
28	.396	.584	.182	.019							
30	.377	.578	.175	.017							
60	.219	.527	.125	.008							
∞		.466	.081	.003							

VORLESUNGEN UBER DIFFERENTIALGEOMETRIE by Wilhelm Blaschke. Volume I: Elementare Differentialgeometrie. Third revised edition. Yellow (Grundlehren) Series. Text in German. English translation of table of contents. German-English glossary-index. 5-1/2 x 8-1/2. xiv + 322 pages. 35 figures. (Originally published at $9.00). *$3.95*

APPLIED MATHEMATICS AND MATHEMATICAL PHYSICS

APPLIED ELASTICITY by John Prescott. ". . . important contribution . . . old material presented in new and refreshing form . . . many original investigations."—Nature. 3 appendices. Index. 5-1/2 x 8-1/2. vi + 666 pages. (Originally published at $9.50). *$3.95*

BESSEL FUNCTIONS, Eleven and Fifteen-Place Tables of Bessel Functions of the First Kind to All Significant Orders by Enzo Cambi. The main tables give $Jn(x)$ for $x = 0(0.01)$ 10.5 and $n = 0(1)$ 29 to 11 places. A supplementary table gives $Jn(x)$ for $x = 0(0.001)$ 0.5 and $n = 0(1)$ 11 to 15 places. Bibliography. 8-1/2 x 10-3/4. Hard binding. vi + 160 pages. 2 graphs. *$3.95*

FOUNDATIONS OF NUCLEAR PHYSICS. Compiled by Robert T. Beyer. Facsimile reproductions with text in the original language of French, German or English of the 13 most important papers in atomic research by Chadwick, Cockcroft, Yukawa, Fermi, etc. 122 page bibliography with over 5,000 classified entries. 6-1/8 x 9-1/4. x + 272 pages. Illustrated. *$2.95*

HIGHER MATHEMATICS FOR STUDENTS OF CHEMISTRY AND PHYSICS by J. W. Mellor. Fourth revised edition. ". . . an eminently readable and thoroughly practical treatise."—Nature. 2 appendices. Index. 5-1/2 x 8-1/2. xxix + 641 pages. 189 figures. 18 tables. (Originally published at $7.00). *$4.50*

HYDRODYNAMICS by Sir Horace Lamb. Sixth revised edition. "Standard work . . . important theories (of the dynamics of liquids and gases), which underlie many present-day practical applications, are dealt with thoroughly and with mathematical rigour."—Engineering Societies Library. Index. 6 x 9. xviii + 738 pages. 83 illustrations. (Originally published at $13.75). *$5.95*

INTRODUCTION TO THE DIFFERENTIAL EQUATIONS OF PHYSICS by L. Hopf. Translated by Walter Nef. "There is a surprising amount of valuable material packed into this small book."—School Science and Mathematics. Dover Series in Mathematics and Physics. Index. 4-1/4 x 6-3/8. vi + 154 pages. 48 illustrations. *$1.95*

PLEASE SEND FOR YOUR FREE CATALOG LISTING ALL DOVER BOOKS IN THE FIELDS OF PURE MATHEMATICS, APPLIED MATHEMATICS, AND MATHEMATICAL PHYSICS, PHYSICS AND CHEMISTRY.

Dover Publications, Inc. 1780 Broadway, New York 19, N. Y.